I'LL BET MY LIFE ON IT

ONE DOCTOR'S EXPERIENCE IN AMERICAN MEDICINE

I'LL BET MY LIFE ON IT

ONE DOCTOR'S EXPERIENCE IN AMERICAN MEDICINE

Ronald G. Connolly, M.D.

Moraga Press
Moraga, California

First Edition

ISBN 0-9634703-0-2

Library of Congress Catalog No. 92-062278

Moraga Press
P.O. Box 6657
Moraga, CA 94570
1-800-732-0059

Printed in the United States of America.

For ~

Gerardine Laffey Connolly, a kind and loving mother,

and

those many men, women, and children in the United States who have no health care coverage.

A Note of Acknowledgment

I wish to express my appreciation to some gracious men and women who have helped me to tell my story: Carl Rubino, for his suggestions and encouragement during the early drafts of the manuscript; Ellen McCarty, for her editorial expertise; Julie Chappell and Andrew Griffin, for their critical reading; and Andra Zamacona and Tracey Hahn, for their talented secretarial support.

Also, I wish to express my heartfelt gratitude to Florence Pullella, my secretary, for her unfailing friendship throughout this battle.

I also am proud to acknowledge Schnucki, Maria, Christina, Ronny, and Anna, for their spirit and courage; and Sieglinde — for her faith and her love and for more than I can ever put into words.

Ron Connolly
November 19, 1992

CONTENTS

I'LL BET MY LIFE ON IT

ONE DOCTOR'S EXPERIENCE IN AMERICAN MEDICINE

INTRODUCTION

My story takes place in Wilmington, Delaware, my home town. I was born in 1939. At that time Wilmington was a small town, and my earliest memories are of growing up in a new development on the outskirts, called Alapocas.

Oak trees lined both sides of our street; on our side were several comfortable single-family homes, and on the other side was Wilmington Friends School. The stone Quaker school building with white framed windows and gray slate roof was constructed in 1937; the school had been founded in downtown Wilmington in 1748.

I remember the black-outs during the war. Mom, Dad, my older brother, Art, my younger brother, Chris and I gathered in the kitchen. Dad explained that in an air attack, a light in our house or elsewhere in the city could become a target for enemy bombers. Later, I remember standing in the kitchen as horns, sirens, and whistles blared outside, and looking up to Mom, who had been washing dishes, as she explained that the war was over.

After the war the United States entered an era of unsurpassed prosperity and optimism, with record-setting accomplishments in everything from science and technology to education and home-building to per-capita income. The horrors and hardships of World War I, the Great Depression, and World War II had passed. The United States led the free world in its quest for peace and democracy.

Serious problems persisted, but the major injustice, repression of Blacks, was finally acknowledged as the 1954 Supreme Court decision, Brown v. Board of Education, outlawed segregation in the public schools. The entire country had good reason for hope as higher levels of productivity and prosperity were recorded yearly, and at the same time American generosity helped Europe and Japan to rebuild.

If optimism and idealism permeated the United States in the late 1940's and 1950's, they certainly permeated its youngest generation; success, we believed, depended on hard work, honesty, a good education, and American opportunity.

To say the least, my life was satisfactory. I liked my home and I liked my neighborhood, and I even liked most things about school—and it was clear that they liked me.

My brothers and I went to Friends School. On late mornings it took me ten minutes to jump out of bed, wash, dress, dash to school, and be in my seat before the bell. When the school year started each September, it was an event if we had one new boy or girl in our class. Surrounding the school were broad lawns and variously-sized athletic fields where Art, Chris, our friends, and I played. Saturdays we often took a bus to downtown Wilmington where, for a few dimes, and with a box of popcorn, we saw a Lone Ranger or Gene Autry double-feature at the Grand Theater. *The Sands of Iwo Jima*, with John Wayne playing Sergeant Stryker, was memorable: great people risking their lives for even greater values. But shortly after I left the movie, my most pressing concern was whether to play football or kick-the-can. Serious problems and upheavals involved distant people and distant places.

Mom often took Art and me to The Monastery of the Visitation, where the nuns taught us catechism. Their contemplative order had been founded in France in 1610 by St. Francis de Sales and St. Jane de Chantal. The serene graystone monastery with its red Spanish-tiled roof was built in 1893.

I remember standing on the wide granite steps leading up to the front door of the monastery, hastily trying to memorize the answers to my *Baltimore Catechism* while waiting for the receiving sister to open the door. The sister then led us into the hallway, with its polished hardwood floor. To the left of the hallway was the wood-panelled chapel with its elegant stained glass windows and its large wooden grille from behind which the cloistered sisters assembled for Mass and prayers. To the right of the hallway were a few reception rooms where one of the sisters reviewed our catechism.

When I was seven years old, the sisters taught me the prayer that Sieglinde and I have taught our children:

Dear little Jesus come to me,
dear little Jesus stay with me;
My heart is so small,
you fill it all;
There is no room for anyone but You and me.

I was seven when I received my First Communion in the Visitation Chapel. As I knelt in the chapel sanctuary, Father McCoy, an Oblate priest, said the Latin Mass while the Visitation Sisters, separated by the grille, responded.

I was not a good student in grade school; I did well with a soccer ball, not with the school books. I remember sitting with Mom, as a fourth grader, at the big desk in the den as she helped me with my workbook, hours after bedtime. The workbook was due the next morning, and Mom patiently helped me, page by page, with work that I should have done a month ago. It was spring and the school year would soon be over. By the time Mom and I had closed the workbook, I could barely keep my eyes open. "Ronny," Mom quietly said, "what's the nicest surprise that could happen to you?"

"Is Mrs. Passmore going to promote me?" I responded. Mom replied that at the recent Home and School Meeting my fourth grade teacher had said I had passed the school year; I would be promoted to the fifth grade.

By the summer of 1949, when I was nine years old, we started going to camp, spending eight weeks playing baseball, swimming and canoeing. Camp Minnewawa was located on Panther Pond in Raymond, Maine. Art was eleven and Chris seven. The camp was run by Alan Hughes, an extraordinary athletic coach, and the athletic director at Friends School. Our camp was small—about 25 boys—but our baseball team was a winner, one of the best in the area.

Every day after meals, or at least it seemed so, Coach Hughes stood—tall, graying hair combed straight back, pipe in hand—and gave us the major league baseball scores with particular attention to the Brooklyn Dodgers, which had been his home team before he came to Wilmington. After giving the scores he routinely exhorted: "Boys . . . be somebody; be yourself! Don't be a flounder."

This admonition, repeated over three summers, was amusing to us; it was part of the camp routine—baseball, swimming, and don't be a flounder!

I was popular and was voted the All-Round Camper Trophy as a ten year old, and again when I was eleven.

By seventh grade my school work had improved, I was a 75-pound quarterback on the Mite football team, and I pitched for the baseball team.

During this time our family had grown. I now had two sisters, Muffy and Mary, and another brother, Tommy. By the time I finished eighth grade at Friends, my parents transferred all of us to Catholic schools. Art and I went to Archmere Academy, run by the Norbertine Fathers.

At Archmere I was sometimes on the honor roll, shy in the class room, comfortable on the athletic field, a 5'9" co-captain of the basketball team, and on the student council. Next to getting into a good college, my greatest concerns at Archmere were our basketball team, whether Bob Cousy and the Boston Celtics were winning, and whether I had the nerve to ask Judy Schmelzer, the auburn-haired class queen from Ursuline Academy, to the senior prom.

The Norbertine Fathers were admirable role models as well as good teachers. In the religion courses we deepened our understanding of our faith: the sacraments, scripture, tradition, and morality. Religion did not constrict; it expanded and fulfilled. I developed a deeper appreciation of Catholicism. I was proud of myself, and exciting challenges lay ahead.

I learned to serve Mass, including the Latin responses, from Father Glen Siebers:

> Introibo ad altare Dei,
> ad Deum qui laetificat juventutem meum.
> (I will go to the altar of God,
> to God the joy of my youth.)

By the fall of 1957, I had followed Art to Georgetown University, and I was now studying philosophy—Aristotle, Augustine, Aquinas—and other liberal-arts courses. During freshman orientation the leaders of the senior class introduced their respective clubs and organizations, each describing their particular advantages. One of the organizations was The St. John Berchmans Society, and its prefect summarized his organization as consisting of a hundred or so college students who assisted the Jesuits at Mass and other liturgical celebrations. "The rewards," he said, "are . . . well, out of this world." After the orientation I joined the tennis team and the St. John Berchmans Society.

During my sophomore year at Georgetown, after one of my friends had switched his major from the classics to pre-med, I also decided that I wanted to become a doctor. I would remain in liberal arts, but add a fifth year of college enabling me to take the pre-med courses necessary for admission.

I liked working with people and initially had thought of becoming a teacher. (I had never been interested in business, politics or law.) As a doctor, I could work with people in a vital relationship, and medicine provided a challenge, as well as independence: success depended on hard work and performance, not on social or political maneuvering.

During these impressionable years, the environment at Georgetown was a source of deep nourishment and strength. Science and spirituality were comfortably integrated. Simply put, science (technology, materialism) fell far short of providing all the answers. And, by itself, spirituality also failed to provide all the answers. The two, when combined, complement and fulfill each other. Neither one possesses the autonomy to dictate to the other; each is essential to the other. (This is *not* an outdated, speculative wish, but rather is the heartbeat of the world's hope for peace, as exemplified by such Nobel Laureates as Mother Teresa, Archbishop Desmond Tutu, the Rev. Martin Luther King, and others.)

Teilhard de Chardin, the French Jesuit and scientist (paleontologist), wrote of the impersonal and universal world of matter conjoined with the personal and transcendent God. He wrote of the evolution of life over the millennia: Just as we witness the physical world evolving, there has been a corresponding evolution of human consciousness. The world has been 'complexifying'; it has ascended from a primeval broth to our level of consciousness today. Matter is being built up, is evolving, and is rising into spirit. According to the Christian faith, God (Pure Spirit) took on matter, flesh and blood, when He became a human person; Christ's birth, His life, His death, and His Resurrection has been, is, and will be central to this evolving process. Christ affirms our humanity, and shares with us his eternal destiny.

At Georgetown, I did well in my studies, started on the varsity tennis team for three years, was the prefect of the St. John Berchmans Society, and was a member of the student council. And although the customary preparation of a student for medical school includes a Bachelor of Science degree, usually in biology or chemistry, for better or for worse, I had a Bachelor of Arts degree; my background included metaphysics, epistemology, the philosophy of man, logic, ethics, and four years of theology.

It would be an understatement to say that medical students work long hours. At Georgetown Medical School I worked between 80 and 100 hours per week—partially from fear of failure, partially from desire to succeed. But I liked my work; it was meaningful; it was a worthwhile challenge, and I was preparing for a bright future.

With my first year of medical school behind me, in a class of 116 students—the majority of whom had been science majors in college and had already taken anatomy, histology and physiology—I was ranked nineteenth.

A liberal-arts major, by hard work, had succeeded in science. To be an athlete, actor, artist, or articulate lawyer, there is no magic or mystery, but a lot of work and sacrifice.

My role models at Georgetown included leaders in American medicine and admirable physicians: Charles

Hufnagel, Chief of Surgery and a pioneer in the replacement of heart valves. Proctor Harvey, Chief of Cardiology, quiet, modest, and world-renowned. William Walsh, founder of Project Hope. Andrew Marchetti, Chief of Obstetrics and Gynecology, had worked with Dr. Papanicolaou in developing the Pap Smear. I remember Dr. Marchetti serving at the twelve-noon Mass in the hospital chapel: standing in profile—snow white hair, white lab coat, strong Roman nose—with cruets in his hands for the priest.

Georgetown was also an exciting place to live. Senator John Kennedy lived a few blocks from campus, on "N" Street. His wife gave birth in our hospital. I remember his inauguration day. As I walked by Holy Trinity Church, a commotion had developed. A moment later the President-elect, surrounded by secret-service men, entered the church to attend Mass, prior to the ceremony on the Capitol steps.

I graduated from medical school in June, 1966. I had been with the Jesuits at Georgetown for nine years. They were great educators and inspired leaders, but it was time to cut the umbilical cord. The next month I started a rotating internship at Kaiser Foundation Hospital in San Francisco. At the same time, the Vietnam War was blazing.

The interns at Kaiser worked an eighty-hour week (plus more hours of study at home), were on-call every third night, and earned approximately thirty-five cents an hour. The long hours at the hospital were challenging, draining, exciting, tedious and fruitful. Back in my studio apartment at 43rd Avenue and Point Lobos, I pored over my medical books on the symptoms, signs and management of my patients.

Doctors my age had the alternative of being drafted into the military or joining the Berry Plan, which enabled them, usually successfully, to request their branch of service, location, and whether they would serve after internship, residency, or fellowship. I joined the Berry Plan, requesting to serve with the Marine Corps, in Vietnam, after internship.

The Flower Children were studying Zen and protesting Vietnam. I was completing my internship and preparing for a three-week indoctrination at the Marine Corps Base, at Camp Pendleton, before reporting to the Naval Support Facility at Cam Ranh Bay, Vietnam.

I was working a night shift at Kaiser a few months before internship ended, when I was called to the floor for a new admission: She was German, with happy blue-gray eyes, dark hair, and an exceptionally soft, kind voice. Sieglinde had come to San Francisco with her sister and brother-in-law, who lived across the bay in Oakland.

She was soon discharged from the hospital and two weeks later I telephoned, asking her how she felt. Just as she was thinking that the follow-up care of these American doctors was extraordinary, I asked her for a date.

Sieglinde and I began seeing more of each other. She was the most trusting person I had ever met, and she had exceptional bearing. She was modest yet confident, gentle and sensitive yet strong.

Sieglinde's childhood experiences had been quite different from mine. She was born in 1940 on a cold winter day in Aschaffenburg, a city in Germany, midway between Frankfurt and Wurzburg. A pan of water placed under her mother's bed by the midwife to assist with the delivery had frozen.

Some of Sieglinde's earliest memories were of Aschaffenburg's air-raid sirens screaming into the night, followed by her parents bundling Sieglinde and her older brother and sister, Kurt and Hildegard, into blankets and running for the air-raid shelters. On leaving the bomb shelter one morning, they found their house had been badly damaged. Soon afterwards, in early 1945, they went to live in Nordheim, a small farming village about 100 miles east of Aschaffenburg where Sieglinde's mother had grown up and where Sieglinde's grandparents, aunt and uncle lived.

One afternoon in 1945 Sieglinde and Hildegard were taking a walk with an elderly woman when a strafing plane angrily bore down on them, firing its .50-caliber machine guns as the fleeing old woman and two young children dove for cover behind large sacks of grain.

The plane passed; grain poured onto the ground from the shredded sacks.

After the war, their small possessions wiped out, the family worked long hours on the little farm owned by Sieglinde's aunt and uncle. Sieglinde, her hair in dark braids and wearing a small apron over her well-worn school dress, went to the village school and wrote her lessons in chalk on a small hand-held slate.

Food was scarce during the war and for several years afterwards; it was an event to have butter on a roll, and meat was usually limited to a few pieces of sausage at the Sunday noon-meal. Staying warm in winter was also a problem. The small house that they shared had no heat except that provided by the black, wood-fed stove in the kitchen; and, once outside, frostbitten toes were common. Homespun woven woolen leggings helped, but itched, so they were lined with newspapers. Sieglinde, even on freezing winter mornings, was often in the seventeenth-century village church by seven o'clock in the morning, attending Mass. After Mass she went to school and then returned home to help with the farm chores.

In 1951 the family moved back to Aschaffenburg, the years passed, and Kurt's ordination to the priesthood, June 1965, came the month before Sieglinde joined Hildegard and her husband, David Melander, to come to California.

A few months after meeting Sieglinde, I finished my internship, and then went to Camp Pendleton, along with thirty or forty other doctors, for induction. One day I was a civilian, the next day I was in the Navy (which supplies the Marine Corps with doctors—the Marine Corps has no doctors of its own), and had two bars (I was told I was a lieutenant). In three weeks I would be in Vietnam.

A few days after arrival at Pendleton I was wearing newly issued fatigues with two sparkling silver bars on my collar. As I walked to the PX I heard rapidly approaching footsteps behind me. Drawing even with me and without breaking stride, two young Marines crisply turned and saluted. "By your leave, Sir!"

Before I could mumble a response, the Marines hastened by. As I was pondering how to respond to "By your leave, Sir", one hundred drilling Marines, precision perfect, swung into the street heading towards me.

"HUT! . . TWO . . THREE . . FOUR."

Row upon row of arms swung in perfect unison; one hundred pairs of boots stomped the pavement in perfect cadence.

Rapidly they approached.

Abreast of me the drill instructor abruptly yanked his head towards me and crisply saluted: "SIR!".

In unison one hundred Marines yanked their heads towards me and crisply saluted.

With maximal indecision I returned their salute: half of my extended right hand protruding above my visor, half below, and my hat knocked ajar.

The marines quickly passed, and I continued into the PX railing at myself. Hopefully, I thought, their sergeant will explain that I'm not a "line-officer," I'm a medical officer; they won't have to follow me into battle. Hopefully, they won't be seeing me in Vietnam.

My three-week crash course passed quickly: "Throw a hand grenade like a football, with a spiral, not like a baseball."

"Here's how you strip a .45," the marine captain said, "and put it back together again in forty seconds." And as he yanked, pulled, inverted, and pulled again, the weapon crumbled to pieces on the desk top. Then, reversing the sequence, the .45 was reassembled with seconds to spare.

"When you're in the field with the marines they're going to protect you. If they get hit, they want *you* with them."

Vaccinations were for plague, cholera, typhus, typhoid, tetanus and yellow fever.

Malaria prophylactic tablets were given once a week; gamma globulin injections every four months.

Iodine tablets make water potable.

Basic was over and I had a few days to get to McChord Air Force Base outside Seattle. From there we would fly, refueling in Tokyo, to Cam Ranh Bay.

On the way to McChord I stopped in San Francisco to see Sieglinde. As I was leaving, she gave me a delicate eleven-inch wooden statue of the Blessed Mother, carved in Oberammergau.

The Naval Support Facility at Cam Ranh Bay was a one-thousand-man base. It had a large naval communication station and well-armed Navy Swiftboats—powered by two 500 horse-power diesel engines and manned by a crew of five or six, which patrolled up and down the jungle-lined coast. Along with six or so corpsmen, I was responsible for the medical care of the base, which included approximately 50 Vietnamese civilian employees. Ten miles north of our facility were a U. S. Army base and an Air Force base, but no Marine Corps. The marines were farther north in the Da Nang area.

A few months after my arrival the Tet (Vietnamese Lunar New Year) offensive began. Cam Ranh Bay was on Red Alert. We expected to be hit within the next twenty-four to forty-eight hours.

"Doc, you better go over to ordnance. Check out a .45 and a couple of hand grenades. And stay in the dispensary tonight; don't go back to your barracks."

During the next several days reports poured into our base from across South Vietnam telling of the casualties and destruction. But we were lucky, we didn't get hit.

During my year in Vietnam, Sieglinde and I corresponded. As the end of my tour came into sight, I requested—and received—assignment, for my second and last year of active duty, to the medical dispensary on Treasure Island Naval Base located in San Francisco Bay. During this year, Sieglinde and I saw more of each other.

As during my internship, I went to Mass at St. Ignatius Church, on the Jesuit campus of the University of San Francisco. The majestic church, with its beautiful main altar, flickering votive candles, statues, murals and stained glass windows of the saints—men, women and children through the millennia with diverse lives yet sharing a great humanity—provided an important dimension to my life.

One Sunday at Mass, a tall, red-haired Jesuit priest—articulate, confident and with a commanding presence—gave an extraordinary sermon to the crowded church. His name was Fr. Bernard J. Bush.

Soon thereafter, Fr. Bush and I became friends. As a college student he had thought of becoming a lawyer; and, judging from his talents, I had no doubt that he would have been a great success. Instead, he chose to follow Christ as a Jesuit priest and to voluntarily take lifetime vows of poverty (he would have no money, nor would he own any material items), chastity (he would never enjoy sexual relations), and obedience (the nature and location of his work would be determined by his superiors).

A short time later, Sieglinde and I invited Fr. Bush for dinner at my apartment. We had also invited three friends: a high school teacher, a business consultant, and a musician who, along with me, comprised a monthly book-discussion club.

As Fr. Bush and the five of us discussed various topics, one of my friends, the teacher, without provocation, suddenly and with visible irritation challenged the priest: "What are you willing to bet that God exists?"

The rest of us, surprised by the bluntness of the confrontation, looked at Fr. Bush. He thought for a moment, then quietly responded, "I'll bet my life on it."

(Another Jesuit, Father William O'Malley, in his book *Meeting the Living God* [Paulist Press], also discusses the "God questions": Does God exist? Does God have a personal interest in you and me? Are we immortal from the moment we come into existence? O'Malley says, "Whichever way you decide the God questions, it will change your whole life. And not to decide *is* to decide.")

By now, I had been discharged from the Navy, and soon thereafter, March 1970, Sieglinde and I were married at Notre

Dame de Victoire Church. I gave Sieglinde a bouquet of red roses, daisies and baby's breath; for everyone else, there were white carnations at the entrance to the church.

Late in 1970 Gerardine Afra was born, named after our mothers (and nicknamed "Schnuckiputz") . . . and then in 1971 Sieglinde Maria ("Mia") . . . and then Christina Ann ("Tina") in 1974.

During this time, I had been working as an emergency-room physician, but by July 1974, with the help of the GI bill, I started an internal medicine residency at Kaiser Foundation Hospital in Sacramento. We rented a small ranch-style house on Lynwood Way, a few minutes from the hospital, as well as a few minutes from Presentation Church and School.

The days and nights at Kaiser Hospital were more than just busy, as my fellow residents and I learned the twelve to fourteen specialty areas of internal medicine, from allergy and cardiology to nephrology and rheumatology.

I remember one morning coming home for a quick breakfast after an on-call night. Sieglinde tiredly greeted me; she had struggled through an all-nighter too: stomach flu had hit the three children. Sieglinde had spoon-fed them sips of ginger ale, hoping to prevent dehydration; a stack of dirty pajamas and bed sheets were in the bathroom waiting to be washed.

But our problems were not the hospital's, so after a twenty-minute visit I was back at Kaiser for a regular day of work, and the completion of my thirty-two hour sleepless work shift. We were convinced though that the hard work, long hours, and low pay were worth it. We were preparing for a bright future.

By July 1976 the internal medicine residency was over, Ronny, our fourth child, was a few months old, and I was concluding my specialty training with a two-year rheumatology fellowship at the University of California-Davis, which staffed Sacramento General Hospital.

Two years later, June, 1978, I was finished with my formal training: college, medical school, internship, residency, and fellowship—fourteen years of work. And this had been supplemented with seven valuable years of experience as a Navy and an emergency-room physician. My education, training, and experience had given me a solid, broad-based foundation which had progressed into greater specialization, culminating with certification by the American Board of Internal Medicine and the American Board of Rheumatology.

My education, training, and experience had also put me on a collision course with organized medicine! Soon, some leaders of the medical profession would charge that I was psychiatrically ill.

1

I'll Bet My Life On It

doctor n. a person licensed to practice any of the healing arts. . . .
vt. to tamper: as, he doctored the evidence.
Webster's New World Dictionary

According to *The Principles of Medical Ethics of the American Medical Association*: "The medical profession . . . . should expose, without hesitation, illegal or unethical conduct of fellow members of the profession." However, when I presented complaints of unethical conduct to leaders of the medical profession in Delaware it caused a convulsive response.

Before proceeding, I should make it clear that this story is NOT meant to be an indictment of the medical profession; there are many talented and dedicated doctors. This story is meant to be an indictment of the autonomy—or licensed monopoly—enjoyed by the medical profession in administering the nation's health care.

It is helpful to understand a few basic facts regarding medicine in the United States. The Health Care Financing Administration (HCFA) reports that the United States spent $751.8 billion dollars on health care in 1991, an 11.4% increase from the 1990 level, and that this expenditure comprised 13.2% of the gross national product. This represents an expenditure of $2,868 per person on health care. The current projections of the HCFA are that by the year 2000 national health care expenditures will be $1.7 trillion annually, or $6,148 per person, and will comprise 18.1% of the GNP!

Not surprisingly, this financial behemoth, the medical profession, is supervised by—the medical profession.

The public and their legislators bestow upon the medical profession unsurpassed autonomy to license, supervise, discipline, and, to a great extent, set its own fees. In exchange the medical profession pledges that the public's welfare is foremost. The linchpin in this transaction is the public's trust.

Betray that trust, and the medical profession will lose its autonomy.

Medicine is a business, as well as an art and a science. But it is a business unlike any other. When you, the consumer, go shopping, you select which items to buy. When, however, you go to your doctor, the doctor, acting on your behalf, is largely responsible for your selections, ranging from which laboratory and X-ray studies to obtain, to which prescriptions to buy, to which surgeries to perform; but *you* are the one who pays the bill.

The medical marketplace is also unusual in that it is unresponsive to the basic economic principle of "cost" as a function of supply and demand. Normally, for any given demand, as the supply of goods and services increases, costs decrease. In medicine, however, as the supply of doctors increases, there is an *increase* in the cost of their services.

Additionally, utilization of medical services for the same illness is significantly different depending upon whether your care is provided through a *pre-paid* program (a Health Maintenance Organization) or a *fee-for-service* program. For example, a patient is much more likely to undergo coronary artery bypass surgery or a hysterectomy if he or she belongs to a fee-for-service insurance program. But the common denominator of both programs is that the medical profession's income is maximized.

Unfortunately, although medical care in the United States is the most expensive in the world, it is not the best—as measured by such fundamental standards as the level of immunization against preventable diseases, the infant and maternal mortality rates, and the life-expectancy rate. The United States is the only industrialized country in the world, apart from South Africa, that does not make health care available to all of its citizens. Thirty-five million Americans are without medical insurance.

Dr. Alain Enthoven and his co-author, Richard Kronick, of the Graduate School of Business at Stanford University, writing in the *New England Journal of Medicine* on January 5, 1989, state:

> The health care economy of the United States is a paradox of excess and deprivation. We spend about 11.5% of the gross national product (GNP) on health care, much more than any other country. And whereas other countries have stabilized the share of their GNP that is spent on health, ours has accelerated in recent years. . . .
>
> At the same time, roughly 35 million Americans have no financial protection from the expenses of medical care—no insurance or other coverage, public or private. This number is substantially higher than it was 10 years ago.... Millions more have inadequate coverage that leaves them vulnerable to large financial risks. And uncounted millions have coverage that excludes preexisting medical conditions.

These medical realities are deplored by legislative bodies in each of the fifty states and in Washington; their economic, political and social consequences daily affect the well-being of every citizen.

Joseph A. Califano, Jr., Secretary of Health, Education, and Welfare from 1977 to 1979, wrote in the *New York Times Magazine* (March 20, 1988):

> Just as history teaches that war is too important to be left to generals, so recent American experience teaches that medicine is too important to be left to doctors and politicians.
>
> Health is devouring an ever-increasing share of our national wealth. . . .
>
> During the two years leading up to the 1986 elections, those in the health-care industry channeled more than $8.5 million through various

> political action committees to members of Congress. Next to financial services, this is more than any other industry—more than the hand-gun and tobacco lobbies, the oil companies and the 100 largest defense contractors. And that $8.5 million does not include direct contributions made by doctors and hospital administrators. For the contributors, those political gifts are a small price to pay to keep a piece of one of America's three largest industries.

Skyrocketing medical costs are often explained by burgeoning technological advancements, an older population requiring more medical services, rising malpractice premiums, and increased costs of labor. A much less frequently discussed component of soaring medical costs is doctor greed, corruption, and fraud. A feature story (February 24, 1992) in *U.S. News & World Report* said, "Experts now estimate that fraud and abuse in the healthcare field cost somewhere between $50 billion and $80 billion each year—a figure that dwarfs the estimated $5 billion lost through criminal fraud in the entire savings and loan debacle."

In light of these facts, does the medical profession in 1993 merit the exceptional autonomy—to license, supervise, discipline, and set fees—that the public grants? The public's answer to date is apparently a resounding "yes": With each passing day medical costs continue to rise, more Americans struggle to obtain basic health care, the income of doctors continues to rise, and yet each of the fifty state medical boards continues to be monopolized by doctors!

At the end of our journey, if we both make it, perhaps you would ask yourself if *you* want your state medical board controlled by the medical profession, or should it be controlled by the public, by those who pay the bills—the consumer, the taxpayer, industry, government.

It may be that my experience in medicine has absolutely nothing to do with these national problems. But then again, it may. You decide.

Let's get down to specifics: The sum of medical care—the whole pie—is no more and no less than the sum of its component parts. Thus each individual medical doctor comprises a small slice of the medical-care pie. And to understand the grave problems in medicine today—from billion-dollar expenditures to quality of care to supervision of the profession—the whole medical-care pie and at least some of its component parts must be viewed.

My experience represents a biopsy, if you will, of American medicine. Only one biopsy, to be sure, but still, as is well known, a single biopsy can portend a grave prognosis.

Some doctors stand out, either because they are fine, dedicated professionals or because they are unprofessional and unethical. When I was convinced that I had run into the latter, I tolerated them for a while, but then—for both personal and public reasons which will become evident—I decided to file formal complaints of unethical conduct against two of my peers. When my complaints were summarily dismissed, rather than dropping the complaints, I pursued them through prescribed channels, although those prescribing obviously did not intend the channels to be used. Thus I began an odyssey that is perhaps unrivaled in the exemplification of medical negligence, greed, and cover-up.

One consideration is appropriate at the very outset. Since this is my personal story the reader can question my bias; this is, after all, one side of a two-sided controversy. However, because of the nature of the events involved, there is extraordinary documentation of the facts from the public record. Most of what has been said about those people and institutions with whom I am in conflict was not said by me; it was said by them, and has been copied verbatim from Court proceedings. These proceedings include written exhibits, sworn affidavits, and sworn testimonies during depositions and at trial.

Elsewhere in the story quotation marks are used in connection with conversations. In these instances, which are self-evident, quotation marks are not intended to represent the exact words spoken, but rather, in a fair and natural manner, to depict the substance and tone of what was said.

It should also be noted that all the names used are real, not fictional; including the names of two patients, both of whom gave written permission.

Well, the kleig lights just clicked on, so let's get back to our story. Does anyone see corruption?

In July 1978, after finishing my rheumatology fellowship and becoming certified by the American Board of Rheumatology, Sieglinde, the children and I visited Mom and Dad, who were still living in my boyhood home in Alapocas, and I inquired whether there was a demand for a rheumatologist in Delaware. Friends of the family in the medical profession were encouraging: Delaware had only *one* full-time rheumatologist, Dr. Russell J. Labowitz.

If I opened a practice in Wilmington I would be only the second full-time rheumatologist in the state—an exceptional opportunity.

I telephoned the doctor and introduced myself. I quickly learned that it was an understatement to say that Delaware needed another rheumatologist. "I'm looking for a rheumatologist now to join me in my practice," Dr. Labowitz said. "I can't keep up with the work. It takes me four to six weeks to see a new patient, and I'm looking forward to a much-needed vacation." Dr. Labowitz encouraged me to come down to his office and discuss the position.

I responded that I planned to open my own office, but if I moved back to Wilmington, perhaps we could provide second opinions and cross-cover for night-call.

The tone in Dr. Labowitz's voice became more urgent. He needed another rheumatologist in his office now. He again asked me to consider his offer.

I reiterated my desire to open my own office. (Even as a student at Georgetown, fifteen years earlier, I had looked forward to the independence—the opportunity to be self-employed—that medicine provided.) A few minutes later we concluded the conversation. We would keep in touch.

Mom and Dad would be elated if we moved to Wilmington. My mother was now sixty-eight. She had devoted her life to her family. Dad was an attorney. Art, my older brother, and his wife Joan lived in Wilmington; he was a partner in my father's firm. But my two younger brothers, Chris and Tom, and my two younger sisters, Muffy and Mary, as well as spouses, nephews and nieces, lived in Boston, Washington, D.C., Aspen, and London.

Sieglinde and I were torn between staying in California and moving to Wilmington. There were also many good jobs available in California for a board certified rheumatologist, but our move to Wilmington would mean much to Mom and Dad.

In September, the children resumed school at Presentation while Sieglinde and I began packing boxes for our new home in Wilmington.

We arrived in Wilmington the week before Christmas, 1978. Sieglinde and I wanted to make the children's holiday memorable yet we also had much work to do. We had purchased an almost-completed new house in Greenville, a suburb of Wilmington; the children were starting in their new school, Ursuline Academy, in mid-year, and less than two weeks later, on January 2, 1979, I was opening my new office.

I had rented a newly furnished medical office at 2300 Pennsylvania Avenue. Now I dug into the numerous chores waiting to be done.

Opening a private practice, building my career, and being self-employed presented for me, as for millions of Americans, a great opportunity. The office would reflect my personality, my taste, and my values. Here my family and I would build our future.

Two months before our move, Dr. Labowitz and I had exchanged letters; he still hoped I would consider working for him. A few days before my opening date, I met him in his office. He was my age, of medium height, large-boned, with a full, brown beard. Dr. Labowitz had opened his office in Wilmington in 1972. He was the Chief of the Rheumatology Section at both the Wilmington Medical Center and St. Francis Hospital, my two main hospitals.

The Wilmington Medical Center, one of the largest community hospitals in the country, has over 1000 beds. The large Department of Medicine consisted of more than 150 internists; but of more than twelve sections within the department, the Section of Rheumatology was by far the smallest, with only three rheumatologists: I would be practicing rheumatology full-time, as did Russ Labowitz, and the third physician split his practice between rheumatology and internal medicine.

As soon as Dr. Labowitz and I had shaken hands, he again encouraged me to join his practice. Surprised, I again reiterated that I hoped we could help each other in our work, but with independent office practices. I told him that within the past week I had signed an office rental contract, with a January 2 opening date. We then talked for a short time, and parted cordially.

I needed one vital addition in order to have a successful medical practice: patients! As a specialist in rheumatology my work depended heavily on referrals from other doctors, and referrals depended on a good reputation.

I took every opportunity to meet the medical community. I also opened an Arthritic Clinic in the towns of Milford and Seaford (an hour and a half and two hours respectively south of Wilmington).

My basic billing policy included *not* being a financial burden to my patients. This was not munificence on my part. I had a good education, a good job, and a bright future. If I thought a patient was financially stressed, his or her bill was stamped: "Pay what you REASONABLY can," or I simply billed a fraction of the fee. If this was still a hardship, I voided the bill.

Being board-certified in both internal medicine and rheumatology, I promptly received privileges at five Delaware hospitals, including the Wilmington Medical Center and St. Francis Hospital.

Gradually, more doctors referred patients to me, but my practice was picking up more slowly than I had anticipated. During my first month in practice, several doctors spoke to me of unfair competition practiced by some influential leaders in the local medical community, which restricted the access of patients to other doctors. Yet I was optimistic; the demand for rheumatology in this community was great, and I was making progress; each new referral and each new hospital consult was another step in the right direction.

Meanwhile, Sieglinde's warmth and kindness quickly made friends for the entire family. By now we had unpacked the last moving box and hung the last curtains. Daisies were blooming in the flower beds, and red geraniums flourished in our window boxes—a touch of Bavaria. Schnucki, Maria, and Tina were settled into their school work; Sieglinde took care of Ronny at home, and she was now in the middle of her fifth pregnancy; Anna Jennifer was due in a few months.

Friday afternoon, October 12, 1979, my budding career began to crumble.

Once or twice a month, Dad, Art, and I met for Friday lunch, usually at the Greenery Restaurant on Market Street. As I returned from lunch this Friday, my secretary said that a Dr. John Levinson, a gynecologist, had called.

I phoned Dr. Levinson. He was admitting one of my patients, the daughter of a prominent doctor, to the Wilmington Medical Center on Sunday afternoon for a second-trimester saline abortion (the woman was twenty-one weeks pregnant with her first child). He wanted me to consult on the patient.

I had recently begun treating the patient for scleroderma, a disease that had caused moderate arthritis and some thickening of her skin. Fortunately there were no signs that the patient had the more severe form of the disease, which causes internal organ involvement.

Dr. Levinson told me that the patient, her husband, her mother and father, the patient's psychiatrist (she had required hospitalization in the past), as well as himself, all concurred with the abortion, but he wanted my consultation because of the scleroderma.

"Dr. Levinson," I replied, "I just saw the patient in my office two weeks ago; her scleroderma is doing well. There's no need for me to consult on her scleroderma at this time."

"Usually I do these as an out-patient," Dr. Levinson said, "but this patient is in her fifth month, and as a precaution I'm bringing her into the hospital. I want you to consult on her scleroderma." As Dr. Levinson continued, it became clear to me that he wanted my medical clearance in order to proceed with the abortion.

I again reassured him that the patient's scleroderma was stable, she required no further management for her disease at this time, and she already had an office appointment to see me in two weeks. But Dr. Levinson once again insisted that I come into the hospital to consult on the patient, and then concluded the telephone conversation saying that the hospital would be notifying me Sunday afternoon after the patient had been admitted.

I was upset: On religious grounds I could not participate in an abortion; for me it would be seriously wrong. My background in science also supported my religious convictions. At conception the DNA programming of the human embryo is that of a genetically unique and complete human being. In order to carry out that programming, the embryo, like every person, requires only oxygen, ambient temperature, water, and nutrition. According to my conscience, I could not participate in terminating this life—either by assisting or by asking another person to assist.

That evening Sieglinde and I talked over the problem. I had spoken with the patient on the telephone within the past week; at that time, she had been excited about her pregnancy.

Saturday slipped by, and Sunday afternoon, as Sieglinde and I were talking in the kitchen, the phone rang. It was the hospital nurse. Dr. Levinson's patient had just been admitted; he wanted me to consult.

"I'm sorry, I can't consult on this patient," I responded. "I discussed it with Dr. Levinson on Friday; tell him to call me back if he wants to talk further."

Five minutes later Dr. Levinson called. Embarrassed, I told him that the patient's rheumatologic condition did not require any additional treatment at this time, and on religious grounds I could not participate in the abortion.

Levinson became irritated and the conversation circuitous as he told me the decision to have an abortion had already been made by the family and other doctors; I was needed to treat the patient's scleroderma. This reinforced my conviction that I had become essential in order for Levinson to proceed with the abortion; he wanted my medical clearance.

As I again tried to explain to Dr. Levinson, he abruptly interrupted. "Dr. Connolly, you either come in to consult on your patient or you get another qualified physician to take your place!"

With further embarrassment, I again said that I could not do what he demanded.

Levinson angrily replied, "Dr. Connolly, you either consult on your patient or you get another doctor to consult on your patient, or I'm charging you with patient abandonment before the New Castle County Medical Society!"

I replied that on religious grounds I could not consult on the patient, and I could not ask another doctor to do what out of conscience I myself could not do. As I tried to explain, Levinson yelled, "I'm charging you with patient abandonment!" And he slammed down the phone.

2
The Letters

"PERSONAL & CONFIDENTIAL"

Christmas Eve.

A letter arrived a few days later from the Executive Director of the New Castle County Medical Society:

> October 19, 1979
>
> Dear Dr. Connolly:
>
> Your presence is requested at the next meeting of the Professional Conduct Committee . . . .
>
> The purpose of your appearance before the Committee is to discuss with you the charge which was made against you that you allegedly refused to honor a request for a hospital consultation on a patient of yours . . . who is currently under your medical care.
>
> Sincerely yours,
> Eugene C. Syrovatka, J.D.

I was furious as I put the letter down. The patient had a legal right to abortion, and Levinson had a legal right to abort, but I also had a legal right not to participate in abortion. This was not a pro-life or pro-choice issue; for having made my choice, I was now being charged with patient abandonment.

I had never before had a complaint filed against me, and now Levinson, without giving me a chance to explain, had formally charged me with patient abandonment.

Sieglinde was as upset as I; my career was being threatened. Together we considered the best way to explain my position to the committee.

I talked to Dad and Art. Art promptly sent a letter to Syrovatka requesting that we receive a copy of Levinson's complaint, and saying, "We assume Dr. Connolly has a right to have a lawyer present at the hearing and to present a defense."

Syrovatka telephoned Art a few days later saying that there must be some misunderstanding, since no official or written charge had been issued; this was merely to be an informal meeting between Dr. Connolly and the committee over "soup and sandwiches" to discuss a complaint. Never in his experience had a doctor brought an attorney to such an informal hearing. However, as the conversation proceeded, Syrovatka admitted that there had been a written complaint by Levinson against me. Art retorted that it was absurd that I was expected to defend myself without seeing a copy of the charges against me. Syrovatka consented, and a copy of Levinson's complaint was sent to Art:

October 16, 1979

Re: Ronald G. Connolly, M.D.

Dear Dr. Syrovatka:

I wish to bring formal charges best described as patient abandonment on the above physician.
On October 12 I notified him that I would be hospitalizing [the patient] in two days for a second trimester pregnancy termination. . . .
. . . . Dr. Connolly however, in spite of an advanced notification when he did not refuse to see this patient, did indeed refuse to see her when advised of the consultation on October 14. The consultation in no way requested his opinion as to the advisability of abortion but only that he would observe and treat as need be her scleroderma. Once he had refused the hospital's request for consultation I personally discussed this with him by phone. . . .I asked if he could get a replacement and he made no effort to do so and I

then explained that I was formally charging him with patient abandonment.

I deeply regret having to accuse a fellow physician of gross misconduct. However, I find I have no recourse. I can assure you that the family is concerned over his actions as are a number of his professional colleagues who have become aware of these circumstances. . . .

Sincerely,
John M. Levinson, M.D.

It was crucial to me that the committee find *no* basis for the charge of patient abandonment. I urgently prepared for the meeting. Morning, noon, and night, my mind was constantly preoccupied with the charges against me. Often, in the middle of the night, I would jump out of bed to jot down a helpful note by the night light. If I carefully explained the situation, selecting the right words, then the committee would have to exonerate me.

For me, it would have been seriously wrong to participate in the abortion, whether by doing the consultation myself or by asking another doctor to do it. My refusal to participate had resulted in Dr. Labowitz's clearing the patient for the abortion. How many minutes of inconvenience had it taken Levinson, or the nurse, to telephone the consultation to Dr. Labowitz? I thought religious tolerance would include not trying to force a person to sacrifice his or her religious convictions for the sake of a phone call. And it obviously had not compromised the patient's health; Dr. Labowitz was a qualified rheumatologist.

Art now replied to Syrovatka:

November 1, 1979

Dear Dr. Syrovatka:

. . . . In regard to Dr. Levinson's charges, we feel the following points should be brought immediately to the attention of the Professional Conduct Committee:

.... Dr. Connolly is charged with patient abandonment. . . .In that the surgery was merely "elective", it is our understanding that Dr. Connolly possesses a right, which is of constitutional proportions, not to become involved in any steps which lead to an abortion. While he is not trying to impose his views on others, certainly Dr. Connolly should not be forced to participate in procedures with which he inherently disagrees when the surgery involved is merely "elective". Nothing Dr. Connolly did or did not do was in any way a threat to the patient's health ....

[Art then summarized our position and continued.]

.... Dr. Levinson's letter states that a number of Dr. Connolly's professional colleagues who have become aware of these circumstances are concerned over Dr. Connolly's actions. We are most interested in learning the details of the publication of these possibly slanderous charges. It seems apparent that until the Professional Conduct Committee has acted, Dr. Levinson should not have circulated to the medical community and to the family of the patient his serious charges of misconduct.

In closing, we are absolutely shocked that Dr. Connolly has been forced to defend a charge of "gross misconduct" for merely exercising his clear right not to become involved in any way with an "elective" abortion. We trust that the Committee will issue written findings that the charge is baseless and frivolous ....

Sincerely,
Arthur G. Connolly, Jr.

Art also sent copies of his letter to the thirteen members of the Professional Conduct Committee and to Levinson.

In the meantime, I wrote to the chairman of the Professional Conduct Committee and to the president of the New Castle County Medical Society, presenting my position. And I sent copies of both of these letters to the Chief of the Medical-Dental Staff at the Wilmington Medical Center (where the abortion had occurred), and to the president of the Medical Society of Delaware. I felt that everyone should be informed about the controversy.

My noon-meeting with the Professional Conduct Committee was to be held at the Delaware Academy of Medicine on Lovering Avenue. The dignified two-story red-brick building had been erected in 1816.

As I walked up the red brick sidewalk, then under the wrought-iron archway leading to the front door, I reminded myself to focus on the facts. Entering the building, I took a flight of stairs to the second floor, where a secretary instructed me that the committee was waiting in the conference room adjacent to the library.

I found the Professional Conduct Committee assembled around a conference table, eating sandwiches. The chairman sat at the head of the table, and committee members lined both sides. The Executive Director, Mr. Syrovatka, who was an attorney but was customarily referred to as Dr. Syrovatka, was also present.

I was directed to a seat at the far end of the table and offered a sandwich, which I declined, and the committee then proceeded to question me for the better part of the next hour. I told the committee that the *sole* purpose of the patient's hospitalization was for the elective abortion. I emphasized that on religious grounds I could not provide medical clearance for the abortion—the termination of human life—and obviously I could not arrange for another doctor to do so.

When the last question had been asked and answered, the chairman told me that I would be notified of their conclusions, and I was then excused.

A few days after Christmas I received the decision of the committee:

December 26, 1979

Dear Dr. Connolly:

Thank you for meeting with the Professional Conduct Committee. We hope that you regarded your appearance as a learning process and not a disciplinary one.

The Committee, at no time, attempted to infringe on your rights. The abortion was not an issue at any time. At issue was the fact that another physician had requested a medical clearance from you on a seriously ill patient, under your care, who was to undergo a surgical procedure.

It is the opinion of the Committee that you should have complied with the request either by clearing this patient yourself or made arrangements with another physician to do so. The Committee feels that you did not act prudently and in the best interests of your patient.

It is hoped that, in the future, should a similar situation occur, you will either personally comply with the request for a consultation or make other satisfactory arrangements.

Sincerely yours,
Eugene C. Syrovatka, J.D.
Executive Director (Exhibit #1)*

* Throughout this book representative exhibits have been copied and may be found in the Appendix. The above letter is Exhibit #1.

"The abortion was not an issue. . . ." Incredible! That was the only purpose of the patient's hospitalization. The requested "medical clearance" was in order for the patient to undergo the abortion!

The "seriously ill patient" had been doing well; her disease was limited to moderate arthritis and patchy thickening of the skin.

For the next few days Sieglinde and I debated our next move; we wanted a mutually acceptable resolution. Since the issue was of public importance, I considered presenting the facts to the local newspapers.

I talked with Dad and Art; they did not recommend further action. And Sieglinde wanted peace; our lives had already been disrupted for three months.

Reluctantly, I finally put the problem behind me, soothing myself with the fact that Art and I had written letters presenting my position to all of the involved doctors. In addition, the deliberations of the committee involved peer review—and were confidential. Therefore, the committee's conclusion, including their hope that I regarded my "appearance as a learning process and not a disciplinary one," should not be damaging. The problem had been unusual; undoubtedly it would never recur. (At a later time, when I would review the hospital records, new light would be shed on this abortion incident.)

As the weeks of January 1980 slipped by, Sieglinde and I resumed our regular schedules at home and at work—busy, but without upheaval.

Gross office income for the twelve months of 1979 had been $43,984. My expenses had been $34,863, which gave me a salary of $9,121 for the year. It was not what I had expected, but I had known that the first year would be the hardest.

In the meantime, Dad supplemented my income with an account that he had started when I was an infant in order to ensure my college education and career; my home expenses, including the children's school tuition, would be covered. And the office was picking up. I reasonably expected that soon I would be covering my home expenses, and some time after that I would be able to install basic office benefits such as a health insurance plan and pension fund.

A few months later, Dad, Art and I were again having lunch at the Greenery Restaurant. The abortion incident and Levinson were distant from my thoughts, when Art began relating a recent conversation. Joe Biden, Delaware's Democratic Senator, held a "Biden Seminar" twice each year for his supporters; cocktails were served, and a political notable spoke. Art said he had been talking with John Levinson at the recent Biden Seminar. Levinson had remarked he was surprised to learn that we were brothers, and he had continued saying that the mother of the patient who had had the abortion, the wife of a well-known doctor, had been extremely upset at me. She had made the comment that she wanted me "run out of town."

Levinson had then concluded his informative comments by suggesting that Art, he, and I get together for a beer some day after work.

That evening I related the conversation to Sieglinde. We had not discussed the abortion incident for weeks since it seemed as though everyone considered it a thing of the past—apparently, even Levinson himself.

In the months that followed, my practice continued to gradually pick up, and I also submitted a study proposal to the Delaware Arthritis Foundation requesting a $5,000 grant made available by the Chichester DuPont Foundation. (I was interested in studying the effect of two medications on the sleep electroencephalogram [EEG] of patients with a common painful condition, called fibrositis.)

Jane Roth—a prominent Wilmington lawyer, and the wife of Republican United States Senator William V. Roth—was President of the Delaware Arthritis Foundation. Mrs. Roth wrote to the Chichester DuPont Foundation enclosing my research proposal, and commenting:

> We are very proud of a Delaware research project which proposes to investigate fibro-

> myositis, one of the most common and least understood types of myofascial pain. . . .
>
> Dr. Connolly's hope of finding clues to relieve chronic pain is not only of interest to Delawareans. Successful findings would also be of great benefit to all people concerned with pain, perhaps not limited to the field of the rheumatic diseases.

Dr. Labowitz and some other Board members of the Arthritis Foundation felt, however, that a proposal for research funding should formally be made to the Medical and Scientific Committee of the Foundation. (Both Dr. Labowitz and I were members of this committee.) So I again submitted my proposed investigation, this time to the Medical and Scientific Committee. I then met with Dr. Labowitz and the other members of the committee in order to discuss my investigation. At the meeting was a new committee member; studious, bespectacled, and bearded, Dr. James H. Newman was Russ Labowitz's new partner.

Sometime later Jane Roth wrote again to the Chichester DuPont Foundation, this time to inform them that my proposal had been approved by the Chapter's Medical and Scientific Committee. She continued, saying, "We find this small local research study exciting and encouraging to the life and work of our Medical and Scientific Committee, as well as to the entire Board of Directors."

By the end of 1980 my work had increased to almost 50% of capacity. Although many patients paid only a fraction of the fee, and some paid nothing, gross receipts were up to $101,343; expenses took $60,909 of this, leaving me with a net of $40,434. And, as I worked towards full capacity, each additional dollar in gross receipts would add proportionately more to net income. Clearly, a doctor could make an excellent income in medicine, and still give financial consideration to each patient.

My office was growing. Two full-time secretaries were now working with me, Florence Pullella and her sister, Josie

Picollelli. I had moved my office one block up the street to 2401 Pennsylvania Avenue, a modern condominium building with handsomely kept lawns and ample parking space. The office was an attractive, bright, first-floor corner suite that I had purchased. Another nice feature was a second entrance into the office; a glass sliding door opened directly from the secretarial area onto the front sidewalk.

Our family was also growing; Anna, the youngest of our five children, was about to have her first birthday.

Publishing medical research is probably the single best way for a doctor to develop a fine reputation. As I worked on my fibrositic study and the effect of these two medications on sleep-EEG's, the *Delaware Medical Journal* was considering a manuscript which I had submitted that described the beneficial results of these two medications in the treatment of fibrositic patients.

The editor of the journal wrote to me that one reviewer queried whether a laboratory test — the sedimentation rate — was within normal limits in all of my patients "since this requirement is a must to allow the diagnostic label of fibromyositis." (The sedimentation rate is a commonly used laboratory test in which a small sample of the patient's blood is placed in a thin capillary tube; the rate at which the red blood cells fall to the bottom of the tube, leaving clear serum at the top, is the rate of sedimentation. Fibrositis, being characterized by normal laboratory studies, has a normal sedimentation rate [less than 30 millimeters per hour]; inflammatory arthritic conditions such as rheumatoid arthritis and lupus have abnormal laboratory studies, including elevated sedimentation rates [above 30].)

I sent the editor the additional data indicating that my patients all had normal sedimentation rates. The journal shortly thereafter accepted my manuscript for publication.

Less than two weeks after the editor queried me concerning my patients' sedimentation rates, I received a surprise from Dr. Labowitz: for the first time since I had opened my practice, he referred me a patient. Her name was Madeline Boone.

Mrs. Boone sat across the desk from me, pale and tired-looking. A middle-aged housewife, she cared for her sick, elderly mother at home. Her husband supported the family by working as an elementary-school custodian.

I was puzzled that, after more than two years, Dr. Labowitz was now referring me a patient. If he needed a second opinion, Dr. Newman was available in his own office.

Madeline Boone leaned across my desk, handing me a referral note from Dr. Labowitz. As I opened and read the note I asked Mrs. Boone, "What's Dr. Labowitz treating you for?"

"Lupus," Mrs. Boone replied.

"Lupus?" I said.

"Yes, lupus."

I then read to her Dr. Labowitz's note:

February 9, 1981

Dear Ron:

I am referring this patient to you for evaluation of non-articular rheumatism, most likely fibromyositis. . . .She may be a candidate for your study. If you need any information please let me know. . . .

Regards,
Russ

Looking up to Mrs. Boone I said, "Dr. Labowitz thinks you have fibrositis."

"Fibrositis? What's that?" she asked. "Dr. Labowitz told me I had lupus." Mrs. Boone then told me that the doctor had ordered laboratory tests on her at the Wilmington Medical Center.

I was concerned. Dr. Labowitz had presented the patient to me as having fibrositis, yet Mrs. Boone emphatically insisted that he had told her she had lupus. The two diagnoses are in sharp contrast: among other things, the diagnosis of fibrositis requires normal laboratory studies, including normal sedimentation rates, whereas patients with lupus have abnormal laboratory studies.

If Mrs. Boone was right and if I had entered her into my fibrositic study on the basis of Dr. Labowitz's note, my research would have been marred if not ruined, sleep electroencephalograms needlessly obtained, and at least part of the $5,000 grant wasted.

I considered the possibility that Dr. Labowitz had intentionally misrepresented his patient's diagnosis and had tried to sabotage my study.

More information would help to clarify the discrepancies. Without expressing my concerns to Mrs. Boone, I told her that we would request her medical records from Dr. Labowitz.

Then, after I questioned her further on her symptoms and examined her, my secretary had Mrs. Boone sign an authorization for records release from Dr. Labowitz and gave her a follow-up appointment for two weeks.

Two weeks later Mrs. Boone returned, but her medical records had still not arrived. My secretary telephoned Dr. Labowitz's office—again requesting the records—and Mrs. Boone signed another records release, which was again mailed to Dr. Labowitz.

A month passed, more office visits, another telephone call to Dr. Labowitz's office, but still no records on Madeline Boone.

Then, finally, someone in Dr. Labowitz's office sent a copy of a four-page letter which Labowitz had sent to an orthopedic surgeon six months before he referred Madeline Boone to me. The letter contained numerous objective abnormalities found on past physical exam and laboratory testing, including an abnormal sedimentation rate of 36 millimeters, that clearly excluded this patient from being a legitimate candidate for the fibrositic study.

I continued to work on my fibrositic study. In the meantime, my article on fibrositis was published in the April 1981 issue of the *Delaware Medical Journal.* The article discussed the significant improvement in nine patients treated with one or both of the medications, as well as the supervision and precautions taken to minimize the possibility of side-effects.

The success of the article was surprising. I soon received reprint requests from other states, as well as Mexico, Bulgaria, Czechoslovakia, Lithuania, and Poland. Patients were now being referred to me specifically for the management of their fibrositis.

I was sitting in my office on a humid August day, and as I looked through the morning mail I came across the August issue of the *Delaware Medical Journal*. As I casually paged through it, I came upon a Letter to the Editor:

> "Appropriate Treatment of Fibromyositis"
>
> We are writing in regard to Dr. Connolly's article in the April issue. . . .
>
> . . . . There is a definite risk (which may be as high as 20 percent) of irreversible [side effects]... complicating the long term use of [one of the medications which I had used in treating my fibrositic patients]. . . .
>
> Any prospective study attempted in this area should not only evaluate the patients from the traditional medical approach, history and physical, laboratory testing, and EEG, but also should include psychological testing. . . .
>
> At the present time, we do not feel that the combination of drugs used in this article should be used by the practicing physician until more reasonable data are available. . . .
>
> Russell J. Labowitz, M.D.
> James H. Newman, M.D.

Angrily, I reviewed the letter. Critical Letters to the Editor are common and often constructive, but Labowitz and Newman's letter for a number of reasons was distinctly uncommon: Both of them had been present at the Medical and

Scientific Committee meeting the year before the journal published my article when I had discussed my research proposal, including my use of these medications. Neither of them at that time or subsequently had ever expressed concern to me regarding these medications; they had gone directly to a public forum for their criticisms.

In addition, if Labowitz did not approve of the use of these medications then why had he referred to me his own patient—Madeline Boone—for probable therapy with these medications?

Further, Labowitz, the Chief of Rheumatology, publicly affirmed in his Letter to the Editor that fibrositic patients should be evaluated according to the "traditional" medical approach of patient history, physical exam, and laboratory testing. But privately he had referred Mrs. Boone to me with documented exclusions in his own medical records to the traditional diagnosis of fibrositis, including at least one abnormal sedimentation rate.

Also, the reviewer (I later learned that it was Dr. Labowitz) of my manuscript for the *Delaware Medical Journal* knew that abnormal sedimentation rates are an exclusion; the reviewer had queried, only weeks before Labowitz referred Madeline Boone to me, whether the sedimentation rate was within normal limits in all of my patients, "since this requirement is a must to allow the diagnostic label of fibromyositis."

I had received only positive responses to my article, including responses from foreign countries. But now there was one noteworthy exception to these affirmative responses: two of my peers in the four-man Section of Rheumatology at the Wilmington Medical Center, Drs. Labowitz and Newman.

Several weeks later, I wrote a follow-up Letter to the Editor. Exercising tolerance and restraint, and without going into Labowitz and Newman's apparent duplicity or reviewing the references which they had cited to support their letter (I assumed they had represented them accurately), I reiterated the precautions and circumstances under which I had used the medications. I also cited a major review article on chronic pain in the *Annals of Internal Medicine* which similarly advocated these medications.

By the end of 1981 my yearly figures showed that the practice had plateaued at about 50% of capacity; although gross income had increased 130% from 1979 to 1980, it had increased only 13% from 1980 to 1981.

The next year, 1982, was even worse; the increase in office gross was only 2%, less than the rate of inflation. Most of my referrals were coming from satisfied patients, and fewer were coming from doctors. While my office was often empty, new patients were waiting weeks for an appointment in Dr. Labowitz's office. My first year in Delaware I had been told that there was unfair business competition in the medical community. Personally, I had run into problems: I had been accused of patient abandonment for not consulting on the abortion patient; there was the suggestion that Labowitz had misrepresented Madeline Boone's diagnosis when he referred her as a possible candidate for my study; and I felt sure that Labowitz and Newman's Letter to the Editor had damaged the acceptability of my article in the *Delaware Medical Journal*. But would these actions alone result in my reception room being empty while patients waited weeks to see Labowitz and Newman?

December 13, 1982, I received a letter from the Wilmington Medical Center:

Dear Dr. Connolly:

We are happy that your application for reappointment to the staff has been approved, however the Credentials Committee of the Department of Medicine has noted less than average performance in the following areas: conference attendance and participation in departmental functions. This information has been passed on to you in the hope that greater participation can be anticipated in the future.

The entire credentials process should be one that stimulates interest within the Department

and the entire hospital. We sincerely hope that
in the next few years you will be more active.

Sincerely yours,
Russell Labowitz, M.D.
Head, Section of Rheumatology
Department of Medicine

Robert B. Flinn, M.D.
Director, Department of Medicine

After reading the letter, I considered: Each conference attended resulted in one hour of Continuing Medical Education (CME) credit, and the Medical Society of Delaware required 17 CME credit-hours per year. For this year, 1982, I had 110 CME credits. (Conference attendance was urged, but not required at the Wilmington Medical Center; like many physicians, many of my credits had been received from other institutions, and I had recently informed the hospital of this fact.)

In addition, my participation at the Wilmington Medical Center included a mandatory three-month per year rotation on the Rheumatology Service, during which time I worked gratis in the Thursday morning Arthritis Clinic (for which the hospital billed the patient) and was on-call 24 hours per day for possible gratis hospital consultations. In return, I averaged only one patient-referral per month from the hospital.

My past experience with Dr. Labowitz clearly indicated to me the measure of his hopes for my future participation.

As the bleak days of December 1982 continued to slip by, I reassured myself, for the fourth year in a row, that it was just a matter of time before my practice was established. In the meantime, I continued to enjoy working with my patients; I continued to study through the various CME programs, and I continued my research. (In June, I would be presenting the results of my fibrositic study at the national meeting of the American Rheumatism Association in San Antonio, and would also be submitting the results of this study for publication.)

It was now December 24, Christmas Eve. I left the office earlier than usual. It was time to celebrate, and Sieglinde and I wanted to finish our preparations for the children's Christmas. As I drove home I was unaware of what awaited me; it would irrevocably change our lives.

As I walked through the front door Maria, blue eyes smiling, grabbed my hand to show me her Christmas presents for the family. Christina was writing a Christmas card to her bunny rabbit, Flipper. Ronny and Anna were playing in the living room, and Schnucki was out walking Fritzi, our German Shepherd.

I entered the kitchen. Sieglinde smiled as she placed a pan on the stove. I kissed her on the cheek, asked about her day, and as we hastily caught up on each other's activities, I looked over the day's mail.

There was a letter addressed to me marked "PERSONAL & CONFIDENTIAL" from Dr. Alfred Lazarus, the representative from Delaware for the American College of Physicians (ACP). (Dr. Lazarus' official title was ACP Governor for Delaware.) The College is the second largest medical organization in the United States, exceeded only by the American Medical Association. The stated aims of the College include improving patient care, fostering medical education, encouraging research, and similar principles. I had applied for membership to the College in May, more than seven months ago, and for months had been awaiting notification of the routine acceptance.

I quickly slit open the envelope:

December 21, 1982

Dear Dr. Connolly:

The credentials subcommittee has deferred your application for membership in the College of Physicians. The reason for this is your lack of adequate participation in the teaching program and meeting the responsibilities of your section according to the reports of the credentials committee of the Department of Medicine of the Wilmington Medical Center. In view of that, the committee and the local committee and I did not feel that your application at this time was sufficient to warrant membership in the college. If this improves next year I would be most happy to endorse your application.

Best personal regards.

Sincerely yours,
Alfred Lazarus, M.D. (Exhibit #2)*

"Those bastards!" I roared. "They've denied me membership in the American College of Physicians!"

"This time they've gone too far!" I said as I handed Sieglinde the letter. "No one gets refused membership in the American College of Physicians. It's like not getting into the Boy Scouts!"

Sieglinde finished reading the letter. "Show it to Dad!" she said, handing it back to me.

This was blatant. This was war. Lazarus had sent me a "PERSONAL & CONFIDENTIAL" letter on Christmas Eve that denied me membership in the American College of Physicians. I had submitted my application to him on May 7; his letter of denial was post-marked December 23.

What "reports" was Lazarus referring to? Dr. Labowitz was my section chief; his only criticism to me during my four years at the hospital was the brief letter he and Dr. Flinn had sent less than two weeks ago, and this was more than six months *after* I had applied to the College. No one had ever told me that my participation in the teaching program was inadequate, nor that I was deficient in meeting the responsibilities of my section.

* Please see Appendix: Exhibit #2.

In more than 15 years of practicing medicine I had never heard of anyone being denied membership in the College; even medical school students were accepted, and I had graduated from medical school in 1966 and had then advanced with additional years of training, credentialing, and experience.

For four years I had been tolerant and accommodating, hoping and expecting that the problems would pass. I had not complained after I was criticized for not participating in an abortion because of my religious convictions; I had not complained when I heard talk of having me "run out of town"; I had not complained about Labowitz's inappropriate referral of a patient for my fibrositic research and his withholding essential information from me in spite of repeated requests, and I had not complained following Labowitz and Newman's letter to the *Delaware Medical Journal.*

Now it was clear that unless things changed I had no future in Wilmington: My practice had been crippled by repeated attacks, and my career was going to go nowhere until these problems were resolved. I had not worked in medicine for twenty years, nor had I volunteered to serve in Vietnam, only to be wiped out by a few of my peers. Accommodation had not satisfied them. Now, for the first time in my life, I would confront.

The same energy, strength, and commitment that I had devoted to medicine for the past twenty years was now being redirected. Whatever it took, Labowitz, Lazarus, Levinson, and I were going to straighten things out.

3
The Board Of Medical Practice

The Code of Ethics is meaningless.

Robert B. Flinn, M.D.
Director, Department of Medicine
Wilmington Medical Center

Autonomy is contradictory to the usual checks and balances which characterize a democracy. In government the legislative, judicial, and executive branches provide a check on one another. A board of directors monitors the activities of a corporation, and a school board can hire or fire the Superintendent of Schools.

In sharp contrast, the medical profession is granted an autonomy by the public that approaches a licensed monopoly. This has been done because the medical profession solemnly pledges that the public's health and welfare is foremost.

As the medical profession supervises the country's health care, a by-product is their unsurpassed domination of an industry that generated over $800 billion in revenue in 1992.

In a democracy, with free enterprise and fair competition, if politicians, corporate executives, or school officials perform poorly, they are replaced—fired. In contrast, even though this country is in the midst of an unparalleled health care crisis, in each of the fifty states the medical profession remains entrenched in controlling its licensed monopoly.

The medical profession in the United States has administrators, committees and institutions whose duties include disciplining their medical peers. The professed purpose of this system is to protect the public from unethical, incompetent and impaired doctors, thus insuring the public's health and welfare. To utilize this system to *conceal* medical fraud would be a perversion of its fundamental intent and a betrayal of the public's trust.

Serious questions have been raised, however, as to whether the medical profession is sufficiently accountable for its actions. A Special Report published in the March 21, 1985 *New England Journal of Medicine*, said "There have been estimates that as many as 5 — 15 percent of doctors are not fully competent to practice medicine." Yet the Federation of State Medical Boards has documented that in some years not one of the 50 states had a disciplinary rate above 1 percent per year. Additionally, in some years there are states which have not disciplined one physician per thousand!

Dr. Arnold Relman, the recent editor of the *New England Journal of Medicine*, editorialized on the above Special Report stating, "All the evidence suggests . . . that most if not all the states have been too lax . . . in their enforcement of medical professional standards."

Several common explanations are given for such gross deficiencies in the self-regulation of the medical profession, such as the failure of legislators to budget sufficient funds and to grant sufficient power to enable the medical profession to discipline itself satisfactorily.

A systematic and calculated refusal by medical authorities to fulfill their public responsibility is infrequently offered as an explanation for these deficiencies.

For the first time, I was now presenting complaints of unethical conduct to the medical authorities. I was following the medical profession's prescribed directions. Little did I imagine what lay ahead.

Taking Lazarus's letter with me, I drove to my parents' house.

Perhaps some background about my parents would be helpful. My mother, Gerardine Laffey Connolly, had been born in Wilmington, and came from a family of attorneys. (Her given name came from St. Gerard who is the patron saint of childbirth, and Gerard is my middle name.) Her uncle, John Laffey, had started the legal department for the DuPont Company in 1903. He was head of the Legal Department and general counsel for the company. He served as a Vice President from 1923 until his death in 1937. My mother's father, Tom Laffey, also an attorney, worked at DuPont with his brother, John, and, after a company divestiture, he started the legal department of Atlas Chemical Company in Wilmington.

My mother, who had brown eyes and dark hair (which I inherited), as a young girl had experienced tragedy. She was only seven years old when her mother died from a fall down a flight of stairs. Afterwards, the slender little girl had hugged her mother's empty bathrobe as it hung behind the door of her parent's bedroom. She had written letters to her absent mother, placing them at the foot of the Blessed Mother's statue in the Chapel at Ursuline Academy, where she went to school. (A kind nun had collected the letters and returned them to my mother when she and Dad married.)

When my mother was fourteen, her stepmother, whom she also loved, died from tonsillitis. And throughout these years her good friends, including the nuns at Ursuline and at the Visitation Monastery, provided great love and support—and my mother reciprocated.

By the time she was twenty, she was strikingly beautiful, with dark brown hair, angular features, and a warm personality: spontaneous and outgoing, yet serious and committed. She was popular, loved horseback riding, and had gone to art school. But, perhaps because of the tragedies in her life, she had an exceptional need for people; she was eminently kind and thoughtful, cared for friends as well as strangers, had more true friends than anyone I have known, and was a devout Catholic.

As a boy, sometimes if I was in a hurry or tired, I would say "I don't care about . . . ."

Mom would gently reply, "Ronny, *care* . . . always *care*."

My father, Arthur Guild Connolly, was from south Boston. His grandfather, John Connolly, my great-grandfather, had immigrated to Boston as a teenager from County Galway in Ireland around 1847 when a million impoverished Irish men, women, and children died from starvation and disease during the potato famine. At that time in the United States, Blacks and Irish often competed for the most menial, lowest-paying jobs. In

1849 my great-grandfather, about seventeen years of age at the time, became a "forty-niner," traveling across the country in a covered wagon to California, where he dug for gold. His industry was modestly rewarded, and he returned to Boston with enough gold to buy a small combination grocery-liquor store located where South Station now stands. Later he fought with a Massachusetts regiment in the Civil War, and his Civil War rifle remains a family memento. When my great grandfather died, my great-grandmother, in order to meet family expenses, sold off the south Boston property her husband had acquired; the once-comfortable nest egg was soon gone.

My father, as a nine-year-old boy, walked the south Boston streets at six o'clock on cold winter mornings delivering 200 newspapers; half went to homes and the rest were sold on the street corner or as he walked through trolley cars. In the hot summer months he labored on a farm outside Boston for ten cents an hour. After South Boston High School, he worked his way through MIT, studying chemical engineering, and then through Harvard Law School. Soon afterwards he took a job in Wilmington as a patent lawyer with the DuPont Company. In 1943 he left DuPont to start his own law firm, and, with exceedingly hard work—seven days a week, year after year— the firm prospered, and he had a national reputation.

"Willpower," Dad often said, referring to self-discipline, hard work, honesty, and healthy living habits, "is the key to success; without it a person won't amount to much." With willpower any accomplishment was possible, especially in America.

After buying our first television in the early 1950's, we often watched Friday night boxing presented by the Gillette Cavalcade of Sports, and, if the under-dog started to take a pounding and needed help, we invariably would see Dad jump up from the couch, unable to restrain himself, throwing left jabs and right upper-cuts at the assailant.

My father was now seventy-seven years old; with gray hair and keen blue eyes, he still practiced law and worked seven days a week. To keep physically fit, several times each week he rode his bike, eighteen miles in all, around the roads of Alapocas, and he still climbed stairs two at a time.

Dad enjoyed his work, and he had enthusiastically supported my decision to open my own practice, to be my own boss.

Now, as we sat at the dining room table, Mom and I watched Dad as he studied Lazarus's letter. "They're using the Wilmington Medical Center as a bottleneck to block your advancement," he somberly remarked, turning towards me.

"You don't have to be on the staff of the Wilmington Medical Center," I angrily responded, "to be a member of the American College of Physicians! I teach and have responsibilities at Seaford, St. Francis, and other hospitals as well. I donate work each year to the Wilmington Medical Center; I rarely get referrals from them, yet they block my membership in the American College of Physicians!"

As we reviewed my four turbulent years in Wilmington medicine, I saw two explanations: Labowitz wanted a monopoly in Delaware rheumatology, and some people wanted to destroy my practice because of the abortion incident.

"I know the president of the hospital, James Harding," Dad said. "I'll arrange for us to meet with him."

Pleased with that prospect, I responded that I would call Lazarus to see what "reports" he was referring to, and to see which doctors were on his "local committee."

Mom, her faced lined and concerned, added her perspective as I was getting ready to leave. "Ron, don't let this spoil your Christmas."

Dad and I were scheduled to meet with Harding on Friday, January 14, and I prepared with a passion. Finally, after four years, my work was going to be freed of interference.

I had never met nor spoken with Lazarus. I now telephoned him. Lazarus confirmed that the "reports of the credentials committee of the Department of Medicine of the Wilmington Medical Center" had originated from Labowitz. They were reports *from* Labowitz *to* the Credentials Committee. On the basis of Labowitz's reports—reports submitted behind my back, since I had not known they existed—Lazarus had denied me

ACP membership without once speaking to me; he never interviewed me; he never gave me a chance to respond.

Lazarus further told me that his "local committee" which had considered my application, consisted of three physicians: John Egan, Wayne Martz, and Richard Morgan. I decided to speak with each of these in turn.

I telephoned Dr. Egan, a hematologist, who told me he was unaware that he was on Lazarus' ACP committee; he knew nothing of my application.

I then called Dr. Martz, an internist and Chief of Medical Education at the Wilmington Medical Center, who confirmed that he was on Lazarus' ACP committee, but he was unaware that I had applied for membership.

Finally, I called Richard Morgan, another internist, who confirmed that he was on this committee, and that Lazarus had discussed my application with him in a brief telephone conversation three to six months previously.

Lazarus's "local committee" that had deferred my application was a hoax! Lazarus—hiding behind a medical committee—had simply used Labowitz's reports to deny me ACP membership.

Next, I reviewed Delaware legislation governing abortion. Code #1791 of the *Medical Practices Act* stated: "No person shall be required to perform or participate in medical procedures which result in the termination of pregnancy; and the refusal of any person to perform or participate in these medical procedures shall not be a basis for civil liability to any person, nor a basis for any disciplinary or other recriminatory action against him."

As our meeting with Harding approached, I also wanted to talk with one additional person—Madeline Boone. I telephoned the patient. She adamantly repeated that Dr. Labowitz had told her she had lupus shortly before he had referred her to me. She had been alarmed by the diagnosis; she had requested and received literature on lupus from the Arthritis Foundation, and she then discussed her disease with her family minister.

A few days later Mrs. Boone signed a statement affirming that Dr. Labowitz had diagnosed her as having lupus prior to his referral of her to me. She also reminded me that Labowitz had ordered blood tests on her at the Wilmington Medical Center.

I then called the hospital requesting Mrs. Boone's laboratory tests. They sent me an erythrocyte sedimentation rate ordered by Labowitz only weeks before he referred the patient to me. The result was 43, well above the normal rate. This was now the second abnormal sedimentation rate in Dr. Labowitz's possession, and yet not made available to me, at the time he had referred Mrs. Boone. According to Labowitz's own criteria, this had excluded the diagnosis of fibrositis in Mrs. Boone weeks before he had referred her to me for possible inclusion in my fibrositic sleep-EEG study.

It was now time for Dad and me to present our evidence to James Harding, president of the Wilmington Medical Center.

As we walked into the first-floor lobby of the administrative wing of the hospital's Delaware division adrenaline coursed through my body. A clear, concise presentation to Harding would resolve my problems; my practice would start reflecting my work of the past twenty years, rather than the interference of Labowitz and others.

I was excited, but my father, with his blue eyes, white hair and spry steps, was relaxed. For fifty years he had been criss-crossing the country as a trial lawyer.

As we entered the president's sumptuous office, James Harding, a heavy-set, amiable man with thinning hair, warmly greeted us. Mr. Harding sat down behind his executive desk and motioned for us to take chairs across from him. As president of the Wilmington Medical Center, he was busy with the final stages of the hospital's new $145 million expansion, consolidating the Center's three geographically distributed divisions (the Delaware, the Memorial, and the Wilmington General). The new consolidated hospital would be called the Medical Center of Delaware and was scheduled to open south of Wilmington within the year. In size, the center, with more than one thousand acute beds, was among the top three percent of U.S. hospitals. Its maternity service handled more than 6,000 deliveries a year, and was the fifth largest in the country. There were more than eight hundred doctors on the Medical/Dental

Staff; the hospital was one of the largest employers in the state; and more than one hundred of the most prominent Delaware philanthropists, professionals, bankers and business leaders served as trustees of the hospital.

After exchanging pleasantries, Dad focused the subject, saying that I was having problems with a few members of the hospital staff. I then handed Mr. Harding a manila folder containing copies of Labowitz's and Lazarus' letters, Levinson's complaint of patient abandonment, and additional data supporting each of my complaints.

As I summarized each of the problems, including the abortion, we reviewed the data together. With each incident Harding spoke of his concern, asked questions, made comments, and promised a prompt investigation.

After more than an hour, the complaints had been thoroughly discussed. Harding wished to keep the manila folder containing his copy of the data in order to help with the investigation. As we were leaving, Dad and I thanked Mr. Harding for his time and obvious concern. As I shook hands I said: "In my opinion, Mr. Harding, Dr. Labowitz and Dr. Lazarus are dishonest and flagrantly unethical."

"In addition, they're stupid," Harding rejoined, in obvious reference to the blatancy of their actions.

"We'll look into the complaints thoroughly," he continued, "and we'll be in touch with you."

My father was smiling as we walked down the stairs of the hospital. "Ron, you did a great job. You made a brief statement, then you showed him the supporting evidence; another brief statement, then more documenting evidence."

I thought of Sieglinde and the upheaval we had been through the past four years. It would be nice to stop fighting and to concentrate on medicine.

Two weeks later my father received a letter from Harding saying that he had referred the problems to the Medical Center's Vice President for Medical Affairs, Dr. Allston Morris, "in order that they may be reviewed and resolved appropriately through our normal administrative channels."

Thursday morning, January 27, Dr. Morris telephoned, asking me to meet him at one o'clock in his office.

I dashed home to put on a suit. As I was about to leave, Sieglinde checked my optimism. She was worried. "Don't be disappointed if they don't do anything."

"They'd be crazy if they didn't," I replied. "I'm not trying to break down walls. I just want an *acknowledgement* of wrongdoing, and an assurance that it's going to stop. If they want, they can even keep Labowitz as Chief of Rheumatology."

I gave Sieglinde a hug and a kiss, and I headed off for the hospital.

Morris's office, at the opposite end of the hall from Harding's, was small and cluttered. Morris, short, bespectacled and intense, had been an internist in private practice before accepting his full-time position at the Medical Center. As we sat down, his secretary handed him a jumbo sandwich. He asked if I would like one. I thanked him but declined.

Sieglinde's premonition was justified. Morris "would have been honored" if, when he had started practice, his section chief had referred him a patient such as Madeline Boone. Other complaints, such as Lazarus's handling of my ACP application, as well as Labowitz and Newman's letter to the *Delaware Medical Journal*, were outside the jurisdiction of the Wilmington Medical Center.

"Dr. Morris," I responded, "Dr. Labowitz is your Section Chief of Rheumatology. His professional conduct is relevant to the hospital. And Dr. Lazarus, your Chief of Gastroenterology, was using Wilmington Medical Center reports from Dr. Labowitz to your Credentials Committee to defer my American College of Physicians application. Lazarus then attributed his deferral to a committee — a hoax committee — composed of three Wilmington Medical Center doctors. And the abortion was done by Dr. Levinson *at* the Wilmington Medical Center."

As I finished, Morris took a mammoth-sized bite from his multi-layered sandwich and struggled to compose himself. A bolus of food ballooned out his left cheek. "Dr. Connolly, if you're interested in pursuing this further, I suggest you talk with your departmental chairman, Dr. Flinn."

Morris then added that my Arthritis Clinic in Seaford (a two-hour drive south of Wilmington where I attended once a month) seemed to be going well; perhaps I should develop my practice there.

We finished our conversation a few minutes later. As I stood up to leave, I saw on Morris's cluttered desk the manila folder supporting my complaints which I had left with Harding. "Will you give the information to Dr. Flinn?" I asked, pointing to the folder. Morris acknowledged that he would.

"I think Dr. Labowitz's and Dr. Lazarus's conduct is dishonest and flagrantly unethical," I said.

Morris picked up a pencil from his desk and facetiously wrote on the front of the manila folder, "dishonest and unethical."

"That's right," I quietly said as I picked up the same pencil and underlined "dishonest and unethical."

Walking back to my car I thought of Morris's statements. So this was the review and the resolution of my complaints that Harding had promised.

Morris had suggested that I present my complaints to Dr. Robert Flinn, the Director of the Department of Medicine. (The department included twelve or so sections, of which one was rheumatology.) Realizing that this was my last chance to resolve my problems, I tried to be optimistic that Dr. Flinn, unlike Harding and Morris, would respond to my complaints. I called the director; our appointment was scheduled for Monday afternoon.

I knew Robert Flinn personally; we had been in the same medical building when I opened my practice in 1979. Dr. Flinn was a leading member of the medical community.

The director's hospital office was on an upper floor of the Delaware division. As I entered, Dr. Flinn—distinguished, wearing a starched white lab coat, with wavy, graying, neatly parted hair—cordially greeted me. He sat behind a small antique desk; behind him were rows of neatly ordered medical books and journals; an Oriental rug covered the floor.

On his desk lay my manila folder of complaints, which Dr. Morris had forwarded.

"Well, Ron, what seems to be the trouble?"

As with Harding and Morris, I related my complaints. Flinn was attentive but noncommittal. During a break in the conversation, since I remembered seeing Flinn's name in a recent Friends School alumni magazine, I mentioned our mutual school. We briefly reminisced over a few of our memorable teachers, including Mrs. Passmore, the fourth-grade teacher who, for two generations of students, seemed to embody character and dignity.

When we resumed the discussion of my complaints, Flinn remained noncommittal. He would not acknowledge the slightest wrongdoing on the part of Labowitz and Lazarus.

Finally, reaching into my brief case, I pulled out three paper binders, and held them up.

"Dr. Flinn," I said, "here are more than 100 pages of Wilmington Medical Center Bylaws, Rules, and Regulations." Then, turning to the last page of the Bylaws, I said: "Here is the Medical Code of Ethics of the American Medical Association as adopted by the Wilmington Medical Center. Section 4 says: 'The medical profession should safeguard the public and itself against physicians deficient in moral character or professional competence. Physicians should observe all laws, uphold the dignity and honor of the profession and accept its self-imposed disciplines. They should expose, without hesitation, illegal or unethical conduct of fellow members of the profession'."

Dr. Flinn flatly replied, "The Code of Ethics is meaningless."

I was disappointed, but not surprised. We discussed the issues for a while longer; then, as I was leaving, Dr. Flinn promised to investigate the complaints and get back to me.

Discouraged, I drove home to Sieglinde.

"They're all afraid," Sieglinde said. "We should just move back to California."

"Whether we move or not," I replied, "we at least have to get a response to our complaints. We've worked too hard to just pack up and leave."

I felt a sad sense of irony: Believing in democracy, I had volunteered for the Marine Corps in Vietnam and served with the Navy at Cam Ranh Bay, and yet now, in Delaware, we were being driven from our home. At the age of 43 I would have to look for a new job. In other parts of the world people risk imprisonment and worse for freedom and justice. Yet, the prestigious medical authorities to whom I had appealed had, like cowards, refused to perform the minimal duty for which they were being handsomely paid.

That night, as so often in the past, I lay in bed unable to sleep. If I could just think of the right words which would prompt Flinn to act. Perhaps I had my foot in the door with our common experience at Friends School. I decided to write a letter to Flinn the next day.

The next morning, February 1, as I worked on an outline of my letter, I received unexpected assistance. The morning mail contained a letter from Flinn addressed to all members of the Department of Medicine. The letter stressed the need for an "open active staff" in the new multi-million dollar hospital, and he urged the members of the department to promptly communicate problems directly to him in order to diminish "the possibility of an elite group forming."

Perfect! That was precisely what I had done the day before! Perhaps there was hope. If Flinn resolved my complaints then my family and I would have a future in Wilmington; we would not have to give up our home and my practice.

I wrote to Dr. Flinn that in order to have an open staff, and out of respect for the ideals that guided admirable teachers at Friends School, he should at least consider that "There has been unethical conduct at the Wilmington Medical Center; a not unlikely assumption given the fact that there are hundreds of physicians on the staff." I then urged him to investigate my complaints, and I concluded my letter, saying, "The problem with the world today lies not with Russia, Poland, Afghanistan, Iran, Central America, etc., but here. The problem lies with people who are free and have an opportunity to make a difference."

That evening I showed the letter to Sieglinde. "It's awfully strong," she said, "talking about Russia and Iran."

"I know it is," I replied, "but that's how I feel. I didn't ask them to do me a favor. I asked them to do their job. Day after day for years I explicitly followed their rules, regulations, bylaws and ethics . . . like a grunt. I crossed every 't' and dotted every 'i'. The first time in my life that I asked the power-movers to respond they ignore me, and tell me the Code of Ethics is meaningless!"

If Sieglinde, the children, and I were going to leave Delaware, I was going to tell Flinn how I felt.

Ten days later Flinn had still not acknowledged my letter. Determined that the hospital was going to respond to at least one of my complaints, I chose Labowitz's referral of Madeline Boone, and I wrote him another letter:

> February 10, 1983
>
> Dear Dr. Flinn:
>
> The Code of Ethics of the American Medical Association, adopted by the Wilmington Medical Center. . . states that a physician "should expose without hesitation, illegal or unethical conduct of fellow members of the profession."
>
> I regret the necessity of filing a formal complaint . . . . However, the ByLaws of the Wilmington Medical Center obligate me to comply. Therefore, by means of this letter, I am filing a formal complaint against Dr. Russell Labowitz for, what I believe to be, unethical conduct . . . .
>
> . . . . As one example [I then presented the evidence that Dr. Labowitz had falsified Madeline Boone's diagnosis: the patient's signed statement, Labowitz's referral note representing the patient as having fibrositis, his withholding medical data on the patient which was incompatible with the diagnosis of fibrositis, including abnormal sedimentation rates] . . . .
>
> I would like a formal reply whether or not the Wilmington Medical Center has found Dr. Labowitz's conduct ethical or unethical. I hope this question can be resolved within the next month. If clarification is still pending one month from now, then I will seek the advice of the Board of Trustees.

Flinn acknowledged receipt of the complaint and referred it to the "Department of Medicine's Credentials Committee for their review and decision."

Weeks passed, but there was no further word concerning my complaint.

It was obvious to me that the Wilmington Medical Center had a conflict of interest in disciplining Labowitz, and also Lazarus. Labowitz was Chief of their Section of Rheumatology and Lazarus was Chief of their Section of Gastroenterology. Both doctors had thriving practices and provided business to the hospital. They also undoubtedly worked, referring patients back and forth, with at least some of the physicians on the Credentials Committee. Also, Lazarus himself was a member of the Credentials Committee!

After more than a month of waiting, rather than turning to the hospital's Board of Trustees, I decided to submit my complaints to the Delaware Board of Medical Practice—the top medical tribunal in the state.

The Board of Medical Practice was located one hour south of Wilmington, in Dover. It consisted of eleven physicians and two lay persons, and although a majority of the physicians were on the staff of the Wilmington Medical Center, at least some down-state physicians would be represented. An additional advantage was that as I presented my complaints, they could not be dismissed as being outside the scope of the Wilmington Medical Center.

During the second week of March, as I worked on my complaints to the state Board, the chairman of the hospital's Credentials Committee, Dr. Charles Reese, a neurologist, telephoned to say that the Credentials Committee would like to meet with me on Monday, March 14, at 5 p.m.

As I sat at one end of the long conference-room table, Dr. Reese—in his early fifties, lean featured and dignified—sat at the opposite end, while committee members lined the sides. Dr. Lazarus was absent.

Dr. Reese asked if I objected to his tape-recording the meeting. I assured him that I had no objections.

As the meeting started Dr. Reese told me that they would only consider the complaint which Dr. Flinn had forwarded to them, namely, Dr. Labowitz's referral of Madeline Boone.

Now, for the fourth time, I presented my complaint, and responded to questions. And, as with Drs. Morris and Flinn, there was not the slightest acknowledgement of wrongdoing. As the meeting concluded, Dr. Reese told me that the Committee would send its report to Dr. Flinn; any reply that I received would have to come from him.

As I was leaving I told Dr. Reese and the committee that I would like to present all of my complaints to the Delaware Board of Medical Practice. Dr. Reese replied that that would be appropriate, since some of the problems had occurred outside of the Medical Center.

As I left the room, Dr. Labowitz entered.

I had not expected the confrontation to escalate to the state Board of Medical Practice, but I deserved an answer to my complaints. The day after the Credentials Committee meeting, I completed a formal twelve-page letter explaining my complaints against Drs. Labowitz and Lazarus. I also related Dr. Levinson's patient-abandonment charge, and the subsequent reprimand that I had received.

During my years in Delaware I had worked hard to be accepted by my peers; I had been tolerant; I had not complained. I fully realized that if I filed a complaint before the Board, some doctors would disapprove and a few would despise me. But I wanted a response to my complaints; it was important if my practice was to be salvaged.

As soon as my secretary, Josie, had left for the post office with my complaints, I felt pleased. I had made my decision; it was now time for the Board to make theirs.

As the Board considered my complaints, I asked Dr. Flinn to transfer me from the Active Staff at the hospital to the Courtesy Staff. I had spent months every year donating my services to the hospital, but there was no evidence of reciprocity.

Meanwhile, I had had success on another front. After meeting with Harding, I had applied for membership directly to the headquarters of the American College of Physicians in

Philadelphia and I had also filed a complaint against the ACP Governor for Delaware, Dr. Lazarus, who had failed to process my application according to regulations. Several weeks later I received a letter from the Regent and Secretary General of the College, Dr. George T. Lukemeyer, congratulating me on being elected to membership, and further stating that he planned "to meet and talk with Governor Alfred Lazarus. Together we will discuss College policies and procedures as it relates to election to Membership. . . ."

On April 8 Dr. Flinn called me to his office; the Credentials Committee had completed their deliberations.

Dr. Flinn, wearing his usual white lab coat, a stethoscope protruding from his pocket, peered at me: "Ron, the Credentials Committee investigated your complaint against Dr. Labowitz and, frankly, felt it was without merit . . . and I agree with them. They also felt your complaint was somewhat inappropriate, and suggested that you have a psychiatric evaluation."

"Why," I exclaimed, "should I see a psychiatrist?"

"Ron, you're so intense in pursuing this issue that we thought a psychiatric evaluation might be helpful."

I assured Flinn that I felt fine, I was not going to see a psychiatrist, and the Medical Code of Ethics required every physician to expose unethical conduct.

Flinn then handed me a letter which he had written a few days earlier, the substance of which he had just discussed with me:

April 6, 1983

Dear Dr. Connolly:

I have received the report from the Department of Medicine's Credentials Committee concerning your complaint that Dr. Russell J. Labowitz had committed unethical conduct. The Committee was unanimous in its feeling that the diagnosis of a referring physician to an investigator conducting a study should have no bearing on whether or not the patient is accepted in the study. It must be the investigator's responsibility to make that decision. Therefore, they felt that Dr. Labowitz was blameless and that your complaint against him of unethical conduct was without merit; and therefore, somewhat inappropriate.

Sincerely yours,
Robert B. Flinn, M.D.
Director
Department of Medicine

Driving home, I angrily reviewed the events. I was sure Flinn's psychiatric recommendation had resulted from my earlier letter imploring him to investigate my complaints and then concluding: "The problem with the world today lies not with Russia, Poland, Afghanistan, Iran, Central America, etc., but here. The problem lies with people who are free and have an opportunity to make a difference."

Flinn evidently had disapproved of my letter. Perhaps I should have included "Vietnam" in my enumeration.

The next week I called Flinn on the telephone. I told him that the Credentials Committee had not addressed my complaint against Dr. Labowitz. They had not mentioned my evidence that he had misrepresented his patient's diagnosis and withheld essential data. "That's a serious charge you're making," Flinn said. "You can't prove it 100 percent."

I was unable to budge Dr. Flinn from his decision, and a few minutes later we concluded the conversation.

Dad urged me to document my request that Flinn reconsider by sending him a letter. Together, Dad and I worked out my reply:

April 25, 1983

Dear Dr. Flinn:

Your letter of April 6, 1983 fails to address my formal complaint that Dr. Labowitz's conduct has been unethical.

There has never been any question that, as an investigator conducting a study, I had the responsibility and right of diagnosing the patients accepted for this study. However, this does not, as your letter implies, excuse Dr. Labowitz's unethical behavior. . . .

Evidently the Credentials Committee prefers to condone such conduct rather than censure it, even though it jeopardized the patient's health and, if undetected, would have invalidated the research project.

Sincerely,
Ronald G. Connolly, M.D.

A few days later, Flinn responded:

April 29, 1983

Dear Ron:

. . . . The Credentials Committee examined each and every bit of evidence that you forwarded. They found no evidence to support your conclusion or charges.

Therefore, it is the Committee's opinion and mine that Doctor Labowitz has behaved in a very ethical fashion and we simply do not agree with your interpretation.

> I hope this clarifies our position on your complaint that Dr. Labowitz's conduct has been unethical.
>
> Sincerely yours,
> Robert B. Flinn, M.D.
> Director
> Department of Medicine

I now consoled myself with the knowledge that the Delaware Board of Medical Practice was reviewing all my complaints. My decision to go to the Board had already been affirmed.

I had mailed my complaints to the Board in mid-March, and as the weeks of April slipped by I waited for some response; perhaps an investigator would meet with me or I would be asked to testify.

If the Board acknowledged Labowitz's and Lazarus's wrongdoing, if they reprimanded them, then I would be satisfied. This would send a clear message, and my future would be unimpeded.

The Board of Medical Practice was established by Delaware legislation with these words:

> Recognizing that the practice of medicine is a privilege . . . it is hereby deemed necessary . . . to provide regulations to the end that the public health shall be promoted and that the public shall be properly protected . . . from unprofessional conduct by persons licensed to practice medicine. (#3)

The Governor of Delaware appoints the Board from a list of nominees submitted by the Medical Society of Delaware.

The *Medical Practices Act*, which governs the Board of Medical Practice, in Code #1732 states:

> It shall be the duty of the Board to investigate, either upon complaint or, whenever it shall

> think proper, upon its own motion, cases of unprofessional conduct. (#4)

I had begun my complaint to the Board saying: "By this letter I am filing formal complaints against Dr. Russell Labowitz and Dr. Alfred Lazarus for what I believe to be flagrantly dishonest and unethical conduct." I had then explained how my practice had been damaged, and that in the process, I believed, Dr. Labowitz had compromised patient care (intentionally misrepresenting Madeline Boone's diagnosis) and compromised healthcare costs (by withholding essential laboratory tests and jeopardizing a $5,000 research project).

April passed. The Board was still silent.

May 6 was a warm, sunny day. A few puffy white clouds lazily drifted across the blue sky; the dogwood and azaleas were in full bloom. Josie had just gone to lunch, and her sister, Florence, brought me the morning mail. There was a letter from the Board of Medical Practice!

> Dear Dr. Connolly:
>
> The Delaware Board of Medical Practice wishes to inform you that after considerable review of your complaint dated March 15, 1983 against Dr. Russell Labowitz and Dr. Alfred Lazarus that your complaint does not come under the jurisdiction of the Board.
>
> Sincerely,
> Vincent G. Lobo, Jr., D.O.
> President
> Delaware Board of Medical Practice (#5)

"Florence!" I yelled. But she had just slipped out the sliding door of the office and was walking up the sidewalk to lunch. I dashed after her.

"Florence! The Board of Medical Practice responded to our complaints!" I handed her the letter.

"That's terrible, Doctor!" she exclaimed as she finished reading.

"It's a joke!" I said. "The Board of Medical Practice is telling me that they have no jurisdiction over patient care and health care costs."

We talked for a few minutes more, and then Florence went to lunch, while I returned to my office. Unable to sit, I paced from room to room. This involved the public! . . . the patients! If the Board of Medical Practice had no jurisdiction over complaints of patient care and health care costs, then who did? Who would monitor the health care of Mrs. Boone and her family? Who monitored the health care of my family, of any family?

The Board of Medical Practice had refused to perform its statutory duty.

It exercised autonomy over an extraordinarily lucrative profession, but refused even to investigate, much less to resolve, complaints of unethical medical conduct.

The Board of Medical Practice had snuffed out my last hope of resolving the problems within the medical community. I now had a decision to make: My family and I could leave Delaware—in which case my work of the past five years would be lost and my opponents would have been successful in running us out of our home—or I could take these doctors before a different tribunal, the Superior Court of Delaware.

The Board's letter made the decision easy.

For years, with no accountability, these doctors had attacked me. Now I was going to put them on an unaccustomed playing field. No longer would the medical profession be able to shield them.

I had no other recourse. For months my time and energies had been consumed in urging the medical authorities, my peers, to respond—to do their job. The problem was not one of selecting the right word or clarity of expression; most of my complaints had not even been considered.

That evening, after getting the children to bed, Sieglinde and I rehashed the Board's letter. Sieglinde was hurt and tired.

"Let's just move," she said quietly. "We don't have to stay here. We were happy in California."

"We can move back to California," I responded, "but I can't let these people destroy everything we've worked for without fighting them. I have nothing to lose by suing them; they've already destroyed our practice."

"It's not worth it," Sieglinde said. "We have to think of the children; too many months have been spoiled already!"

"What future do the children have if I don't fight back? We move, and if someone doesn't like us, then they wipe us out, and we move again!"

"It's not worth it," Sieglinde replied.

"I have clear evidence," I argued, "of unethical conduct—letters signed by these people. A lawsuit would document under oath and publicly expose this fraud, and we'd have a good chance of re-establishing our practice."

"It's not worth it," Sieglinde repeated. "We've done our job."

Over the next week, Sieglinde and I wrestled with our problem.

I talked with Dad and Art. They both were opposed to a lawsuit. They recommended further negotiations within the medical community. I was not, however, being impulsive; for four years I had quietly tolerated these problems before finally complaining to Harding, and for the past five months I had stayed awake nights trying to think of means to implore these medical administrators to respond. Five months of negotiations had failed.

What *was* important, if not this? Was anything important? Was there *any* meaning to what I had learned at home, in church, in school, in Vietnam, or anywhere else?

I needed a lawyer. The confrontation was no longer going to be behind closed doors. It was going to be open—before the public. I was going to Court.

4
The Incredible Depositions

> I communicated with Dr. Gorsuch [Associate Executive Vice President for Membership of the American College of Physicians] . . . . I was concerned . . . as a result of my action, there might be a suit against me, and I asked the College, 'If there were a suit, would they support it?' They said, 'Yes . . . . You have a way out. Turn it over to the Credentials Committee and that absolves you.'
>
> Dr. Alfred Lazarus
> American College of Physicians
> Governor for Delaware

On a clear spring afternoon in May, as I looked out the eleventh floor windows of the elegant law office, I had a panoramic view of Wilmington, the Delaware River, and southern New Jersey. It had been two weeks since I had received the Board of Medical Practice's letter.

Far below me at street level was Rodney Square, the central city block of downtown Wilmington. A well-kept lawn was surrounded by park benches, on the left an American flag gently tugged atop a towering pole, and on the right a larger-than-life-size statue of Caesar Rodney astride a galloping horse commemorated Rodney's urgent eighty-mile ride to the Continental Congress in 1776 to cast Delaware's vote for independence.

Across the street from the square on my left was the granite, three-storied neo-classical courthouse, buttressed in front by a row of imposing Ionic columns. There in the not too distant future my medical opponents and I would stand side by side publicly accounting for our actions. I was proud to stand on my record of professional conduct and patient care.

The lawyer listened attentively as I explained my various complaints and the damages to my practice. He concluded the conversation saying that he wanted to review the facts; he would give me his decision soon.

Several weeks later he completed his review: I had struck out. Although it was clear to him that I was "not one of Labowitz's favorite people," he did not recommend embarking on a lawsuit.

As I considered which attorney to try next, I thought of Jane Roth, my associate at the Delaware Chapter of the Arthritis Foundation. She was President of the foundation and the wife of Delaware's Republican Senator, William V. Roth. She was a graduate of Harvard Law School, a partner at the prominent firm of Richards, Layton and Finger, and a distinguished leader in the legal community.

As a Board member, I had worked with her at the Arthritis Foundation for the past four years. We had a cordial relationship, and she had played a role in the $5,000 fibrositic research grant, which would be one of the issues in the lawsuit.

I had been impressed by her, as well as by her credentials. She generously donated her time to the Arthritis Foundation and seemed modest and unpretentious. I doubted, however, that she would represent me. She was involved in medical litigation, but as far as I knew she represented defendants, not plaintiffs. Another problem was that her law firm represented the Wilmington Medical Center, and although the hospital would not be a party to the lawsuit, its Chief of Rheumatology, and perhaps others, would be.

But Jane Roth's advice could be valuable: She could recommend a lawyer who would represent me, she might have other legal suggestions, and, apart from the lawsuit, she should be informed of these problems since they directly affected the Arthritis Foundation and the Wilmington Medical Center.

Unfortunately, I struck out again. During our telephone conversation Jane Roth showed no interest in my prospective lawsuit, nor in any of the issues, and in the middle of our conversation she excused herself saying that her husband was telephoning from Washington.

I then called another attorney . . . and another . . . and another. May had slipped into June, and now it was July. I had trekked from office . . . to office . . . to office.

The lawyers spoke of the need for a "smoking gun." Several attorneys told me I had "no cause of action." Labowitz might hit me, and them, with a "malicious prosecution suit."

Perhaps, I thought, I should file the lawsuit myself and obtain an attorney later. I wanted the suit filed by August 1: One of the issues would be Labowitz and Newman's letter to the editor which had been published in August 1981, and the two-year statute of limitations, after which this issue could not be included, was quickly approaching.

Finally, with a few days left in July, I connected. Tom Neuberger—a tall, dark-haired attorney in solo practice, and strongly opposed to abortion—agreed to take my case. We would file on August 1.

The financial arrangement would be fee-for-service, costly for me, but not nearly as costly as losing my practice. And, if we won, the award might cover my legal expenses, as well as compensatory and punitive damages. At any rate, I now had a fighting chance. My opponents could no longer attack and then hide behind medical committees.

In the meantime, more facts had surfaced. An ex-patient of Dr. Labowitz's, LaRaye Thomas, an indigent, disabled, 35-year-old black single mother, had recently become a patient of mine. She related that Dr. Labowitz had sued her for $272.50 for non-payment of her bill. (#6) She had managed to pay $120.00 of her debt; Dr. Labowitz continued to pursue her for the $152.50 balance.

As the woman related her story, she was factual, with no trace of bitterness or self-pity. Who had placed her on disability because of severe arthritis? Dr. Labowitz.

After Dr. Labowitz sued her, for more than two years she had no medical care for her painful, crippling condition.

Meanwhile, the status of my privileges at the Wilmington Medical Center remained unsettled. Dr. Flinn and I exchanged several letters without reaching an agreement. The Credentials Committee would not grant me Courtesy Staff privileges; I would not work in the hospital's Arthritis Clinic or Ward Consultation

Service (after four years of service from me, the hospital had denied me even a token resolution of my complaints against Labowitz and Lazarus); and Dr. Flinn insisted that in order to maintain Active Staff privileges—the only privileges available to me—I was required to serve in both the Clinic and on the Ward.

August 1 arrived. A day for celebration! Our complaint was ready to be filed at the New Castle County Prothonotary's Office. Also, for the past several days, Dad, who had originally opposed the lawsuit, had been helping Tom Neuberger.

The lawsuit would be against Dr. Labowitz; bringing in the others, at least at this time, would increase expenses and case complexity. The abortion problem, much to my disappointment, would not be included; it was a controversial issue that might lead to a hung jury.

My determination to present the evidence of improper conduct and negligent peer review to the Superior Court was mixed with trepidation. The litigation would publicly embarrass prominent doctors and administrators. Irrespective of the merits of my complaints, many peers in the medical community would ostracize me. For them, nothing justified a lawsuit; the medical community handled *everything* behind closed doors.

Would members of the medical profession actively help Labowitz? Would they resent the exposure of deep flaws within the state's medical industry? Those people who would be embarrassed might consider themselves "locked in" to Labowitz's position: if Labowitz lost, they would have to explain publicly their refusal to address basic complaints involving medical care.

Would colleagues continue to refer patients to me? Two friends, physicians, had voluntarily suggested that I file a lawsuit against Labowitz. Now that the lawsuit would soon be a reality, would they support me?

I tried to prepare mentally for the alienation I knew would come. Passing a friend on the street who no longer recognized me would be a price I would have to pay, and my doubts were superficial compared to my deeper convictions. I was comfortable with my decision to proceed: My practice had been crippled, and Sieglinde, the children, and I would be uprooted from our home and our community unless the Court provided us relief. What did we have to lose?

Our lives would be changed and there would be hardships, but the change and the hardships for all of us were going to bear fruit.

Later that morning, with the hot August sun shining overhead, I drove over to Tom Neuberger's. We then went to the Prothonotary's Office located in the basement floor of the courthouse.

Entering the building's marble lobby, we rode the elevator down one floor. With satisfaction I handed my complaint to the prothonotary clerk, along with the filing fee.

She placed the front page of the complaint in a stamp-clock: "SMACK!!!"

Filed

August 1 11:44 AM '83

Prothonotary

The defendants were Russell J. Labowitz, M.D., his corporation, and John Does (referring to our belief that Labowitz had conspired with others, who, after suitable discovery, would be added by us as co-defendants). The plaintiffs were Ronald G. Connolly, M.D., and his corporation.

The complaint read as follows:

> This complaint states a cause of action for defamation . . . interference with professional and business relations; and pursuing a scheme of improper conduct, the purpose and effect of which has been to damage plaintiffs' reputation and interfere with . . . [his] professional practice . . . .
>
> On information and belief, many of the illegal and improper activities described . . . [above] have been conducted as an integral part of a scheme and conspiracy between defendants

> and others . . . . The objective of this conspiracy is to improperly monopolize and control the treatment of numerous patients throughout Delaware and the professional practice of Rheumatology. The effect of these activities is to compromise patient care, to excessively interfere with the Wilmington Medical Center's operations, to substantially increase health care costs, to continually damage plaintiffs' professional reputation and continually interfere with plaintiffs' professional practice.

I had just accomplished the first of my two goals: getting my complaints before the Superior Court! The complaints were now official; an authoritative body had accepted jurisdiction.

Now, with an equal passion, I was determined to accomplish my second goal: being among the 10% of cases that get to trial. The judge and the jury—the people—were going to review and render a decision on the medical profession's conduct.

The next move was Dr. Labowitz's.

Weeks passed. Labowitz was still arranging his legal representation; he needed an extension before responding to our complaint.

Meanwhile, the Gannett-operated daily newspapers, the *Wilmington Morning News* and the *Journal Every Evening*, ran an article under the headline: DOCTOR FILES SUIT AGAINST COLLEAGUE. Dr. Labowitz was quoted: "I am sorry this happened. It's to his detriment, my detriment and the detriment of the medical community."

Finally, in mid-September, Neuberger telephoned me. "Doctor, it finally looks as though Labowitz has a lawyer. Do you have any objections if he's represented by Jane Roth?"

My surprise was surpassed by my relief that after more than six weeks of waiting we could finally proceed with the lawsuit. "No," I replied. "She's familiar with my complaints, and I think she'll be fair. Let's get the lawsuit moving."

A few days later, September 16, 1983, an "Entry of Appearances" was submitted to the Court by Jane Roth of Richards, Layton and Finger, and another attorney, Morton Kimmel, of Kimmel and Spiller, whose firm had represented Labowitz in the past. They denied all charges of our complaint, and, astonishing us, Jane Roth filed a motion before the Court:

MOTION FOR PSYCHIATRIC EXAMINATION
AND FOR A PROTECTIVE ORDER

Defendant Labowitz hereby moves the Court for an Order that plaintiff submit to a psychiatric examination to determine his competency to maintain this action. Good cause for the psychiatric examination is set forth in the Affidavit of Charles L. Reese, III, M.D. attached hereto.

An appointment has been made for the examination to be done by David E. Raskin, M.D., on October 7, 1983, at 10:00 a.m., Department of Psychiatry, Delaware Division, Wilmington Medical Center, Wilmington, Delaware.

Defendant Labowitz further moves the Court for a protective order, staying all discovery and proceedings in this matter, pending the completion of the psychiatric evaluation.

Jane R. Roth
Richards, Layton and Finger (#7)

A smashing entry into the lawsuit for Ms. Roth!

For more than four years I had worked with her at the Arthritis Foundation and I had spoken with her when I was seeking an attorney shortly before filing the lawsuit. What was the "Good cause . . . set forth in the Affidavit of Charles L. Reese, III, M.D." that would warrant the Court to order a psychiatric examination of me?

The Affidavit of Dr. Reese, the Chairman of the Credentials Committee of the Department of Medicine, accompanied Roth's motion. Dr. Reese told the Court:

> He . . . has had occasion to review the complaint filed by Ronald G. Connolly, M.D. with the Wilmington Medical Center, against Russell J. Labowitz, M.D. He also heard the presentation made by Dr. Connolly concerning the allegations he made against Dr. Labowitz . . . .
>
> In his opinion, Dr. Connolly's grievance against Dr. Labowitz was not justified under the facts as presented by Dr. Connolly. It is Dr. Reese's opinion, as a physician, that as a matter of reasonable medical probability Dr. Connolly's complaint against Dr. Labowitz, as he, Dr. Reese, is familiar with it, is a manifestation of a psychiatric condition suffered by Dr. Connolly.

I had never had a psychiatric illness, nor had anyone ever suggested that I had a psychiatric illness. My record of the past 43 years—personally, scholastically, militarily, and professionally—was open for review.

But now Roth and Reese had publicly stated that I was psychiatrically ill. Why had they made this charge? Was it because of my behavior? My conduct? My medical performance?

They had made the charge because in their opinion my "grievance against Dr. Labowitz was not justified under the facts as presented by Dr. Connolly . . . . [and] is a manifestation of a psychiatric condition."

I now discussed Roth's motion with my attorneys. I reassured them that there had been no problems at my hearing before Reese's Credentials Committee. Reese had tape-recorded the meeting; my lawyers could listen to the tape themselves!—if Reese would let them.

Discovery in the lawsuit, in which Labowitz was the defendant, was now delayed while the court scrutinized me and considered Roth's motion for a psychiatric exam.

One week later Roth and Kimmel amended their answer to the complaint by adding the Affirmative Defense that "[Dr. Connolly] lack[s] capacity to sue due to incompetency, caused by mental illness." (#8) They also amended their motion for a psychiatric examination and for a protective order, saying:

> Good cause for a psychiatric examination exists further in the allegation of plaintiffs that they have suffered monetary loss to their professional practice due to the actions alleged in the Complaint. It is the contention that any failure of plaintiffs' professional practice has been caused by plaintiff Ronald G. Connolly, M.D.'s mental illness, and not by any action or conspiracy on the part of defendants. (#9)

As we prepared our response to Roth's motion, two volunteers called Neuberger saying they had read about the lawsuit in the newspaper and had had personal experience with Dr. Labowitz.

One caller was an attorney, who had been involved in a 1979 lawsuit in which Labowitz was deposed as an expert witness in rheumatology. In the course of citing his credentials, Labowitz had said that he was Board Certified in rheumatology. The attorney later checked with the Board in Philadelphia and learned that Labowitz had *never* been certified in rheumatology. (Thus in 1978, when Sieglinde and I had moved to Delaware, and Labowitz had repeatedly asked me to join his office, I had been the first and only board-certified rheumatologist in the state. Now, the only other board-certified rheumatologist in Delaware besides me was Labowitz's partner, Newman.)

Neuberger's other caller was an ex-secretary of Labowitz's who had worked for him for approximately six years. She signed an affidavit stating:

> I recall many instances of Medicaid abuse by Dr. Labowitz. The Medicaid program [which provides federal and state funds, derived from taxes, to indigent members of society for their medical care] does not have forms that must be signed by a patient. Dr. Labowitz would see approximately six Medicaid individuals per day. Approximately ten of the individuals scheduled per week would not appear for their appointments. For approximately half of these individuals, about five patients per week, Dr. Labowitz would bill Medicaid as if they <u>had</u> appeared for their appointments. This was improper and could be done because there was no form for the patient to sign verifying that services were actually rendered.

Medicaid regulations prohibit a doctor from billing for no-shows. To further support that this prohibited billing was customary in Dr. Labowitz's office, the woman referred Tom Neuberger to another ex-secretary of Labowitz's. She also signed a similar affidavit.

Meanwhile, I had received a strange "invitation" from the Peer Review Committee of the New Castle County Medical Society. Their Chairman, Dr. Gustave Berger, was "inviting" me to attend their lunch-time meeting, in a week and a half. Attached to the invitation was a response card: "Yes, I will attend," or "No, I will not attend." (#10)

Tom Neuberger wrote to Dr. Berger, requesting more information.

> Before Dr. Connolly can agree to attend any such meeting, could you please advise me in writing of the nature of the meeting, its purposes, and any procedures which govern its conduct.
>
> If the meeting relates to . . . [Dr. Connolly's] lawsuit, due process and Dr. Labowitz's right

to a fair trial prohibit Dr. Connolly from discussing this litigation in any extra-judicial proceeding.

Dr. Berger telephoned Tom, providing general information on the Peer Review Committee, but it was still unclear why I had been invited to the meeting. Tom promptly wrote to Dr. Berger his understanding: "Dr. Labowitz has asked your Committee to review the question of his standard of care with reference to Ms. Madeline Boone. I respectfully request a copy of any documents relating to his request since I am unclear as to the precise nature of his inquiry." My attorney then again explained that because the issues were pending before Superior Court, he was not able to permit me to appear before the Committee. In closing, he said:

> For all the above reasons, I respectfully request that your Committee postpone its meeting until either the above impediments that I have raised are removed, or the lawsuit in the Superior Court is resolved. At a later time your Committee can appropriately review any questions it feels fall within its jurisdiction. I believe this is a satisfactory resolution of these problems and I will assume you agree unless I hear from you otherwise in writing.
>
> Should your Committee feel that it has to proceed, I ask that you make my [previous] letter . . . and this letter a part of its record. In addition, I respectfully request a copy of any written rules, regulations, or guidelines which govern the operation of your Committee as well as a statement in writing of any potential adverse consequences to Dr. Connolly if he does not appear. I also would like a copy of the record developed by your Committee.

There was no response from Dr. Berger.

A month later I received another "invitation" from Dr. Berger to attend the next Peer Review Committee meeting.

Neuberger again replied—his third letter to Dr. Berger—but, again, there was no response.

The decisions, whether I must submit to a psychiatric examination and whether discovery could proceed, were now pending before Superior Court Judge Joshua Martin.

Briefs were filed. Neuberger told Judge Martin that Roth's motion was a "transparent attempt to substitute a psychiatric associate of Dr. Labowitz for the Court and jury in disposing of this lawsuit . . . ."

Meanwhile, we wondered how Roth would attempt to bolster her psychiatric motion. Her comments at Judge Martin's office conference were a revelation.

Roth, donning the hat of a psychiatrist, explained to the Court: "This is the first time in eighteen years of practicing law that I have ever brought a motion to have a party examined to evaluate their capacity to be a party. The reasons I did so are twofold. Number one, Dr. Connolly called me on the telephone several months ago and . . . [in] a lengthy conversation . . . I became quite concerned about his state of mind . . . ."

Roth then explained to the Court that, at a later date, she was asked to represent Dr. Labowitz and: "At that time, I became aware of the fact that Dr. Connolly had been recommended to have a psychiatric evaluation [by Dr. Reese's Credentials Committee] . . . . Through my own experience, through my discussion with Dr. Reese, as set forth in the affidavit by Dr. Reese . . . I have brought this motion." (Roth—a lawyer representing my opponent—had rendered *her medical opinion* to the Court, in support of her motion to have me psychiatrically examined!)

Neuberger countered, saying that Roth's psychiatric motion was "a tactic by Dr. Labowitz to slow discovery, confuse the issues, and intimidate Dr. Connolly by threatening to invade his privacy and subject him to a gross indignity."

Neuberger continued: "I want the record to be clear here that I think it improper for Ms. Roth to be testifying as to Dr. Connolly's state of mind."

A few weeks later, Judge Martin signed his Order:

> . . . the Court has determined that at this time, discovery has not proceeded to a point where a psychiatric examination of the plaintiff should be taken and the Motion is denied, with leave to resubmit the request for a psychiatric examination at a later time, if appropriate. The Motion to Stay Discovery is denied.

The Wilmington newspapers blared the court action with a five-column headline: WILMINGTON DOCTORS TRADE CHARGES IN COURT FIGHT. The article covered the charges of mental illness and alleged Medicaid fraud.

As I read the article, I remembered the times before filing the lawsuit when I had mentally prepared for what was to come. Never could I have anticipated these tactics from my opponents. I worried about the effect of the public accusations on Sieglinde and our five children.

Often, as Sieglinde and I passed a friend, we would want to explain that the mental illness charges were a travesty. But where would we start? Did they have the time and interest to listen? Would they believe Roth or us?

To exonerate myself it was now even more imperative that I substantiate my complaints against Labowitz. Day and night I lived the lawsuit: analyzing submissions by our opponents, preparing for further discovery, and reviewing the Court pleadings.

Constantly, whether I was at work or eating at the dinner table, whether I was jogging or doing homework with the children, whether I was attending Mass, mowing the lawn, or trying to sleep, I would think of a new perspective, a new dimension, to the lawsuit. On Sunday I would sometimes resolve not to think about the lawsuit and not to bother Sieglinde by discussing it, but rarely if ever was I successful. One side was going to lose and it was not going to be ours!

Meanwhile, Sieglinde—often bothered by abdominal symptoms, her hair graying—worked 16 to 18 hours a day keeping the children's life balanced, while at the same time supporting me.

We also worried about another development. Mom had had abdominal surgery, and an incidental finding was that of a carcinoma involving the right colon, which was excised, as was a cancerous mesenteric lymph node. The other excised lymph nodes were negative for cancer, as were the liver exam and the laboratory studies. We hoped that the surgery was curative.

As the lawsuit resumed, some of our discovery attempts, such as our request for Labowitz's state and federal tax returns from 1979 to the present, were frustrated. Labowitz's lawyers objected to our request as being "irrelevant and not calculated to lead to the discovery of admissible evidence." (We held that Labowitz, his employee, Newman, and I were the only full-time rheumatologists in Delaware, and that any deterioration in my practice and income would be directly reflected in Labowitz's and Newman's income.)

At the same time, other areas of discovery were fruitful. Labowitz, in his interrogatories, admitted that in a hallway conversation at the Medical Center more than a year ago—and several months before Lazarus's Christmas Eve letter to me—he had told Lazarus that I had not met the requirements for promotion at the hospital. (Not once in more than four years had Labowitz discussed promotion with me.)

Lazarus also surprised us. In response to our subpoena, he gave us a copy of a letter he had sent to the American College of Physicians in Philadelphia on May 28, 1982, a few weeks after I had submitted my application to him.

> "Dr. Connolly has been well recommended for membership in the College of Physicians by his proposers. I endorse his proposals for membership without hesitation."

Then, September 1, 1982, he sent the College another letter:

> On May 28th I endorsed a proposal for membership on Dr. Ronald G. Connolly.

> I have subsequently learned that he has failed to meet his obligations for teaching at the Medical Center and his Chief of Section has found him deficient in this area . . . .
>
> I have discussed this with my committee on membership and they are in unanimous agreement.
>
> I would like to withdraw my recommendation for membership on Dr. Ronald G. Connolly.
>
> Sincerely yours,
> Alfred Lazarus, M.D. (#11)

Although Lazarus had written to the ACP September 1 withdrawing his recommendation for my membership, he had then waited until the day of Christmas Eve to notify me of his decision.

I had no inkling what "obligations for teaching" Lazarus was referring to. My "Chief of Section," Labowitz, had *never* told me I was deficient in teaching obligations; he had attacked me behind my back.

Meanwhile, Roth's psychiatric motion had escalated the lawsuit. My father's law firm, Connolly, Bove, Lodge and Hutz, had now entered an appearance before the Court on my behalf and would be working with Tom Neuberger.

I eagerly awaited Dr. Lazarus's approaching deposition, to be held in my father's law offices on the 18th floor of the Girard Bank Building in Wilmington. I never, however, could have anticipated the dimension that the doctor would add to medical professionalism and medical peer review.

Lazarus, a short, mild appearing man in his fifties, had been Chief of the Section of Gastroenterology at the Wilmington Medical Center for approximately twenty years. He had been Governor of the American College of Physicians for about five years, and he and Labowitz had served as medical consultants for each other's patients.

Tom Neuberger and Jim Woods, an attorney from my father's firm, were representing me at the deposition. Lazarus was represented by a Philadelphia attorney, and Labowitz was represented by Robert Katzenstein, an attorney with Richards, Layton and Finger who was replacing Roth for the day, as well as by an attorney from Kimmel's office. In addition, Roth's firm also represented the Wilmington Medical Center.

Dr. Lazarus was duly sworn to tell the truth, the whole truth, and nothing but the truth. Mr. Katzenstein then made a statement: "Before we begin, I would like to state that I am appearing today as counsel for Dr. Labowitz, but also, if the occasion arises, I will be imposing objections if questions are asked on information which is protected by 24 Delaware Code #1768. . . . I am acting as counsel to the Wilmington Medical Center, because it is my understanding that the witness is a member of one of the Credentials Committees in the Medical Center . . . ."

[Statute 1768 was legislated in order to encourage medical peer review and thereby protect the public from incompetent or unethical doctors. It provided medical peer review committees, and doctors submitting information to them, with immunity from legal claims; it also provided that the records and proceedings of such committees were confidential and not available for Court subpoena or discovery. Thus, if a doctor thinks that a peer is incompetent or unethical, the doctor is encouraged to submit the evidence to the peer review committee. In such a case, both the doctor submitting the evidence and the review committee is immune from possible legal action initiated by an angry doctor who resents having his or her performance reviewed. (#12)]

The deposition continued. Lazarus admitted that, as a result of Labowitz's remarks, he had concluded that I "had the worst performance of any physician in the Medical Center." (Yet another criticism by Labowitz behind my back to Lazarus and perhaps to others.)

Neuberger: Are you aware that the American College of Physicians early in 1983 did approve Dr. Connolly's application?

Lazarus: Yes.

[Lazarus was then asked if there had been any phone conversations between himself and the American College of Physicians.]

Lazarus:	I communicated with Dr. Gorsuch [the Associate Executive Vice President for Membership at the ACP] . . . . With regard to the application, I was concerned—I don't know how I was concerned or why— but as a result of my action, there might be a suit against me, and I asked the College, "If there were a suit, would they support it?" They said, "Yes." I asked them—they said, "You have a way out. Turn it over to the Credentials Committee and that absolves you." That is the mean by which they acted. (#13)
Neuberger:	Were you aware at that time that Dr. Connolly sought to bring you before the Credentials Committee of the Wilmington Medical Center?
Lazarus:	I think that's what prompted this. Yes, I was aware of it. I think Dr. Morris informed me there was some question of that.
Neuberger:	Were you aware that sometime after that Dr. Connolly tried to bring the dispute between you and he before the Board of [Medical Practice] in Dover?
Lazarus:	I think somebody told me about that, but I don't know who . . . .
Neuberger:	Do you recall anything else Dr. Gorsuch said to you?
Lazarus:	Well, pretty much, that at least for membership, they were getting very relaxed, and if somebody hadn't raped somebody, they would accept them for membership . . . . (#14)

Extraordinary! Apart from relaxed standards, state law grants to Credentials Committees immunity from legal claims in order to facilitate the medical profession's discipline of misconduct.

The governor, who is now concerned about his own misconduct, says he was told by a senior ACP official: "You have a way out. Turn it over to the Credentials Committee and that absolves you."

Lazarus's admissions, however, were, for the time being, buried in the courthouse basement—in the Prothonotary's Office.

Dad and I reviewed Lazarus's deposition. "We should tell the American College of Physicians about Lazarus's statements," I said. "I'm sure they'll be glad to help us."

"The problems are more complex than that," my father replied. "We first need more discovery."

Roth now scheduled my deposition. Finally, I had a chance to substantiate my charges for the public record, but I was also apprehensive. My work, my reputation and the future of my family were at stake. My position was consistent and substantive; I wanted my deposition to reflect the same. I reminded myself to concentrate, to focus, to think before responding. A mistaken response could provide a loophole for the defense.

I rehearsed critical points that I wanted in the record; I anticipated Roth's questions, and I reviewed pitfalls to avoid. Then, when I awakened in the middle of the night, unable to sleep, I rehearsed more.

On the morning of my deposition, wearing a new suit and tie and sitting at the kitchen table with the children, I picked at a bowl of cold cereal while Sieglinde made school lunches. As I was leaving the house, Sieglinde gave me a hug. "I'll be thinking of you, and I'll be at noon Mass for both of us."

As I dropped the children off at Ursuline and headed for Richards, Layton and Finger, I felt more relaxed. I had important things to say; this was my day!

I wondered whether the *News-Journal*, when they did their next update on the lawsuit, would tell the people of Delaware that the Delaware Board of Medical Practice "had no jurisdiction" over complaints of unethical medical conduct? Would they note that the Code of Medical Ethics was "meaningless," and that the "blameless" Chief of Rheumatology was suing an indigent crippled patient?

Looking out the window from the luxurious offices of Richards, Layton and Finger, on the tenth floor of One Rodney Square, located across the street from the courthouse, I viewed the law offices across the square where I had begun my pursuit of a legal resolution six months earlier.

My deposition would be starting in a few minutes. I was apprehensive but controlled. Roth—a few years older than I, with dark, short-cropped hair, and a self-assured manner—bantered with the other lawyers about a recently opened restaurant. It was another business day for the lawyers. I looked out the window at the blue sky with a few gentle clouds slipping by; the American flag snapped in the breeze over Rodney Square, and across the way was Caesar Rodney on his horse, heading towards the Continental Congress.

The court reporter took his seat at the head of the conference table, unfolded his tripod, secured his keyboard, and inserted a new packet of paper into the receptacle.

As we took our seats at the long table, I was on one side of the court reporter and Roth on the other side. Neuberger and Woods sat on my left, and Labowitz and Kimmel on Roth's right.

The court reporter was ready; he administered my oath, and we proceeded.

Roth, referring to a yellow legal pad crammed with page after page of notes, questioned; I responded; the court reporter's fingers danced over his keyboard; and Labowitz—bearded, wearing a blue blazer, and slouched in his chair—riveted his eyes on me.

Roth: Haven't you been criticized for patient abandonment?

Connolly: Yes. But that——

Neuberger: I am going to register an objection here. The objection is multi-fold. . . . I am going to direct him not to answer any questions in this line of questioning and I want to state for the record the reason for that.

Roth: Well, you don't need to state it for the record. He is saying he has lost practice and I think if a doctor has been criticized for patient abandonment, that that is a prime situation.

Neuberger: I understand your position.

Roth: Have you ever been criticized for patient abandonment?

Neuberger: And I am directing him not to answer for the following reasons——

Roth: I don't want to hear your reasons right now. Let me just say when the court directs him to answer the questions, I am going to make an application for attorneys' fees.

Neuberger: I want the record to reflect that the reason why I am directing him not to answer this question is because of Section 1791 of . . . the Medical Practices Act. Additionally, I believe this question goes into an inquiry concerning his religious beliefs and—

Roth: Well, that is perfectly appropriate.

Neuberger: I believe it is inappropriate to inquire into his religious beliefs. To use the mechanism of a court to inquire into his religious beliefs would violate his First Amendment rights. Lastly, I believe it would annoy, embarrass and the other reasons stated in the rule. And for these three reasons I am directing him not to answer questions relating to that event in 1979....

[I still wanted the abortion incident in the lawsuit. I believed that the jury, the public, should consider the issue and resolve it. My lawyer still felt, however, that it was too controversial, and he adamantly opposed Roth.]

Roth: The reasons have no bearing in the present case. If you wish to withdraw any complaint about any loss of professional practice, fine. But I think if a physician has been criticized by his peers for patient abandonment, that that is an entirely appropriate field of exploration when one is considering his professional practice.

Neuberger: Counsel, the General Assembly in the Medical Practices Act passed an immunity statute in Section 1791. I will stand on that immunity statute. . . .

[Neuberger held in his hands a copy of statute 1791, which said: "No person shall be required to perform or participate in medical procedures which result in the termination of pregnancy; and the refusal of any person to perform or participate in these medical procedures shall not be a basis for civil liability to any person, nor a basis for any disciplinary or other recriminatory action against him." (#15)]

Roth, surprised, said, "Let me see that. May I?" Neuberger handed the statute to Roth, who studied it.

Roth: Doctor, have you been subjected to a disciplinary action?

Neuberger: I direct him not to answer any questions in that regard if it relates to this 1979 incident.

Roth: Well, if it has been the basis for disciplinary action it is obviously not covered by 1791. Right? Because it says that it will not be the basis for disciplinary action. [Visibly pleased with herself, she continued.] So therefore I think that is an appropriate question to determine whether 1791 covers it or not. Has he been the subject of disciplinary action?

Neuberger: I think it is an inappropriate basis for the question and I'm directing him not to answer.

Roth: You're saying that Section 1791, which states that such action will not be the subject of disciplinary action, covers a matter which was the subject of disciplinary action?

Neuberger: If there has been a disciplinary action, it has been in violation of the Medical Practices Act. In addition, this line of questioning violates his First Amendment right to religious freedom and it is designed to annoy, embarrass and oppress him and I am directing him not to answer it for those three reasons.

Roth: I think I am perfectly entitled to annoy, embarrass and oppress him! Am I not? (#16)

Neuberger: I think you are not, under the rules. Of course not.

And the hours slipped by.

Shortly after 5:00 p.m. the attorneys recessed my deposition; it would be resumed later.

In the meantime, discovery continued.

Two days later the lawyers from both sides reassembled, this time at Connolly, Bove, Lodge and Hutz. The distinguished chairman of the Credentials Committee was about to have his deposition taken by my attorneys. Specifically, he would be interrogated on the reasons for his psychiatric affidavit against me.

Dr. Charles L. Reese was now in the spotlight. And yet another dimension was about to be added to medical professionalism and medical peer review.

5
The Rheumatologists

> One hundred percent of the people in our practice have the ability to pay . . . . We take on outpatients, office patients, assignment on no one ... with the one exception of medical relatives of physicians practicing in the community, husbands, wives, children.
>
> James H. Newman, M.D.

Discovery on Reese was as illuminating as it had been on Lazarus. Reese was the Chairman of the Credentials Committee that had considered my complaint on Labowitz's referral of Madeline Boone. He was about to throw more light on the machinations of medical peer review.

Reese—in his early fifties, with a lean face and straight hair groomed back from a receding hairline—sat with Roth at the deposition table. The court reporter administered the oath: "Do you swear to tell the truth, the whole truth, and nothing but the truth, so help you God?"

After Reese's affirmative response, one of my attorneys, Jim Woods, began the interrogation.

Woods: [Dr. Reese,] what in your background qualifies you to make psychiatric evaluations or diagnoses?

Reese: Nothing very much, really, but we are actually Board Certified by the Board of Psychiatry and Neurology. Neurology and psychiatry used to be a joint thing back in the thirties. . . .We have to take a little bit of psychiatric training in our Boards. . . . We do have to try to recognize psychiatric disease, but we refer it to a psychiatrist, you know.

[Woods then began questioning Reese on the Credentials Committee's processing of my complaints.]

Reese: . . . I don't want to bring up any of the proceedings of the Credentials Committee... because it's privileged.

Roth: Let me state at this time on behalf of the Wilmington Medical Center, I would object to any proceedings or documents before the Credentials Committee being discussed because they are protected by Section 1768 of Title 24 [the statute providing immunity and confidentiality for medical peer review committees]....

Woods: Are you instructing Dr. Reese not to answer?

Roth: I am instructing him not to answer except concerning submissions by Dr. Connolly in communications to Dr. Connolly.

Woods: Just for the sake of the record, do you represent Dr. Reese?

Roth: I represent the Wilmington Medical Center; and the Credentials Committee being a body of the staff of the Wilmington Medical Center, and [Dr. Reese] being a member of that Committee, it is my position on behalf of the Wilmington Medical Center, I can instruct him not to answer . . . .

Woods: Just so I have this straight: You represent Dr. Labowitz and the Wilmington Medical Center, and you also represent, through your representation [of the] Wilmington Medical Center, Dr. Reese, who is a member of the Credentials Committee, to which Dr. Connolly presented a complaint about Dr. Labowitz?

Roth: Right. My representation of the Wilmington Medical Center, the firm of Richards, Layton and Finger does generally represent the Medical Center. It's in that capacity that I am exercising my objection.

Woods: Let me respond to the objection. Our position is that Dr. Reese's affidavit which was filed in this case is a waiver . . . . The case law shows that the privilege under Section 1768 can be waived. Dr. Reese is the Chairman of the Credentials Committee, and we believe he acted on the Committee's behalf in making that affidavit, his affidavit. We feel it's a violation of due process to use some evidence of the Credentials Committee proceedings as a sword and to use Section 1768 as a shield, regarding the rest of the evidence of those proceedings.

[The Court would decide the validity of Roth's objections. In the mean time, Reese was asked what he had relied upon in forming the conclusion of his affidavit that my complaint was "a manifestation of a psychiatric condition suffered by Dr. Connolly."]

Reese: The reason that that statement was made is because Dr. Connolly's response seemed out of proportion to the usual, to this situation.

Woods: What do you mean by, "Dr. Connolly's response"?

Reese: His response of taking action against Dr. Labowitz for unethical conduct, which seemed out of proportion to the complaint where a patient has been referred for a study. She was referred for the study in a fairly standard way. Maybe without all the information that Dr. Connolly would have liked to have had, but it did not seem that Dr. Labowitz was acting against Dr. Connolly in an unethical way, in the way he referred the patient to the study . . . .

Woods: So the disproportionate reaction was one factor in your determination that Dr. Connolly had some kind of psychiatric disorder?

Reese: That he and perhaps the rest of us would benefit from a psychiatric evaluation.

[A minute later:]

Woods: Did you do anything to verify whether Dr. Labowitz had or had not told Madeline Boone she had lupus?

Reese: No.

Woods: Did you interview Madeline Boone?

Reese: No.

Woods: Did you consider Madeline Boone's medical records?

Reese: No.

[And:]

Woods: Was that abnormal sedimentation rate a factor in your conclusion?

Reese: . . . I'm not a rheumatologist. I guess we have to let that go.

[A short time later:]

Woods: Is it fair to say that those paragraphs [referring to that part of my letter of complaint in which I quoted Section 4 of the Code of Ethics] indicate that Dr. Connolly felt he was under an obligation, ethical obligation to expose what he believed to be unethical conduct of other doctors?

Reese: Well, this again I think is out of proportion, because I can't think of another member of the staff who would be presented with—how can I speak for the whole staff—but I can't imagine anybody, and I could go up to two hundred people in the Medical Department, given this information or was in this spot that Dr. Connolly was in, would take this type of action. So Dr. Connolly may have felt that he was under compulsion to expose this unethical conduct, but I don't think anybody else would have thought it was unethical any more than I did or my Committee did.

Woods: Let me ask you this: Suppose you learned of another physician's conduct and you believed or thought it was likely that that physician's conduct was unethical, doesn't Section 4 of the Code of Ethics of the American Medical Association require you—

Reese: Oh, sure.

Woods: —to take steps to determine whether in fact it was unethical?

Reese: Yes, that's right.

Woods: And that duty is not mitigated in any way by a later finding that the conduct was not unethical in the opinion of some reviewing committee?

Reese: Well, you might say then that the opinion of the Credentials Committee, which is on record as saying that there was no grounds to the complaint or that the complaint as to Dr. Labowitz was not found to be unethical, was a finding by a body. That should have reassured Dr. Connolly that we reviewed it very carefully and did not feel there was any breach of ethics.

[And later:]

Woods: Doctor, are you saying that the Credentials Committee reached its conclusion about Dr. Labowitz' behavior without considering (A) Madeline Boone's medical records, [and] without (B) interviewing Madeline Boone? . . .

Roth: I object to the question and direct the witness not to answer it, in that it refers to deliberations of the Credential Committee....

Woods: Let me ask you this, Doctor: Did you draw the conclusion from Dr. Connolly's presentation and from his complaint that Dr. Labowitz had not acted unethically?

Reese: Yes.

Woods: And you yourself in drawing that conclusion did not interview Madeline Boone . . . and did not consult Madeline Boone's medical records?

Reese: That's right.

Woods: Is there anything else in Dr. Connolly's submission—I'm talking about his complaint—that led you to believe that a psychiatric evaluation was indicated?

Reese: No.

Woods: So what you have told us is the sum of the factors to which you relied?

Reese: That's right.

Woods: What did you observe about Dr. Connolly at the hearing that you relied on in forming your conclusion that a psychiatric evaluation was indicated?

Reese: I really can't tell you that. I don't think—

Roth: Let me object, in that the language of the affidavit refers to Dr. Connolly's presentation to the Committee, which I think is an independent item, in that Dr. Connolly, not being a member of the Committee, can acknowledge what he presented or did not present; and any actual proceedings before the Committee, I would object to testimony thereupon.

[Later:]

Woods: Which . . . other members of the Wilmington Medical Center staff knew that you had made or were going to make your affidavit for submission to the Superior Court before Mrs. Roth actually submitted it to the Court?

Reese: I think the only person who knew was Dr. Morris. I talked to him. He's the . . . Vice President for Medical Affairs.

Woods: Allston—

Reese: Allston Morris, yes.

Woods: Dr. Flinn?

Reese: I don't believe I talked it over with Dr. Flinn. I might have mentioned it to him.

Woods: Did Dr. Morris . . . approve the substance of the affidavit?
Reese: Yes, Dr. Morris approved of it. I can remember that.

[Later:]
Woods: Would you consider it a breach of medical ethics not to forward all pertinent medical records in a situation such as the Madeline Boone situation?
Reese: No, I would not.

[Then, as Reese's deposition was concluding, the witness wished to add a comment about the Credentials Committee.]

Reese: We are not a punitive body or a body that is disciplinary . . . . But we try . . . to help our fellow doctors, educate them as to various things which we think are necessary. So in a recommendation such as this, although they are not very usually made or not meant to be a punitive-type thing, it's more of a situation where we feel that maybe somebody could use some—it might be helpful to educate them, help them to see how their thinking could be maybe brought into line with the regular medical community . . . .

By the time Reese's deposition had concluded, another fact was clear: My lawyers and I had no access to the tape-recording of the Credentials Committee meeting; it was being held safely in the files of the Department of Medicine, protected, for the time being, by Roth's claim of immunity under Statute 1768.

Discovery, although just beginning, had been a revelation. It was clear to me that, inadvertently, I had hit a nerve center of the medical profession and I was witnessing the resulting convulsions. And yet more was to come.

The *News-Journal* article prior to Reese's deposition had simply said: ". . . Dr. Charles L. Reese III recommended that Connolly see a psychiatrist after Reese's credentials committee at the medical center decided that Connolly's internal complaint was groundless." My lawyers and I now knew the facts behind Reese's public support of Roth's psychiatric motion, but the public did not. As our knowledge of medical peer review grew, my practice contracted—fewer new patients were being referred and old patients were going elsewhere. I needed relief; I hoped the newspapers would soon update the public's knowledge.

It was now time to interrogate Dr. Labowitz's partner, Dr. James Newman. As we took our seat in a conference room at Connolly, Bove, Lodge & Hutz, we wanted more information on several issues, including the defendant's policy of billing patients.

As Dr. Labowitz's bespectacled, studious, brown-bearded associate of the past three years took his seat and was duly sworn, the interrogation proceeded.

Neuberger: Let me just give you a little background. I'm going to try to create a pie consisting of one hundred percent of the patients [seen by you and Dr. Labowitz] . . . . I'm asking you what percentage of the total patients seen have no insurance, no financial resources whatsoever to be able to pay for the services that either yourself or Dr. Labowitz render.

Newman: My response to that would have to be that one hundred percent of the people in our practice have the ability to pay.

[And:]

Neuberger: What is your rate for a patient visit?

Newman: It's a set office fee. A routine office visit is twenty-eight dollars [in November, 1983]. . . .

Neuberger: Do you know what percentage of your patients you take assignment on?

["Taking assignment" refers to accepting as payment what the insurance companies allow, as opposed to billing the patient directly for the full amount.]

Newman: We take on out-patients, office patients, assignment on no one . . . with the one exception of medical relatives of physicians practicing in the community, husbands, wives, children.

Neuberger: Does Dr. Labowitz' policy on assignment differ from yours?

Newman: I don't believe so.

As Newman's deposition progressed, we also needed information on Labowitz's "reports" to the hospital's Credentials Committee. I had not known they existed; I had been criticized behind my back. We now wanted to know whether Newman realized that his employer, the Chief of Rheumatology at the hospital, was submitting "reports" evaluating him.

Neuberger: Have you ever been evaluated by Dr. Labowitz and Dr. Flinn as Director of the Department of Medicine—

Newman: No.

Neuberger: Let me just finish the question. Evaluated concerning your performance at the Medical Center within the Department of Rheumatology?

Newman: No.

[And:]

Neuberger: Have you ever heard Dr. Labowitz make any disparaging remarks of any nature whatsoever concerning Dr. Connolly?

Newman: To the best of my recollection, no.

Later, Newman, who had by now testified that during his more than three years' association with Dr. Labowitz he had engaged in no independent research, was interrogated concerning his public criticism of my research.

Neuberger:	Who wrote the Letter to the Editor?
Newman:	It was a joint effort.
Neuberger:	All right. What portions of it did you write or did somebody do a first draft and somebody else did—
Newman:	I did a first draft and Dr. Labowitz went over it and rewrote part of it.
Neuberger:	Okay. Do you know how many drafts it went through?
Newman:	I think just that. I think I wrote a first draft.
Neuberger:	Yes?
Newman:	And then he went over it and changed it around a little bit, and then we—I looked at it and said, "well, that seems okay," and we submitted it. . . .
Neuberger:	Approximately how much time was involved in putting this [Letter to the Editor] . . . together?
Newman:	Oh, not much. Maybe an hour or two.

A few weeks later a new voice was heard. Every year, Harry Themal, the *News-Journal's* public editor and ombudsman, had been instrumental in publishing the *News-Journal's Code of Professionalism and Ethics*:

> A newspaper's most important asset is its integrity. Lose it, and the newspaper loses the very power that makes it a community force. . . .
>
> The *News-Journal* papers recognize that the power we have as the dominant source of information for residents of Delaware [the sole daily newspaper in the Wilmington and northern Delaware area] . . . carries with it special responsibilities to face the public with politeness and candor . . . .
>
> When an issue involves two or more sides in conflict, all significant interests should be given an opportunity to respond. Fairness in stories requires

completeness, relevance, leveling with the reader and straight forwardness ahead of flashiness.

Now, in a surprising Sunday editorial, Themal discussed the Connolly v. Labowitz lawsuit:

> . . . The pre-trial action had included charges of mental illness and [Medicaid] fraud.
>
> Such professional disputes seldom hit the press. In this particular case, Dr. Ronald G. Connolly chose to go into Superior Court to make his accusation against Dr. Russell J. Labowitz. Reporter Jane Harriman duly reported the details of the suit in an August story.
>
> Two months later, Harriman wrote another story that summarized some of the depositions that had become part of the public record. These included the nastier counter charges . . . .
>
> The last story about the Court deposition was followed by letters to the editor in support of Labowitz. Such letters are a proper way for the community to express itself about the matter. . . .
>
> Doctors and lawyers prefer to use their own associations and committees to police such charges. The doctors with whom I have spoken are unhappy that the rheumatologists' dirty linen is being aired in public.

Themal's public pledge of high standards contrasted sharply with his editorial, which had failed to mention that for more than six months before I "chose to go into Superior Court," I had urged five different levels of medical administrative review, culminating with the state Board of Medical Practice, to fulfill their public responsibility.

Also unmentioned by Themal was that there had been Letters to the Editor in support of me—a fact verified by my patients—but the *News-Journal* had elected not to publish them. They had selectively published only letters favorable to Labowitz.

In other developments, the Medical Society of Delaware held its 194th Annual Meeting and the President's Award was presented to Vincent G. Lobo, Jr., D.O., the President of the Delaware Board of Medical Practice (and the man who had notified me that my complaint "does not come under the jurisdiction of the Board").

Also, Dr. Flinn and I were still corresponding concerning my hospital privileges:

Dear Ron:

I got your letter refusing to fulfill your obligations by accepting your assignment in the Arthritis Clinic. Although I stated to you several times that your obligation to the hospital has nothing to do with your conflict with Dr. Labowitz, you obviously are unwilling to separate the two issues. Since your request for Courtesy Staff privileges has been denied and since you have refused after my repeated pleading and warning to accept your obligations to the Medical Center as a member of the Active Staff, I am unfortunately left with no alternative other than to forward our correspondence to the Credentials Committee for their recommendations.

Sincerely,
Robert B. Flinn, M.D.
Director
Department of Medicine

I responded to Flinn's letter:

Dear Dr. Flinn:

. . . On the contrary, the Wilmington Medical Center is directly involved in this conflict. Dr. Charles Reese, with the approval of Dr. Allston Morris, submitted an affidavit stating that "as a matter of reasonable medical probability Dr. Connolly's complaint

> against Dr. Labowitz . . . is a manifestation of a psychiatric condition suffered by Dr. Connolly. . . ." Dr. Reese's affidavit was submitted to the Superior Court . . . and subsequently publicized in the *News-Journal* paper.
>
> Active Staff membership entails a mutual obligation between the physician and the Wilmington Medical Center.
>
> . . . I request a transfer to the Consultant Staff.
>
> Sincerely,
> Ronald G. Connolly, M.D.

Meanwhile, into the spotlight now came Dr. Russell J. Labowitz. Both sides prepared for his deposition. I knew the issues better than anyone, and, as usual, my attorneys and I worked up the interrogation questions. I thought it was important that I be present for the depositions; not only did my future and the future of my family depend on the outcome, but I could assist my attorney if questions developed concerning a detail of the case, or if the deposed doctor inserted medical jargon.

As the deposition got under way—with the court reporter again seated at the head of the table, flanked on one side by Labowitz, Roth and Kimmel, and on the other side by Neuberger, Woods, and me—Labowitz, bearded, wearing his customary dark blue blazer, slacks and loafers, was ready.

"Dr. Labowitz, do you swear to tell the truth, the whole truth, and nothing but the truth, so help you God?"

After Labowitz's affirmative response, Neuberger began the interrogation, which continued throughout the day. My deposition was then resumed by Roth; then Labowitz's deposition was resumed, then mine, and again Labowitz's.

Jim Green—about my age, brown hair, broad shoulders—was another attorney with Connolly, Bove, Lodge & Hutz. He had joined Tom Neuberger and Jim Woods.

Green: Doctor, you are not, are you, a diplomate of the American Board of Rheumatology?

Labowitz: No.

Green: And you never have been. Is that correct?
Labowitz: That's correct. . . .
Green: When were you denied certification?
Labowitz: When was I denied certification?
Green: Yes, sir.
Labowitz: 1974, I believe. . . .
Green: Did you take the examination for the board certification?
Labowitz: Yes.
Green: And did you fail the examination?
Labowitz: Yes.
Green: Did you ever reapply?
Labowitz: Yes.
Green: When was that?
Labowitz: In 1976. . . .
Green: Did you take the examination a second time?
Labowitz: Yes.
Green: And did you fail it that time?
Labowitz: Yes.

Also during the deposition, my attorneys wanted to interrogate Labowitz on his "reports" critiquing my performance at the Wilmington Medical Center. We knew of no legitimate reason for Labowitz's disparaging comments, and we wanted to know the nature of these reports: Why—if Labowitz was concerned about medical performance and patient care—had he never discussed these reports with me? Roth objected, however, saying: "Concerning any evaluation done of Dr. Connolly by Dr. Labowitz in his role as Section Chief of Rheumatology, we claim the privilege under 24 Delaware Code, Section 1768."

[And:]

Woods: Do you know if Dr. Connolly has ever been considered for promotion at the Wilmington Medical Center and not promoted? In other words, passed over for promotion.

Roth: I object to the question insofar as it may involve any privileged determination of the Credentials Committee, and direct him not to answer insofar as any answer is encompassed.

Woods: Even though [Dr. Labowitz is] not a member of the Credentials Committee?

Roth: Well, he's section head——chief of the section.

Woods: Can you answer a question without reference to any Credentials Committee proceedings?

Labowitz: No, because the Credentials Committee is a component of the promotion process. So, no. They are obviously involved in all decisions regarding promotion.

[Labowitz was also interrogated on Madeline Boone.]

Neuberger: Is it common to have. . . [a skin] rash across the face [in lupus]?

Labowitz: You could have a typical butterfly rash across the face.

[Labowitz's subpoenaed records on Madeline Boone revealed that he had documented, in his physical exam two months *before* referring the patient to me, that she had a "rash across eyebrows, across nose, almost butterfly distribution."]

Neuberger: Is a sedimentation rate within normal limits a must to allow the diagnostic label of fibromyositis?

Labowitz: Yes.

[A short time later Labowitz testified that lupus and fibrositis are mutually exclusive diseases. Later, my attorney continued the interrogation.]

Neuberger: Are you aware of any fibromyositic publications which discuss fibromyositis in conjunction with lupus?

Labowitz: No. I testified earlier that they are mutually exclusive.

[And:]

Green: How many cases of fibrositis have you treated?

Labowitz: This would be an estimate. I would have to say 2,000 [or] 3,000. I can't—That's a very hard figure to come by. . . .

Green: Upon what laboratory tests, if any, did you rely in making your diagnoses of fibrositis in [these] patients?

Labowitz: . . . the criteria that are now in vogue for the diagnosis of fibrositis include normal laboratory studies. And the patients would have to have normal laboratory studies over the period of time that they were evaluated by myself and other physicians who might have been caring for them.

[Madeline Boone's subpoenaed records from Labowitz and the laboratory tests that he had ordered at the Wilmington Medical Center had by now documented that the last three sedimentation rates on Madeline Boone, prior to Labowitz's referral of her to me, were all abnormal.]

Green: Do you have an estimate of how many fibrositis patients you were treating in January . . . of 1981 [the time when Mrs. Boone was referred]?

Labowitz: I would say active and inactively, probably 500.

Green: That is, 500 where you were satisfied that the disease was fibrositis?

Labowitz: Yes . . . .

Green:	You had approximately 500 patients at that time who definitely had fibromyositis, did you not?
Labowitz:	I just stated that I did.
Green:	Of all your patients in January 1981, was Madeline Boone the best candidate for a fibrositic study, in your opinion?
Labowitz:	For a fibrositis study?
Green:	Yes, sir.
Labowitz:	I believe, yes. I would have to say that, if that's the only patient I referred for that reason.

Additional laboratory studies on Madeline Boone had by now confirmed that indeed she did have lupus, and, unfortunately, she had recently undergone a total hip joint replacement because of avascular necrosis (diminished blood circulation to the joint), a condition caused by various illnesses, including lupus. Did Madeline Boone have lupus in 1981, at the time Labowitz referred her to me? Mrs. Boone's unequivocal answer was to the affirmative.

As Labowitz's interrogation continued, he testified that his Letter to the Editor had been solicited by the editor of the *Delaware Medical Journal*, Dr. Bernadine Paulshock.

The rheumatologist was then probed on his billing of federal- and state-financed health insurance, Medicaid (instituted to cover the poorest members of society). Two of Dr. Labowitz's ex-secretaries had signed affidavits stating that he had often billed medicaid for services not rendered.

Green:	Did you ever bill for services rendered to Medicaid patients when those services were not rendered?
Labowitz:	To my knowledge there was a period of time, a short period of time where office policy was that if a patient did not show, whether they're Medicaid, private or whatever, that they were billed for it. Now, I'm not sure whether Medicaid was

billed for that. But I know that there was a time when my practice was very busy .... During that period of time it's possible that Medicaid patients were billed for not showing. But it was done uniformally in the practice, not just for Medicaid patients. (#17)

Green: . . . . Did you know that charging for a no-show to Medicaid . . . is prohibited by their rules?

Labowitz: No, I didn't know that.

Green: Do you know that now?

Labowitz: You're telling me that.

[And:]

Green: What period of time was that?

Labowitz: I would have to guess. It was probably no more than over a year or two time. . . probably around a two-year period. But I don't know; I can't remember off hand.

[Later:]

Green: Have you ever had any discussions with Mr. James Harding about Dr. Connolly?

Labowitz: No. . . .

Green: Allston Morris?

Labowitz: No.

Green: Ignatius Tikellis [the President of the Delaware Medical Society]?

Labowitz: Yes.

Green: When was that?

Labowitz: That was in mid-1983 . . . .

Green: What was the occasion of that discussion?

Labowitz: I talked to Dr. Tikellis in his role at that time as President of the Medical Society of Delaware, and I felt that I wanted to lodge complaints against Dr. Connolly in front of either the Professional Conduct Committee or the Peer Review Committee of the New Castle County Medical

Society. I thought that Dr. Connolly was acting in an unprofessional, undignified and unethical manner in the way he was proceeding to in essence defame my character, the very charges he was making against me. His methods I felt were very unethical and I wanted to bring those charges to the medical society, and in that context I talked to Dr. Tikellis. . . .

Green: Has a formal complaint been lodged?

Labowitz: Yes.

Green: And by "formal", I mean a written complaint or the phone conversation?

Labowitz: Oral and written complaints have been forwarded. . . .

Green: . . . By the complaints having been filed, is the body with whom they have been filed the Medical Society of Delaware?

Labowitz: They have been filed [with] the Peer Review Committee, which it's my understanding is a medical society committee but also is under the auspices of the New Castle County [Medical Society] . . . .

Revelation! This was the reason that Dr. Gustave Berger, the Chairman of the Peer Review Committee, had "invited" me to attend their luncheon more than three months earlier. Neuberger and I had had no inkling that Labowitz had filed complaints *against* me. We had understood that Labowitz had asked the Committee to hear my complaints against him. And although Neuberger had asked repeatedly for clarification of the meeting's purpose, this most elementary fact had been denied us by Berger and the Committee. They had "invited" me to the luncheon to defend myself against complaints I had never seen and of which I was not aware! Thus, another extraordinary dimension had been added to the performance of the cowardly medical authorities as they abused the autonomy granted to them by the public.

The medical authorities had been active on all three sides of a triangle—the Wilmington Medical Center, the Delaware Board of Medical Practice, and the New Castle County Medical Society—in order, I felt, to squelch my complaints that a doctor had unethically interfered with my practice, compromised patient care, and ignored health-care costs.

The interrogation now returned to Labowitz's billing of patients.

Green: What percentage of Medicare patients do you accept assignment on?

Labowitz: For hospital services, Medicare patients who are hospitalized, I have accepted assignment one hundred percent of the time since I have been in practice. As to office procedures, those patients who may have some problems with fixed income or problems paying for their visit . . . I accept assignment of those patients.

[And later:]

Woods: Earlier in your deposition you stated that . . . you accepted assignment on patients who were having trouble or were on fixed income, for example . . . . Do you recall that, Doctor?

Labowitz: Yes.

Woods: I'd like to show you Madeline Boone's ledger card [from Labowitz's office]. . . and ask you to read the notation . . . next to 3/1/78.

Labowitz: "Called patient and she said she sent it. I gave her one week to make payment and told her we cannot see her until account is paid in full."

Woods: I take it that is your secretary or nurse who was referring to herself as "I told"?

Labowitz: It's the secretary.

Woods: Was that done at your direction?

Labowitz: No. Not that I remember.

Woods: Is that general policy?

Labowitz: The general policy is to contact a patient if they go beyond three or four months and haven't paid, despite the fact that the patient has been billed, and they are asked if there's a problem. If there's a problem, then we try to make out—make satisfactory arrangements for them so that they can pay out the bill in terms that are convenient for them.

Woods: Is it standard policy to tell patients that you will not see them until they pay their bill?

Labowitz: No.

Roth: For who to tell them?

Woods: For anyone from Dr. Labowitz' office.

Labowitz: Not to my knowledge.

Woods: Do you know if that has ever happened, more than on this occasion?

Labowitz: No, I don't.

Roth: If what has happened?

Woods: That a patient was told that she would not be seen until she paid her bill.

Labowitz: No. I'm not—I honestly was not aware of this, and I'm not aware of any others.

Woods: Was your secretary out of line in doing what she did?

Labowitz: If I knew of that, I would have said something to her.

Woods: What would you have said?

Labowitz: I would have told her the policy of the office, which is what I just expounded upon.

Woods: Did you ever have a patient named LaRaye Thomas?

Roth: Do you have authorization from this patient for Dr.—

Woods: No, I don't.

Roth: Then I think we'd better skip it.

Woods: Let me put it this way: Have you ever filed a suit against a woman named LaRaye Thomas?

Labowitz: I don't know. I don't remember.

[Labowitz was handed a copy of the complaint he had filed in the Court of Common Pleas against the patient.]

Labowitz: This is a complaint lodged against LaRaye Thomas for nonpayment of her bill.

Woods: For what amount?

Labowitz: $272.50.

A short time later Labowitz's deposition was again recessed. The court would decide whether to sustain or overrule Labowitz's claims of immunity, as well as those of Lazarus and Reese, but for now we had the information we needed. The judge had previously denied Roth's motion for a psychiatric exam, but with leave, if appropriate, to resubmit it at a later time. We now had sworn testimony and exhibits documenting the merits of my complaints and showing that they were not the manifestations of a psychiatric illness, and in the process we had documented the machinations of medical peer review.

It was now time to present our discovery to the Superior Court of Delaware.

6
The Abortion

> I can assure your Honor that I have never filed any pleading in any matter in bad faith and I specifically did not file the Affirmative Defense in bad faith.
>
> Jane R. Roth, Esq.

The Court had the power to strip the immunity facade from my opponents. Dad, Jim, and I now worked on a motion asking the Court to do so. Our "Omnibus Pretrial Motion" would specifically ask the Court to order Section 1768 inapplicable to Labowitz, Reese, and Lazarus because we believed that the proceedings of the Credentials Committee had been used in bad faith and for an improper purpose, and that the statutory immunity had been waived by Reese's affidavit. We would also ask the Court to deny Labowitz and Roth's motion for a psychiatric examination; to strike their Affirmative Defense that "plaintiffs [me and my corporation] lack capacity to sue due to incompetency, caused by mental illness"; and to impose sanctions against our opponents and award us costs incurred as a result of the defendants' actions, including reasonable attorney fees.

Meanwhile, my deposition had been resumed. My opponents had correctly faulted me for a mistake. In my study which I had reported in the *Delaware Medical Journal*, I had treated refractory fibrositic pain with two medications. I had used these medications in the same manner and in the same dosages as had been recommended in other medical articles I had reviewed. These articles recommended therapy with one of the medications at a dosage of 1 milligram, three times per day. I started treatment in my patients at this same dosage, and, after noting the encouraging results, I wrote my article. Eight to ten months passed, however, before I submitted the article to the *Delaware Medical Journal*. During these intervening months, I noted that some patients were responding equally well when *started* and maintained on just 1 milligram per day, while in other patients the optimal dosage resulted from increasing to 2 or 3 milligrams per day. The two methods—starting at 3 milligrams daily and working down, or starting at 1 milligram daily and working up to 3 milligrams—were equally acceptable, and both were well within the standard of medical care. (The medication was approved by the Federal Drug Administration, and the pharmaceutical company recommended a daily dosage between 2.5 and 10 milligrams per day.) The advantage with starting at the higher dose, 3 milligrams, was that prompter relief of symptoms was usually achieved, while starting at the lower dosage was preferable in that it minimized the amount of medication which the patient received. Before I submitted the article to the *Delaware Medical Journal*, I revised it in order to reflect this new information. In the revision I said that patients were started on 1 milligram and, if necessary, gradually increased to 3 milligrams. This was incorrect. I had tried to avoid what I then considered an unnecessary and prolonged explanation. But I should have taken the extra time to explain that the patients described in my article were started on 3 milligrams daily and tapered downward, whereas now I preferred starting at 1 milligram daily and working upward; or I simply should have said that all patients received between 1 and 3 milligrams daily of the medication. At any rate, my opponents' criticism on this issue was well taken.

In the meantime, the secretive Peer Review Committee of the New Castle County Medical Society had written to its Board of Directors:

January 27, 1984

Dear Doctors:

Your Peer Review Committee has reviewed the complaint filed by Russell J. Labowitz, M.D. in great detail. We have reviewed letters and records made available to us and the oral testimony of Dr. Labowitz, who made himself available for questioning. Dr. Connolly was invited to appear, but declined. We are of the unanimous opinion:

> . . . That questions have been raised concerning the patterns of practice of both physicians. Since we do not have subpoena power, we would recommend that the Board of Directors refer this matter to the Board of Medical Practice for further investigation and review....
>
> Sincerely,
> Gustave K. Berger, M.D.
> Chairman
> Peer Review Committee

Copies of the letter were sent to Labowitz and me.

And the president of the New Castle County Medical Society, Dr. Jane Straughn, then wrote to the Board of Medical Practice in Dover:

> February 2, 1984
>
> Gentlemen:
>
> The Board of Directors of the New Castle County Medical Society . . . reviewed the recommendations of the Peer Review Committee . . . . It was decided that this entire matter should be referred to the Board of Medical Practice.
>
> Sincerely yours,
> Jane C. Straughn, M.D.
> President

Copies of this letter also were sent to Labowitz and me.

I called Jane Straughn and complained that it was absurd that the Peer Review Committee had never notified me that a complaint had been filed against me; Berger had never responded to Neuberger's inquiries. I asked Dr. Straughn to meet with me. She refused; the entire matter had been turned over to the Board of Medical Practice.

Eight months earlier the Delaware Board of Medical Practice had told me that they had no jurisdiction over my complaints. Now they were in a dilemma: Would they accept jurisdiction over Labowitz's complaints?

Meanwhile, my practice continued to deteriorate. Dad supplemented my income, enabling me to cover home expenses, of which by far the greatest, about $17,000 per year, was Catholic-school tuition for our five children.

Medical colleagues continued to distance themselves from me. Many resented that I had spotlighted the medical profession by filing a lawsuit against a fellow physician. Only a handful of doctors continued to refer patients.

It had been more than twenty-two years since I had started medical school, and for the past fourteen years Sieglinde and I had worked and sacrificed together. But now, at a time when I should have been in my professional prime, I was being ostracized by the community.

My circumstances had dramatically changed from those of a respected physician with a bright future to those of a medical embarrassment; from a U.S. Navy Lieutenant Commander who had served in Vietnam, to an outcast in American society.

And I began to change. I became much more interested in politics, took courses in public speaking (which had always been a major fear), and I broadened my reading in literature, history and religion.

I also decided that I was going to write about my experiences. The public should be informed—they have a personal interest in the medical and legal professions—and I had a need to express in my own words what was happening. I could no longer reconcile the community and country which I had known and loved all my life, with what I now saw as blatant corruption.

The months of discovery had been extremely expensive, as well as incredibly time-consuming and emotionally draining, but we had been richly rewarded. On May 2, 1984 Jim Green submitted to the Court our pivotal "Omnibus Pretrial Motion."

Meanwhile, on still another front, although medical administrators had refused to investigate my complaints, I proceeded with my own investigation. I learned that Dr. John Levinson, the gynecologist who had charged me with patient abandonment in

October of 1979, had himself been a focal point for a June 7, 1979 *News-Journal* article that reported:

> The attorney general's office is investigating abortion practices and procedures at the Wilmington Medical Center as the result of a complaint about conditions that led to two live abortion births last month.
>
> Subpoenas were issued yesterday afternoon for several hospital employees, but none were to be issued initially to the doctors involved, according to Joseph J. Farnan, Jr., chief deputy attorney general. . . .
>
> [One allegation,] Farnan said, "is that there has been life outside the womb and it has been ignored. . . . "
>
> The medical center . . . claims that within the ten years that abortions have been legal, only these two live births have resulted.
>
> Both those infants were born recently, and are in good condition in the newborn intensive-care unit . . . .
>
> One of the infants was apparently believed to be stillborn and placed in a specimen container for laboratory investigation. However a nurse later detected a pulse in the umbilical cord and immediate life-support measures were taken. . . .
>
> The medical center has refused to name the . . . doctors involved, but hospital sources confirm that one abortion was done by Wilmington gynecologist Dr. John M. Levinson.

I also went to the Medical Records Department at the Wilmington Medical Center, where I reviewed the hospital records of the one patient Dr. Levinson and I had in common. I came upon Levinson's request to me for consultation. Levinson had written: "Patient for abortion—please advise & therapy re: scleroderma while in hospital & follow-up. Any contraindication to intrauterine saline for abortion? Thank you. John M. Levinson."

Thus, Levinson had planned to abort the patient by injecting a concentrated salt solution into her uterus (this would induce uterine contractions, followed by abortion), and he had wanted me to tell him if there was "any contraindication to intrauterine saline?" Levinson had told the New Castle County Medical Society, "The consultation in no way requested [Dr. Connolly's] opinion as to the advisability of abortion but only that he would observe and treat as need be her scleroderma." Yet, before he proceeded, he had wanted my medical clearance on his *technique* of abortion!

I had emphasized to the Professional Conduct Committee that the patient's scleroderma did not require further management while in the hospital for the abortion. I had told the Committee that it was obvious to me that Levinson had wanted my clearance to proceed with the abortion, yet the Committee had concluded that "the abortion was not an issue at any time."

Reading further in the hospital record, I came across a nursing note written on the patient the morning of the abortion:

> Upset and crying, says, "she does not want to have the abortion."

I read further. Dr. Labowitz had given medical clearance for the abortion, writing in his consultation to Levinson:

> Would agree that patient has progressive systemic sclerosis [scleroderma] with no clinical manifestations of organ systemic involvement at present. . . . See no contraindication to use of saline. Probably would agree with termination of this pregnancy. . . .

So Labowitz's pre-abortion assessment agreed with my office assessment that the patient had no clinical sign of organ systemic involvement.

The abortion was then done. The next day Levinson submitted his complaints against me of patient abandonment, and thereafter the patient's mother, according to Levinson, had wanted me "run out of town." In the meantime, the patient had chosen to have her scleroderma managed by Dr. Labowitz.

In further reviewing the patient's hospital records, I saw that six weeks after her abortion the patient had again been admitted to the hospital, this time for severe hypertension, renal disease and exacerbation of her scleroderma. In his discharge summary, Dr. Labowitz had written:

> One week post-abortion, [the patient] had an episode of vomiting, diplopia, confusion and walking into the walls and was found on examination to have a significant increase in her blood pressure which has remained relatively refractory to treatment. She also had rapid progressive stiffness and contractions in both hands since the abortion. Her vision had gotten worse over the past few weeks and complains of blurred vision, double vision and blindness. On examination by an ophthalmologist, she was found to have malignant changes in her eyegrounds and was admitted to the hospital.

The patient's condition progressively worsened, and, tragically, she died a few months later.

The day after reviewing the woman's hospital records, I talked with my attorneys. The attorneys now scheduled Levinson's deposition.

On the day of the interrogation, I picked up Jim at the law firm. Driving to Levinson's office, we talked about Dr. Newman's recent termination of his association with Dr. Labowitz and his decision to open his own office.

As we walked into Levinson's reception room, we met the court reporter. A few minutes later Roth and Levinson appeared. The gynecologist, in his mid-fifties, looked tired.

"Do you swear to tell the truth, the whole truth, and nothing but the truth, so help you God?"

Levinson responded affirmatively, and the deposition proceeded.

Green: Doctor [Levinson], was the comment made or the threat made by any member of the patient's family that they would try to have Dr. Connolly run out of town as a result of this incident?

Levinson: I do not recall any statement of anybody saying—I think there were statements—at the time, there was a heated portion somewhere along the line. Again, I don't remember all those kind of things. They were very, very upset about this, that a professional should treat a sick girl this way. . . . [The patient's father] was a member of the regular medical fraternity . . . . They were just appalled that the daughter of one of our Staff Chiefs should be treated this way. (#18)

[And later:]

Green: Doctor, while asking [Dr. Connolly] to advise you as to whether there were any contraindications to the use of intrauterine saline for an abortion, you are asking him to assist you in the abortive process or the abortion; were you not?

Levinson: No, I don't think I was. . . . I wanted to know if using saline would have any damage to her kidneys. If it would, I would have used another drug in the uterus rather than the salt solution. I was not asking him to help me. I was asking him the reverse. I was asking him, "Was there any danger to the patient's kidneys?" I would not ask Dr. Connolly for one help regarding an abortion. This would be an affrontary of the same degree that he has afforded the patient and myself. (#19)

[And later:]

Green: And would you agree, doctor, that Dr. Connolly had an absolute right to refuse to participate in an abortion?

Levinson: I never asked him to participate in an abortion. And Dr. Connolly told me, Mr.

Green, he would be available to help with that patient's scleroderma. Two days later, he changed his mind. He refused to get a substitute. And both I and the Medical Society agreed that he abandoned a patient. I will pursue this, and the way I am being badgered, I will make every effort to go to the Court to make this completely clear. I am being badgered, and I don't like it. And it is unfair. You've got a man [Dr. Connolly] that has some problems here. And I think they are rather deep. And I would like to help him. I would sit down tomorrow and work out details and say, "Let's stop all this silliness. It's counter-productive. It helps no one." But I don't like being badgered because I was doing my job to the community. And again, many physicians have raised these same charges. You know it and so do I, not only in the State of Delaware.

Green: I do not know it, doctor . . . the record is clear that you asked him for his opinion on the advisability of the abortion, and he refused to do it.

Levinson: I did not. I did not.

Green: I'm not going to argue with you.

Levinson: I did not ask for his opinion on an abortion. I respected his faith and said, "There is no way I am asking you." I wanted to know if saline would bother her kidneys.

Later, Roth cross-examined Levinson and asked him if, during the course of his 1979 telephone conversation with me, he had formed any opinions as to my thought process or mental status?

Levinson: There was something strange about the conversation. . . . That day, when he refused to come in, I gained the impression that his thinking was not as clear as it might be, yes . . . . I felt that the man's mental health might be a question . . . . I indeed thought that emotionally this man was under pressure or needed some sort of help, the way he was talking to me.

A short time later the deposition concluded, and on July 3, Roth finally filed her Answering Brief in response to our May 2 Omnibus Motion.

> . . . From his observation of Dr. Connolly, Dr. Reese was of the opinion that there was "good cause to have psychiatric examination done of Dr. Connolly insofar as it will clarify the basis for Dr. Connolly instituting the above-entitled action and determine the competency of Dr. Connolly to maintain it." (Reese Affidavit). . . .
>
> We have established by the affidavit of Dr. Reese that this is a material issue concerning Dr. Connolly's competency . . . .
>
> Plaintiff Ronald G. Connolly has been unsuccessful in his medical practice and has been looking for a cause to which to attribute his lack of success. The world now appears to him as a conspiracy to thwart his success but he is frustrated in his attempts to persuade others that such a situation does exist.

A few weeks later, Roth submitted an "addendum" to her brief consisting of excerpts from Levinson's deposition in which he had supported Roth's charge of psychiatric illness, and also including an affidavit signed by a Wilmington psychiatrist—whom I had never met, nor heard of—Dr. Lester Bronheim, stating that "it may prove of value if Ronald G. Connolly, M.D. would have a psychiatric examination."

We replied to Roth's submissions:

It is apparent that Bronheim's abysmal ignorance of what actually transpired in this case, and the background facts, completely disqualifies him as an expert . . . . This Affidavit is nothing more than counsel's attempt to fabricate support for a frivolous defense without any underlying evidence . . . .

Levinson's incentive for attacking Connolly has been established beyond a doubt by the preceding facts. His credibility as a witness is nonexistent. At the prompting of defendants' counsel, he would say anything which served to justify his abandonment complaint.

At a more fundamental level, the Levinson deposition pages demonstrate the extent to which defendants must reach to support their Psychiatric Motion. Of all the vain attempts to bolster this Motion, none has reached the level of ridiculousness that the Levinson deposition has reached.

As the Court considered our pleading, my practice continued to deteriorate. Florence was now handling all of the secretarial chores, while Josie, who recently had been working only part-time, arranged for full-time employment elsewhere.

Flinn and the Credentials Committee had denied my request to be transferred to the Consulting Staff. They offered me instead a transfer within the Active Staff from the Section of Rheumatology to the Section of Internal Medicine. Flinn concluded his offer writing, "If this is acceptable to you, please let me know in writing within two weeks of the receipt of this letter." (#20)

Ten days later I hand-delivered my reply to Dr. Flinn: "I accept the position in the Section of Internal Medicine." (#21) However, six weeks after I accepted Flinn's offer of transfer to the Section of Internal Medicine, he sent me a letter qualifying his offer:

. . . if you are to have an appointment at the Wilmington Medical Center, it will be necessary for

> you to have a psychiatric evaluation by a mutually agreeable psychiatrist. If the psychiatric evaluation finds you in good mental health and recommends continued staff privileges, I will be happy to forward your application on to the Central Credentials Committee.
>
> In an attempt to come to a conclusion on this matter, I would like to request that the evaluation be completed before the first of September. Should you choose not to go along with this request by the first of September, we will be forced to consider that you have resigned from our Staff . . . .
>
> Sincerely yours,
> Robert B. Flinn, M.D. (#22)
> Director, Department of Medicine

The Court had already denied Roth and Labowitz's motion for a psychiatric examination and was considering our motion to impose sanctions against the defendants for submitting their motion, yet now, the Wilmington Medical Center was demanding that I have a psychiatric exam—or resign from their staff!

Would the "mutually agreeable psychiatrist" performing the psychiatric evaluation be Dr. David Raskin, chairman of the hospital's Department of Psychiatry and the one whom Roth had scheduled me to see in her initial motion?

My decision was easy. I would *not* submit to a psychiatric exam! The motives of my opponents were transparent.

I should be judged—like everyone else — on my performance, my work, and my actions, not by a psychiatrist selected by my adversaries. It would be absurd to submit to such a travesty.

On September 7 Flinn wrote to me:

> . . . [I] stated . . . that should you choose not to go along with our request for psychiatric evaluation to be completed by the first of September, we would consider that you were resigning from the staff. In follow-up of that letter, I note that we have not heard from you and, therefore, it is with some regret that I

> accept your resignation from the staff of the Wilmington Medical Center.

On September 26, 1984 I became the subject of a memorandum from Allston J. Morris, M.D., Vice President for Medical Affairs, to eight administrators at the hospital, including the Director of the Admitting Office:

> Please be advised by copy of this memorandum that effective immediately, Ronald G. Connolly, M.D., is no longer a member of the Medical-Dental Staff of the Wilmington Medical Center. He may not under any circumstance admit patients, care for patients presently in the Wilmington Medical Center, nor care for patients in the Emergency Room.
>
> Thank you for your attention to this matter.

This highlighted yet another inconsistency: The Medical Center had now "resigned" me from their staff, ostensibly because of their concern for my psychiatric health. Their concern, however, did not extend to patient care elsewhere since they did not notify the four other Delaware hospitals where I was on staff, nor did they notify the Delaware Board of Medical Practice.

Meanwhile, the Delaware Board of Medical Practice was still struggling with their own dilemma. It seemed that they were in a state of paralysis. After more than seven months, no action had been taken on Labowitz's complaints, which had been forwarded to them by Dr. Straughn of the New Castle County Medical Society.

The Board's silence was finally broken in mid-September, when its vice-president, Dr. Leroy Buckler, wrote that he was investigating Labowitz's complaints against me and, incredibly, my complaints of a year and a half ago against Labowitz!

Buckler, who also had been a member of the Board which had refused to consider my original complaints, made no attempt to explain the Board's flip-flop.

Jim Green replied to the Board. He sent Buckler self-explanatory pleadings and papers filed in the lawsuit, and he cautioned: "This entire matter is before the Superior Court for trial and judgement. . . . I am sure you are well aware that it would be most inappropriate for the Board of Medical Practice to usurp the function of the Court and express any opinion, formal or informal, on this matter while it is before the Court. This letter and the enclosures are being forwarded subject to that understanding."

Buckler replied to me instead of my attorney:

> With regard to the letter of Mr. James S. Green, Esq . . . . I wish only to comment that it is the full intention of the Board of Medical Practice to proceed with its investigation. It is the responsibility of the Board of Medical Practice to be the "sole competent authority" in the state of Delaware to supervise, regulate, and discipline doctors. We must not confuse any litigation currently ongoing, which would seek to adjudicate business practices or professional contractual relationships as a substitute for the Board's responsibility. The responsibility cannot be moved into the courtroom when we are charged with setting standards and enforcing them. There is a certain responsibility that the Board of Medical Practice has in investigating charges such as those brought dealing with unprofessional conduct and skill, including possible negligence or incompetence, including any suggestion of mental illness or mental incompetence which might temporarily or permanently affect the physician's ability to practice.... The fact that the Board of Medical Practice has an immediate and on-going responsibility to the patients of Delaware is supported by the specific charges given to the Board within 24 Del. C. Chapter 17.
>
> Mr. Green claims . . . that the Board would not want to "usurp the function of the court". The

Board clearly feels that this is not usurpation, since the Board's jurisdiction and charge is clearly independent of normal civil judicial processes.

In my mind, Buckler was a phony and the Delaware Board of Medical Practice was a public fraud!

In the meantime, there were other developments. The Delaware Attorney General's office, perhaps as a result of reading the newspaper article relating the affidavits of Labowitz's two ex-secretaries concerning Medicaid abuse, had embarked on an investigation of Dr. Labowitz.

Also, I had continued my own investigation of my opponents. I was interested in learning whether Labowitz had sued any other patients besides LaRaye Thomas.

The civil index of the Court of Common Pleas included suits filed from August 1, 1980. These records revealed that from this date through December 1982 Dr. Labowitz—who lived with his family in an expensive home with a swimming pool and tennis court in his back yard, whose tastes in cars ranged from a new white Cadillac to a sleek gray Jaguar—had sued forty-eight people. Although most of the files were closed, we were able to confirm that the defendants in thirty-five cases were patients of Dr. Labowitz and that the majority involved medical bills for amounts from under $100 to $200. (#23)

Interestingly, Dr. Labowitz, as an adjunct to his medical practice, did laboratory testing and had X-ray facilities, as well as physical therapy. Like many doctors, he also had a financial interest in these services. With each patient that Dr. Labowitz (or any doctor) sees, a decision is made whether that patient would benefit from the doctor's ordering laboratory tests, X-rays, or physical therapy, as well as other medical services. Each decision requires medical competence and honesty.

October 25, 1984 was a clear, pleasant autumn morning as Jim Green, Collins J. Seitz, Jr. ("C.J."), an associate in the law firm, and I walked over to the courthouse for a 9:00 argument. Jim and Jane Roth would be arguing our Omnibus Motion before a Superior Court Judge who had been assigned to our case for a few months now, Judge Vincent Bifferato.

I opened the glass door of the courthouse as Jim and C.J., carrying litigation briefcases, entered. We walked up the circular marble stairs to the second floor, turned right, and walked down the hall to Court Room 9. A few young attorneys, perhaps doing clerkships, sat in the spectator seats talking quietly. Also present was a *News-Journal* reporter, Jane Harriman.

Jim had had much trial experience. He was bright and articulate, yet relaxed and amiable. As he quietly prepared his papers for the argument, Jane Roth entered, exchanged a few words with him, and took her seat at the opposing counsel's table. A few minutes later the bailiff entered, all those present stood, and Judge Bifferato—dark hair, black robes—entered, took his chair, bade us good morning, and began the proceedings.

Jim strode to the podium and politely addressed the Court.

Green: Your Honor, I believe that an understanding of the nature of the case and some of the clearly established facts of record is essential to the Court's consideration of . . . the motion. This is a case [of] business interference, unfair competition, and defamation brought by Dr. Connolly . . . against another physician . . . Dr. Russell Labowitz. . . . It is a business tort case, and plain and simply . . . the defendants have maliciously used the immunity statute and a trumped-up, unprecedented mental illness defense to delay the litigation, to embarrass Dr. Connolly, to destroy his business and reputation. Unfortunately, more than a year after the case was commenced, they have succeeded. It is time, we believe, to put an end to these tactics. Not only is a determination of the present motions of grave concern to Dr. Connolly, they involve matters of tremendous [public] importance, including treatment of indigent patients, standards of health care in the community, health care costs in the community, and the accountability of some doctors for these important public concerns.

[He proceeded to summarize our discovery findings and pleadings for the Court, and then concluded.]

Green: In closing . . . I would respectfully request that Your Honor grant the motion allowing discovery into the areas which have been withheld under the pretext of the immunity statute, and as I asked earlier, to deny the motion for a psychiatric examination, to strike the Affirmative Defense, and to impose appropriate sanctions including the attorneys' fees that have unnecessarily been generated by our struggle to get these spurious issues out of this case . . . Thank you, Your Honor.

The Court: Thank you.

Roth: May it please the Court, let me deal, first of all, with the question of the privilege statutorily enacted in 24 Delaware Code, Section 1768. I think at the present time, we are all very much aware of the need for quality medical care from the physicians in this community and throughout the nation. And there is a great deal of talk about the need for physicians to police themselves, about the need for physicians to judge the quality of their physicians in the community. I think that we all must recognize, and it's well recognized in the case law, that in discussing the competency of a colleague, many people are loath to be frank in their opinion if they know that tomorrow that colleague will see their opinion. Therefore, in getting an . . . evaluation of the physicians in the community, it is of vital importance that there be some means of granting immunity to very frank discussions of physician competency and physician ability to perform the area of medical practice to which they have put themselves out as being qualified . . . .

[Later:]

The Court: [You] told me that the Credentials Committee is to protect the public. Isn't it more important to protect the public against Dr. Connolly, if he is psychotic, from practicing [medicine] than from filing a lawsuit?

Roth: Well, if Dr. Connolly's mental condition will interfere with his practice of medicine, I think it is important that appropriate steps be made to determine that.

The Court: Well, my point is this: I mean, the doctors in this case have come forward and said—before Dr. Connolly can go on with this lawsuit, he ought to be psychiatrically examined. I find that terribly offensive if they haven't done something before the Credentials Committee. I think anybody can file suit in this state, in a civil case, and if it is determined by the Court that he needs a guardian appointed, we will appoint him a guardian. But for the doctors to come forward and say, Dr. Connolly should be examined before he can proceed with a legal suit, but yet we are going to continue to allow him to practice medicine, is frightening to me. I just don't see where they have any backbone or character. And I don't mean to defame them, because I don't know who they all are. That doesn't bother me. It bothers me that these doctors come forward with affidavits saying he needs an examination, but yet they are allowing him to continue to practice medicine and treat people, which is more important to me than to bring a lawsuit.

Roth: . . . . The bringing of the motion in this Court . . . was my determination. That was my determination because of my concern.

[And, Roth continued:]

. . . I saw the recommendation of the Credentials Committee that Dr. Connolly should have a psychiatric evaluation. I was concerned myself from the [telephone] conversation that . . . I had with Dr. Connolly about Dr. Connolly's mental equilibrium. Therefore, on the basis of that alone, I would have not done anything. But I saw the recommendation ... of the Credentials Committee saying they felt his complaint against Dr. Labowitz was unfounded, and recommending that he have a psychiatric evaluation. I was concerned that Dr. Connolly is bringing now in the courts of this state a lawsuit against Dr. Labowitz based upon the same unfounded contentions that he won't give up. . . . I talked to Dr. Reese . . . . I said . . . are you of the opinion that the bringing of this suit is a manifestation of a psychiatric condition?

> That doesn't mean [Dr. Connolly] can't go and treat a patient, but just in his ability to deal with his complaints about Dr. Labowitz, is his mental status affecting his ability to deal with these complaints rationally, or is he using the courts of this state in an effort to get a vindication which, in his mental condition, he feels is necessary, but legally isn't so. This lawsuit has caused great personal concern . . . to Dr. Labowitz, also. There are papers filed by Dr. Connolly saying that Dr. Labowitz was involved in Medicaid fraud. That was printed in the newspaper. There was an Attorney General's investigation of Dr. Labowitz because of these allegations of Medicaid fraud. And the Attorney General's office, after fully investigating this claim, said that it is entirely without basis . . . . And they go on to say, moreover, it appears that Dr. Labowitz is a caring and competent physician. This is a letter from Alex J. Smalls, Director of the Medicaid Fraud Control Unit, of August 13, 1984. So that the complaints that Dr. Connolly is making . . . are complaints which are directed at his apparent vendetta against Dr. Labowitz, which is without justification . . . . And I am concerned on the basis of Dr. Reese's opinion, on the basis of my own observations, that this complaint, this vendetta against Dr. Labowitz is a manifestation of Dr. Connolly's mental condition. (#24)

[I was shocked: Labowitz had been exonerated by the Attorney General's office in spite of his own deposition admissions and the sworn testimony of two of his ex-secretaries! . . . But Roth was not yet finished.]

Roth: And I think it would be valuable to have a psychiatric review of his mental condition. I think this issue is in this case in another aspect, also, and that aspect is, Dr. Connolly says, my medical practice has failed. I haven't succeeded. He is saying, it's got to be because of this conspiracy of Dr. Labowitz. I think if his medical practice has failed, that there are other reasons that his medical practice has failed, and one of them is, is he mentally able to conduct a successful medical practice.

[And, a few minutes later:]

Roth: I think [the privilege under Section 1768] has been properly invoked . . . and I think it is important for the quality of medical care in the State of Delaware that this privilege should stay in existence.

After Jim's rebuttal, Judge Bifferato made a closing statement.

The Court: . . . I know there is more at stake than what moves lawsuits, or concern with money. I think one of the problems we have in this case is that everybody feels close to the medical profession because they provide health care service to the public, and that has put more emphasis on this case than anything else. I will try to dispose of these . . . issues as soon as possible.

The judge concluded his remarks, and recessed the Court.

As Jim, C.J., and I walked out of the courtroom, Jane Harriman from the *News-Journal* came over to talk with Jim. My attorneys repeatedly had cautioned me not to talk with reporters: My case was being tried in Court—not in the newspapers.

As Harriman departed, we headed back to the office. "I hope the *News-Journal* picks up," I said, "the story that there is more at stake to the public than just a lawsuit between two doctors."

"Our goal," Jim reiterated, "is to win in Court, not the newspapers."

A few weeks later, Friday morning, November 16, as I walked into my office Florence glanced up from the morning newspaper. "Doctor, you got another bad article."

The four column headlines blared:

PROBE CLEARS DOCTOR OF MEDICAID FRAUD

The state attorney general's office has cleared Wilmington rheumatologist Dr. Russell J. Labowitz of charges that he defrauded the Medicaid program.

Deputy attorney general Alex J. Smalls said Thursday that at the conclusion of his investigation, he wrote Labowitz and told him he is "a fine doctor, the kind we want in the [Medicaid] program."

Medicaid is state and federal health insurance for people on welfare.

As part of a suit against Labowitz, one of his former employees claims he billed Medicaid for services to patients who did not keep their appointments with him.

"I really expected to be exonerated since I did nothing wrong," said Labowitz. "They [the attorney general's office] concluded I was a competent and caring physician."

Labowitz said his attorney received a letter from Smalls about two months ago announcing the results of the attorney general's findings . . . .

> Ronald G. Connolly, also a Wilmington physician who specializes in arthritis . . . is suing Labowitz for allegedly conspiring to destroy him professionally. The charges of Medicaid fraud are in depositions in that suit, which was filed in the summer of 1983.
>
> This fall, Connolly lost his staff privileges at The Medical Center of Delaware, where Labowitz is chief of rheumatology, but neither Connolly or the hospital administration will discuss why.
>
> Smalls said his letter to Labowitz exonerated him of all charges, and that the investigation had "found no instance where he billed the state when he didn't see the patient."

"Florence," I said, "that's ridiculous! Labowitz at his deposition admitted that there was a period of time when it was his office policy to bill for no-shows whether they were Medicaid, private or whatever!"

"I know," Florence replied, "but the *News-Journal* readers don't know it."

"No wonder Medicaid is running out of funds," I responded. The circumstances had become ludicrous: The public's tax dollars, including mine, were supporting the Attorney General's office and Medicaid; Labowitz had been cleared of Medicaid fraud, and his attorney, Jane Roth, had argued to the Court that my insertion of the Medicaid issue in this case was yet another example that my complaints were without justification and the manifestation of mental illness. Meanwhile, Ms. Roth's husband, Senator William V. Roth, R-Del., Chairman of the Senate Governmental Affairs Committee, had been exposing waste, fraud and abuse in the Pentagon, including the Defense Department's purchase of $600 toilet seats. And simultaneously, Labowitz's malpractice insurance carrier was financing his legal defense, while across the country higher malpractice premiums were being passed on to the public—to patients.

Compounding my problems, the power and prestige of the Wilmington Medical Center, one of the largest hospitals of its kind in the country, was publicly behind Labowitz. They had taken away my staff privileges.

What patients would go to a doctor who had lost his hospital privileges?

During the next week I had a surge of patient cancellations at the office. Administrators at St. Francis Hospital saw the newspaper article and were concerned, and their Vice-President for Medical Affairs wrote to his counterpart at The Medical Center of Delaware (the new name for the Wilmington Medical Center), Dr. Allston Morris, asking for information regarding "the current status of Ronald G. Connolly, M.D. as a member of your medical staff, and if he is no longer a member of your staff, the circumstances surrounding his loss of privileges."

Morris provided no information to St. Francis Hospital concerning the circumstances surrounding my loss of privileges. He simply stated: "At the present time Dr. Ronald Connolly is not a member of the staff of The Medical Center of Delaware."

Meanwhile, at home, Sieglinde and I found that some old friends no longer knew us. Again, as so often in the past, I wondered about the effect of all this on our children. Schnucki was now thirteen years old; Maria, twelve; Christina, ten; Ronny, eight; and Anna, four.

As the cold days of December 1984 slipped by, a problem which I had thought of in the past began increasingly to bother me: Not only was the coverage in the newspapers damaging my practice, but I seriously doubted whether I would be able to get a fair trial. Would there be potential jurors who had not been influenced by the press?

On December 18, Tuesday, I stayed home from work. It was Sieglinde's birthday. We were going to take a hike at the Brandywine Nature Center and then go to a country tavern for lunch. Sieglinde's blue-gray eyes, exceptional bearing, gentle voice and spontaneous manner were as refreshing and strong as ever. But the past two years had been a torture, and with every brief, every affidavit, and every pleading that our opponents submitted to the Court, as well as with every newspaper article on our lawsuit, the torture intensified.

In mid-morning, my father, now seventy-nine years old but daily working long hours with Jim on my case, telephoned: Bifferato had struck our opponents Affirmative Defense, awarded us attorney fees, and overruled many of Roth's claims of immunity!

Later, I read Bifferato's decision:

> Privileges are repugnant to the adversarial judicial system in the United States and are therefore narrowly construed . . . . The integrity of our system relies on full disclosure of all relevant facts . . . .
>
> [The Court then ruled on specific objections in Labowitz's, Lazarus' and Reese's depositions, overruling some and sustaining others. The Court then proceeded.]
>
> An attack on an individual's capacity in open court is a sensitive matter which should only be used in most dire circumstances. The harm to the individual's reputation will be immeasurable, especially where the claim is unfounded . . . .
>
> . . . . The party seeking a mental exam must show that the mentality is in controversy and good cause exists for an examination . . . .
>
> The issue in a defense of lack of capacity is whether the plaintiff suffers from a mental condition that renders him unable to make responsible decisions with respect to the litigation . . . . Defendant must allege with specificity facts which show that plaintiff lacks such capacity so that it is properly in controversy in the case . . . .
>
> . . . Defendants have not alleged any facts in the affirmative defense to put forth in controversy plaintiff's capacity to sue. Defendants rest their argument on the affidavits of Drs. Reese, Bronheim and Levinson. The doctors' affidavits say little more than the doctors' opinions that plaintiff might benefit from psychiatric help. This allegation does not put in controversy his ability to make responsible decisions relating to this litigation. Defendants' allegations

> seem to challenge plaintiff's perceptions of the events in the complaint. It is those perceptions that form the basis of a lawsuit, and the question for the jury, where perceptions differ, is whose perceptions were right and what are the consequences of the correct perception. There are no grounds alleged sufficient to challenge plaintiff's capacity, and thus defendants' . . . affirmative defense is stricken.
>
> This Court has, in the past, heard and considered many claims and defenses that lacked merit and were filed without good grounds to support them. When a claim or a defense is filed and it tends to embarrass a litigant, it must be supported by good grounds and filed in good faith.
>
> . . . The defendant's claim that plaintiff is not competent to maintain this suit is embarrassing, especially since defendant at oral argument agreed that plaintiff was competent to practice medicine. The Court has found that there are not good grounds for the affirmative defense of lack of mental capacity of plaintiff. The Court, therefore, is of the opinion that plaintiff's motion to strike must not only be granted, but that he should be awarded reasonable attorney's fees in the preparation and presentation of such motion. Plaintiff is to submit an affidavit stating the number of hours spent on this matter and stating a reasonable hourly rate charged by his office.
>
> IT IS SO ORDERED.

Super! After more than sixteen months of litigation, the Court was with us and had taken the extraordinary action of imposing attorney fees against our opponents.

Ms. Roth was upset. A few days later she sent the Court a letter:

> Dear Judge Bifferato:
>
> I was extremely distressed by the language used in your Opinion of December 17 . . . implying that I had filed the Affirmative Defense in bad faith.
>
> I can assure your Honor that I have never filed any pleading in any matter in bad faith and I specifically did not file this Affirmative Defense in bad faith. That anyone reading your Honor's Opinion might conclude that I had acted in bad faith, when, in fact, I did not, is a source of very great distress to me . . . .

Apart from Jane Roth's distress, the lock on the Credentials Committee had been broken. Also, a new battle front was developing.

7
The Board on Professional Responsibility

It is the unanimous decision of the Board that it is not in the best interest to you, Dr. Labowitz, or the Medical Profession to pursue this matter any further.

I. J. Tikellis, M.D.
President
Delaware Board of Medical Practice

The *News-Journal* headline blared the Court's decision:

DOCTOR CAPABLE OF SUING, JUDGE SAYS

A Superior Court Judge has rejected a claim that Wilmington rheumatologist Dr. Ronald G. Connolly lacks the mental capacity to sue his colleague, Dr. Russell J. Labowitz . . . .

Thus, despite Roth's and Richards, Layton and Fingers' efforts, I, like other Americans, was now "Capable of Suing."

But my restraint in speaking to the press was exhausted. The negative publicity was affecting my patients, my practice, my family, and my chances in the lawsuit. I was not trying my case in the press; they had already publicized the case—but with major inaccuracies and deletions.

January 2, 1985 I called a *News-Journal* columnist, the resident satirist, Ralph Moyed. He feasted on notable charlatans, hypocrites, and public sleaze. I believed that the stark contradictions between Delaware statute and the Delaware Board of Medical Practice's conduct would be of interest to him; as would the contradictions between the public intent of immunity granted medical administrators under Section 1768 and medical administrators use of this immunity; as well as the contradictions between the attorney general's office exoneration of Labowitz versus Labowitz's own admissions. Also of importance were the contradictions between the Medical Code of Ethics and actions of medical administrators at The Medical Center of Delaware; as well as the contradictions between the *Code of Professionalism and Ethics* publicized by the *News-Journal's* public editor and ombudsman, Harry Themal, and his editorial on Connolly v. Labowitz.

The public was affected by these issues. It was only reasonable that they should be informed. The public also might have an opinion on another issue in the lawsuit: Must a doctor, against his or her religious convictions, consult or obtain another doctor to consult on a patient having an abortion?

It was 4:30 the next afternoon when Ralph Moyed, somewhat overweight, graying hair, glasses and wearing a tweed sport jacket, walked into my office. As we discussed the various issues over the next hour, he seemed genuinely interested. As we concluded, Moyed asked if he could take some of my exhibits with him; he wanted to follow up with the attorney general's office. He also advised that I discuss my complaints with his Editor-in-Chief, Donald Brandt.

At about the same time, I received bad news from Mom's doctor. He had been following her at regular intervals since her cancer surgery, and he now notified me that the most recent studies revealed a recurrence of the cancer, with metastases to the liver. Chemotherapy, including perfusion through the artery going to the liver, might provide some palliation.

For as long as I can remember, my mother had always been afraid of "the Big C"; many of her close friends had died from cancer. Sieglinde and I drove over to Alapocas to break the news to Mom and Dad. As the four of us sat in the living room, I told them about the test results. Mom was composed, serene, positive, and uplifting to Dad, Sieglinde, and me.

"Well, Ronny," she said, "when do we start the chemotherapy?"

Meanwhile, Jim Green had spoken on the telephone with and also written to the Delaware Attorney General, Charles M. Oberly, concerning the conflicting statements surrounding Labowitz's Medicaid practices.

Jim requested that the Attorney General, in view of the conflicting (if not conclusive) evidence, put the facts in perspective "by at a minimum advising the public that there was another side to the story," and he requested a meeting for us with Oberly.

Later, Jim had a chance meeting at the courthouse with the Attorney General. Oberly said that he had reviewed the entire matter and he was satisfied that the Medicaid investigation had been thorough and complete; there was "no proven instance of [Medicaid] fraud." He also declined Jim's request for the three of us to meet.

I then telephoned the Director of the Medicaid Fraud Control Unit, Deputy Attorney General Alex Smalls, asking for clarification of the discrepancies between Labowitz's admissions and Smalls' exoneration. Although the Deputy Attorney General had responded to inquiries from the *News-Journal* and was quoted in their article, he would not respond to my inquiry. He said if I had complaints I should go through my attorney to the Attorney General.

As I hung up the phone I was still determined to get an answer: Roth had used the exoneration to support her psychiatric motion in the argument before Bifferato, and both Medicaid and the attorney general's office were supported by taxes—and I was a taxpayer.

Like many physicians, I received the *Medicaid News Letter*, as well as similar notifications with the latest updates on Medicaid and Medicare. The memoranda and letters often focused on the importance of "stopping health care providers who defraud or abuse the Medicare and Medicaid programs" and a "Hotline 1-800-" number was often provided to report suspicious circumstances.

For an hour I telephoned various federal offices in Washington and Philadelphia. I called the Medicaid Hotline Number, the Office of the Inspector General, the Section of Health Financing Integrity, the Department of Health and Human Services, and the Section of Consumer Affairs. I was referred from one office to another, to another . . . One official suggested that my attorney again try the Delaware Attorney General; another suggested that I write to my congressman or senator—Senator Roth or Senator Biden. But none of the government officials, in spite of their public posture, were themselves interested in investigating Labowitz's exoneration despite his own admissions.

In the meantime, my medical practice continued to deteriorate. My gross income for 1984 was $69,669, approximately half of which was paid out in office expenses. If this continued, I would have to close my office.

Something was seriously wrong with American medicine, and my experience was but an example. I was convinced that top medical administrators and institutions had systematically betrayed their public duty, and while I routinely treated all patients, including indigent patients, my waiting room was empty, while Dr. Labowitz, who had sued many of his own patients, had patients waiting in line.

In addition, my 24-month confrontation with medical peers was now turning into a war of attrition. My father continued to subsidize my home expenses with a monthly check drawn from the funds that he had been saving for me since I was a child, and Connolly, Bove, Lodge & Hutz had now spent more than $100,000 on my litigation. Our financial resources were limited; I could not indefinitely pursue my opponents.

Later in January, in accord with the Court's decision of the previous month, my attorneys submitted their fee for the preparation and presentation of our motion to strike the defendant's Affirmative Defense and psychiatric examination; the fee was $19,455. The Court would consider my attorneys' submission, then render its decision on the sum the defendants would pay.

My deteriorating practice also was compounded by another development. I had been taking night-call and weekend-call every day of the year with the few exceptions of when I was out of town. Now, the physician with whom I had shared "on-call" scheduling over the past four years, wrote me a note saying that he was "going to make a change in [his] coverage system. Therefore our mutual coverage system must come to an end." There was no further explanation.

Meanwhile, more doctors with whom I had been on a first-name basis for years now ignored me.

The Medical Center of Delaware, which by now had opened its new multimillion-dollar hospital, had been ordered by the Court to make additional information available to us. The Credentials Committee, via their attorneys, Richards, Layton and Finger, now turned over to Jim the tape recording of the meeting in which I had presented my complaints against Labowitz.

"Jim," I asked, "did I sound inappropriate, or psychiatrically ill, during the meeting?"

"No," he responded. "There was nothing there whatsoever. It sounded to me like they were helping Labowitz to excuse himself."

"I hope we can use the tape at trial," I replied. "Reese's deposition and this tape contradict his affidavit."

Returning to another battleground, Buckler, of the Delaware Board of Medical Practice, had interviewed me in my office concerning my complaints against Labowitz and his complaints against me.

As we discussed the various complaints, including Labowitz's referral of Madeline Boone, Buckler commented that he did not have the "certainty of God" that Labowitz's misrepresentation was intentional. As he was leaving my office, Buckler said that the Board would inform me of their conclusions.

I was never informed of the outcome (if any) of Labowitz's complaints against me, but only of my complaints against him. On January 21, 1985, the board sent me a letter:

> Dear Dr. Connolly:
>
> I wish to inform you the Board of Medical Practice has carefully considered all your complaints against Dr. Russell J. Labowitz.
>
> None of the complaints that could be documented were of the magnitude that would warrant any action by the Board of Medical Practice against Dr. Labowitz.

The Board has spent considerable time on the merit of the complaints and it is the unanimous decision of the Board that it is not in the best interest to you, Dr. Labowitz, or the Medical Profession to pursue this matter any further.

The Board urges immediate resolution of this controversy.

Sincerely,
I.J. Tikellis, M.D.
President
Delaware Board of Medical Practice (#25)

Although Tikellis and the Board felt that my lawsuit was not in the best interest of the medical profession, they had no apparent objection when the American Medical Association filed a lawsuit in Federal Court charging that the federal government's Medicare physician fee freeze provisions of the 1984 Budget Reduction Act were unconstitutional.

For two hundred years, since 1789, medicine in Delaware has been organized. The state has one of the oldest medical societies in the country. Perhaps the Delaware Board of Medical Practice will claim that they require still more time and money in order to function minimally. And perhaps the governor will form a prestigious "blue-ribbon commission" to make further recommendations. The public, however, can budget billions of dollars, and legislators may pass "perfect" statutes regarding medical practice and ethics, but if the people charged with making the system work state, for whatever reason, that the Code of Ethics is meaningless, or that complaints of unethical conduct are not within their jurisdiction, or if they randomly choose to discipline Dr. X but not Dr. Y, then the system is doomed to habitual failure—an expensive failure, and one that becomes more expensive with each passing day.

Discovery now resumed on Labowitz's ex-partner, Dr. James Newman, who was still under oath to tell the truth.

Green: Were you aware on July 1, 1980, when you became an employee of Dr. Labowitz that he was not Board Certified in Rheumatology?

Newman: No, I was not aware of that.

Green: Have you since become aware of that?

Newman: Yes.

Green: When did you become aware of that?

Newman: It wasn't for several years after I was working with Dr. Labowitz that I knew that for certain. I'm not sure in what context it was.

[And, even though Newman had worked in Labowitz's office for more than three years, he, like me, reiterated that he did not know that Labowitz was evaluating him.]

Green: Do you know if Dr. Labowitz was the person . . . who evaluated your performance at the Wilmington Medical Center, or was that your understanding of one thing he did as section chief?

Newman: I never felt that .... I don't know that I have anybody policing my activities in the Medical Center.

Green: Is it your understanding that as your section chief Dr. Labowitz does not have an additional duty of critiquing your performance on a regular basis?

Newman: I don't believe that Dr. Labowitz has any responsibilities or obligations to the department of medicine to comment or critique my performance.

[Later:]

Green: Was there a particular reason for your termination of your [professional] relationship or Dr. Labowitz's termination of the relationship?

Newman: Well, I think it reflected philosophic differences between us that from my point of view made continuing to practice together unfeasible.

[A minute or two later:]

Green: Was there anything that you learned about Dr. Labowitz as a result of this litigation which affected your decision.

Newman: Absolutely not. . . .

Green: Did Dr. Labowitz meet your standards of being an ethical physician? Was that a philosophical difference?

Newman: I felt Dr. Labowitz was an ethical physician.

Green: Did he meet your standards?

Newman: Yes. I found his behavior to be acceptable to me. (#26)

And Labowitz was again deposed.

Green: Did you not criticize Dr. Connolly's refusal to participate in an abortion [to] Dr. Newman?

Labowitz: No.

Green: You never did?

Labowitz: No, I never criticized Dr. Connolly for not participating in an abortion. You're putting words in my mouth.

Green: Did you criticize him for patient abandonment to Dr. Newman?

Labowitz: That's correct.

[A short time later:]

Green: Were you concerned over [Dr. Connolly's] actions at that time [1979]?

Labowitz: Yes.

Green: Why?

Labowitz: Because I felt it was Dr. Connolly's obligation to see that this woman was properly treated, as a physician.

Green: Wasn't Dr. Levinson indicating to you that what he wanted from Dr. Connolly was medical clearance to perform an abortion?

Labowitz: Yes.

Green: Did he make clear to you that that is what he wanted from you?

Labowitz: Yes.

Labowitz's deposition was adjourned a short time later.

The next Friday, February 1, 1985, I read the headline in the morning *News-Journal*:

JANE ROTH MAY GET JUDGESHIP

Sen. William V. Roth, Jr., R-Del., confirmed Thursday that his wife is being screened for the upcoming vacancy on the U. S. District Court bench in Wilmington.

Jane Richards Roth, an attorney with Richards, Layton and Finger, has the support of her husband in seeking the seat. And Roth is the man who usually picks the judicial candidate, who is then formally nominated by the president.

"It's awkward, admittedly," Sen. Roth said. "But at the same time, in a world where there are many two career families, it's not fair to stand in her way . . . . She is a very able trial lawyer and qualified for the position . . . . I'm strongly behind her."

Jane Roth, 49, said she has sought a judgeship for several years . . . .

While all federal judgeships are presidential appointments, the senior senator in the president's party usually makes the recommendations for the district court.

In this case, "It puts us both in a very awkward situation," Sen. Roth said. Roth said that the administration already knows of his wife's interest and he would probably not have to make a formal recommendation.

On February 4 Ms. Roth, still objecting to the Superior Court's decision in our Omnibus Motion, filed with the Court a "Motion to Reconsider," stating: "On January 28, 1985, the Court [at a conference] granted to defendants permission to submit a motion to reconsider the Opinion of the Court of December 17, 1984, determining that the affirmative defense of lack of capacity was not supported by good grounds or filed in good faith and awarding attorney's fees in the preparation and presentation of the motion to strike the . . . affirmative defense."

Three days later, Jim objected in a letter to the Court: "From the outset of this litigation, Mrs. Roth has demonstrated a disdain and disregard for both the Rules and Orders of this Court. Her ill-conceived and woefully tardy 'Motion to Reconsider' is but the latest example. It should be denied and stricken, with sanctions ordered against both her and defendants for their delaying and harassing tactics."

In the meantime, I had scheduled a meeting with the Editor-in-Chief of the *News-Journal*, Donald Brandt. Brandt had told me that he wanted his managing editor, Norman Lockman, and his public editor, Harry Themal, to be present.

As I entered the red brick News-Journal building at Ninth & Orange Streets, I signed in at the front desk, received a security pass, and was directed up a flight of stairs to the second floor. A secretary ushered me into a drab conference room with a littered table covered with dirty ashtrays and partially eaten lunches. Turning to leave, she said, "Mr. Brandt will be with you in a few minutes."

As Brandt entered—gray hair, lined face, tired eyes, cigarette in hand—we greeted each other. He then introduced me to a small, middle-aged, studious-appearing man behind him, Harry Themal. We cleared off part of the conference room table, and shortly after I began presenting my complaints, a well-dressed, middle-aged black man entered—Norman Lockman.

I systematically reviewed the stark contradictions between their newspaper coverage and documented facts from the public record—sworn depositions and affidavits, briefs, letters, and statutes.

The editors studied my evidence. Themal asked me whether, "Any contraindication to intrauterine saline?" wasn't directed to the patient's scleroderma, rather than to the abortion.

Lockman asked why Reese had submitted the psychiatric affidavit. I responded that the affidavit was based not on misbehavior or misconduct, but on Reese's conclusion that my "grievance against Dr. Labowitz was not justified . . . . [but] is a manifestation of a psychiatric condition." As I showed Lockman and the other two editors Reese's short affidavit and the deposition in which he had repeatedly claimed immunity when asked to specify the basis for his psychiatric affidavit, Lockman, as if in disbelief, simply shook his head.

I told them also that the medical administrators had found Labowitz "blameless" and "very ethical," and then, only *after* the Superior Court began reviewing my complaints and had denied my opponents' motion for a psychiatric exam, had the medical administrators demanded a psychiatric exam, and then "resigned" me from their staff.

Before adjourning our meeting—which would be resumed in a few weeks—I asked them to publicly correct the misrepresentations.

Two and a half weeks later, as the four of us resumed our conference, Donald Brandt looked at me, saying that after thorough review of the material and after discussion among themselves they had come to the conclusion that there was no need for the newspaper to do a correction since the reporting was "accurate, but not as complete as it might have been," but they would do "an update."

It would take several weeks to assign a reporter, review the facts, and interview the parties concerned. Also, the newspaper would have to check with their legal counsel, since the matter was in litigation. Brandt said that Richards, Layton and Finger usually represented them, but he was sure that the law firm would acknowledge the conflict of interest and refer them elsewhere for legal advice.

I emphasized to Brandt and his assistants that it was my opinion that The Medical Center of Delaware had refused to respond to complaints of unethical conduct, and the Delaware Board of Medical Practice had refused to perform its statutory duty.

Brandt acknowledged that the Board of Medical Practice was obligated to investigate my complaints; he intended to have this investigated. He also said it was obvious—by Labowitz's own admission—that the attorney general's office was wrong. "Dr. Connolly," Brandt said, "who got to the attorney general's office and persuaded them to exonerate Labowitz?"

"All I know," I responded, "is what I heard from Roth at the Court argument and what I read in your newspaper regarding Labowitz's exoneration."

As I left the News-Journal building I was elated. Three editors, after spending a total of two and a half hours reviewing documented contradictions, were interested. They were going to investigate everything, including the state Board of Medical Practice, and then write an update.

A few weeks later, Bob Leary, a feature writer from the *News-Journal*, called, saying that the Editor-in-Chief had assigned him the story.

Leary came to my office for a lengthy taped interview. As a photographer took rolls of film, and Jim Green sat in attendance, Leary interrogated me on the conflict from beginning to end.

Over the next several weeks Leary continued his investigation, interviewed other participants, and often telephoned me to clarify various points.

The feature article was scheduled for publication Sunday, April 21.

On Wednesday, April 17, I took Mom down to Georgetown University Hospital where surgeons, the next day, would be inserting a permanent hepatic artery catheter for direct perfusion of chemotherapy into her metastases-filled liver. As Mom lay in her hospital bed, she talked warmly and personably with the hospital personnel as they came, did their chores, and left. Her brown eyes were alert and kind, but she was pale and losing weight. She had been nauseated and had had no appetite for months; her cancerous liver extended down to the pelvic brim.

That evening, as I stood in the glassed-in hallway outside Mom's room, I looked across the darkened Georgetown University campus which had been my second home for nine years: the gothic spires of Healey Building, McDonough Gymnasium, the tennis courts, and athletic fields. Overhead, planes glided over the Potomac on their way into National Airport as Washington prepared for another busy day.

My mother, filled with cancer, had a few months to live. She had never gone to college; she was unable to discuss politics, business or most social movements. At the same time she had an exceptional kindness, love, and trust for strangers and friends alike. She cared.

The day after surgery we would be returning to Wilmington. In the meantime, Leary had more last-minute questions for me, and from Mom's hospital room I returned his phone calls.

The surgery went well. We hoped that it would add a few months to Mom's life. Returning home, Sieglinde and my sister, Mary, who now lived in Wilmington with her husband, Wilson Braun, helped with Mom's nursing. There was now only one more day to await the *News-Journal's* Sunday publication. A fair article would at least partially rectify some of the damage done by the newspaper.

Early Sunday morning I awoke at 4:30, unable to get back to sleep. The paper boy usually did not arrive until 7:30 or 8. A few hours later, I slipped into a bathrobe, went downstairs and picked up the bulky Sunday *News-Journal* from our front door step.

Across the front page was an oversized feature article entitled: "M.D. vs. M.D.: A BITTER PILL FOR PROFESSION."

Adjacent to the headline was a large cartoon depicting two doctors standing on a rock fighting over a caduceus:

> Delaware medical and legal circles are being shaken by a controversial case called "Connolly vs. Labowitz," a case that involves a rare public battle between two prominent physicians each represented by an attorney from a well-known law firm.
>
> It has elements of almost novelistic proportions—accusations of mental instability, a dispute over an abortion, a long running feud between two competing physicians, assertions of professional privilege, accusations of vendettas and claims of professional ruin.
>
> Subplots involve religious convictions, medical credentials and a judge who became unhappy enough with the proceedings to criticize, in court, a defense tactic of a respected attorney who is married to a U.S. senator.
>
> The main participants are Ronald G. Connolly, M.D., a rheumatologist who is the scion of a prominent Wilmington family and Russell J. Labowitz, M.D., who for years was the only full-time practicing rheumatologist in Delaware.
>
> The case is believed to be without precedent in Delaware and it holds a kind of peek-through-the-fingers horror show fascination for the medical community. Because of the prominence of those involved, it is equally engrossing to the legal community.

Sitting at the kitchen table, I finished reading the four-page article: The Delaware Board of Medical Practice was never mentioned! The contradiction between Labowitz's own deposition admissions and the Attorney General's Medicaid exoneration was never mentioned! In its place, the *News-Journal* quoted Roth as saying:

> . . . there are papers filed by Dr. Connolly saying that Dr. Labowitz engaged in Medicaid fraud. That was printed in the newspaper. There was an Attorney General's investigation of Dr. Labowitz because of these allegations . . . and the attorney general's office, after fully investigating this claim, said that it is entirely without basis . . . and they go on to say it appears that Dr. Labowitz is a caring and competent physician . . . .

The newspaper elaborated on the support Labowitz had received from medical administrators at The Medical Center of Delaware—supporting the psychiatric accusations and denying me privileges. The newspaper did not mention that *before* the lawsuit had been filed it was these same medical administrators who, contrary to their Code of Ethics, had refused even to consider some of my complaints and, while ignoring fundamental facts, had declared Labowitz "blameless" of other complaints.

[As the months and years passed, the *News-Journal's* public avowals of fairness continued, as annually they devoted an editorial page to their *Code of Professionalism and Ethics*: "When an issue involves two or more sides in conflict, all significant interests should be given an opportunity to respond. Fairness in stories requires completeness, relevance, leveling with the reader and straightforwardness. . . ."]

Gannett's *News-Journal* was a major problem. Perhaps, I thought, I should contact a large out-of-state newspaper.

In the weeks that followed, my practice continued to deteriorate: more patients canceled, some requested that their records be transferred to Newman, weeks passed without an office referral from another doctor, and months passed without a hospital consultation.

My office income was not even covering office expenses. If the Court did not provide relief soon, I would be closing my office.

In the meantime, a new battleground had developed. It was obvious to me that my chances of a fair trial were being compromised by Roth. It was also clear that her professional conduct should be addressed, as she was being considered for a federal judgeship. In March, 1985, I filed a formal complaint against Jane Roth with the legal profession's Board on Professional Responsibility, which functioned under the auspices of the Supreme Court of Delaware

My complaints to the legal peer review committee included: Roth's psychiatric motion and lack of credible evidence to support it; repeatedly supporting her psychiatric motion by giving *her* personal medical opinion of me, which she based on the telephone conversation we had had prior to the lawsuit's being filed and at a time when she knew I was seeking representation by an attorney; supporting her psychiatric motion by submitting testimony that I was psychiatrically ill when I had exercised my statutory right and refused to participate in the abortion of a five-months-pregnant woman; and saying at my deposition that she was "perfectly entitled to annoy, embarrass, and oppress [me]!"

I submitted my complaints to the Disciplinary Counsel for the Board of Professional Responsibility—Susan Faw, Esquire. Within a few days Ms. Faw informed me that the complaints had been forwarded to Richard E. Poole, Esquire, an assistant disciplinary counsel, who would conduct a preliminary investigation to determine whether there was sufficient basis upon which to initiate formal disciplinary action against Ms. Roth.

A few days later Roth sent Mr. Poole a letter, with a copy going to me and to Jim Green, stating that:

> . . . . in the interest of full disclosure, I believe Dr. Connolly should . . . be made aware of the following matters:
>
> 1. Susan Faw, the Disciplinary Counsel, was formerly an associate of Richards, Layton & Finger.
>
> 2. Edmund N. Carpenter, a partner of mine, has been retained by you [Mr. Poole] as an expert witness in [another lawsuit].
>
> I bring these matters to Dr. Connolly's attention at this time in order that he may express

any concern he has on conflicts of interest that he feels arise from these relationships.

After careful consideration of the pros and cons of objecting to Mr. Poole's investigating my complaints, I responded that I had no objections. At the same time, Mr. Poole assured both me and Roth that "Ms. Faw assigned this matter to [him] so that as a former member of Richards, Layton & Finger she would have no involvement whatsoever in the matter."

Roth then wrote a response to my complaints, and, as directed, I responded with a rebuttal.

On May 9, Mr. Poole interviewed me for several hours. As he concluded the interview, he said that his job was to determine whether Jane Roth had gone beyond the bounds of advocacy. He would render his decision in the near future.

Later that same day the investigator met with Roth and her attorney, Henry Herndon.

Meanwhile, as Poole was investigating my complaints, I felt that there was a chance of blocking Roth's confirmation as a U.S. District Court Judge. I wrote to the Special Counsel for Judicial Selection, Jane Swift, in the Office of Legal Policy at the Department of Justice in Washington, who was involved in the background investigation of Roth's judicial appointment. I also forwarded to her a copy of the ethics complaint which I had submitted to the Board on Professional Responsibility.

I now needed additional support in order to block Roth's confirmation. Because the Right to Life organizations would be interested in the abortion incident, as well as the manner in which Roth had used it in this lawsuit, I contacted the president and founder of March for Life, Nellie Gray, a constitutional lawyer whose office was in Washington.

I had already spoken several months earlier with Senator Joseph R. Biden, a neighbor, about the lawsuit, but not about Roth's nomination. I would have to get this additional information to him. Senator Biden, a Democrat, was the ranking minority member on the Senate Judiciary Committee that would be considering Roth's nomination.

As I was making plans to go to Washington for interviews, a Superior Court office conference was held with a new representative from the bench, Judge Vincent J. Poppiti. I was unable to attend, but when I read the transcript it was clear that Ms. Roth had promptly provided background information for the new judge:

> Your Honor, at the commencement of this litigation . . . I filed a motion for a psychiatric examination of Dr. Connolly supported by an affidavit of a physician, Dr. Charles Lee Reese, III . . . who stated in his affidavit that . . . as he was familiar with the complaint made by Dr. Connolly to the Credentials Committee that he felt he was a manifest nut. It was a manifestation of a psychiatric disorder. . . . (#27)

May 16, I took an Amtrak train to Washington for a 10:30 meeting at the Justice Department with Dwight Rabuse at the Office of Legal Policy. Later in the afternoon I met with the minority counsel for the Senate Judiciary Committee, a staff aide of Senator Biden, Chip Reid, who was going to discuss my complaints with Senator Biden.

Riding the train home that evening, I mused over the events of the day, and tomorrow an FBI investigator would be meeting with Jim Green and Dad concerning Roth's nomination. (Routine screening of a federal judicial nominee includes investigations and recommendations from the FBI, as well as the American Bar Association). In the near future, I planned to telephone the chairman of the American Bar Association's Federal Judiciary Committee in New York City.

Late the next day, Dad told me that his meeting had covered a variety of issues, but that during their discussion the FBI agent had said he was not going to resolve the conflicting evidence on the Medicaid exoneration since Delaware's attorney general's office had already investigated. The FBI did not want to criticize the investigation by reopening the issue!

By now, Mr. Poole had completed his investigation. A few days later I received a copy of his conclusions:

May 17, 1985

Dear Ms. Faw:

On March 6, 1985 you referred [complaints filed by Ronald G. Connolly, M.D. against Jane R. Roth, Esquire] . . . to me pursuant to Rule 9(b) of the Rules of the Board on Professional Responsibility of the Supreme Court of Delaware to conduct a preliminary investigation in my capacity as an assistant disciplinary counsel. I have completed my investigation and I conclude that there is not a sufficient basis upon which to initiate formal disciplinary action against Mrs. Roth. . . .

Pursuant to Rule 9(b), I recommend dismissal of all complaints against Mrs. Roth by Dr. Connolly.

Respectfully submitted,
Richard E. Poole

On June 4, Susan Faw wrote to me:

Dear Dr. Connolly:

As you are aware, Mr. Poole has investigated your complaint and has concluded that there is not a sufficient basis upon which to initiate formal disciplinary action against Mrs. Roth. I have reviewed his report to me of May 17, a copy of which you received, and I concur with Mr. Poole. Accordingly, I consider my file in this matter closed.

Thank you for cooperating with Mr. Poole in the course of his investigation of this matter.

Sincerely,
L. Susan Faw (#28)

As Sieglinde and I discussed the decision of the Board on Professional Responsibility, she said that she wanted to move, to leave Delaware. I was angry, but not discouraged. I had done my duty; the Board's actions were their responsibilities.

I mulled over the irony that I had gone to court because medical administrators had totally dismissed my complaints, and now legal administrators had done the same thing. Neither of the two professional peer-review systems had found a single complaint necessitating disciplinary action. They had not found a single breach in their professional standards!

Meanwhile, although Roth's peers had dismissed my complaints, her judiciary nomination was still pending, and we were winning in Court: We had a victory with our Omnibus Motion, the Court was considering our award of attorney fees, and further discovery had further strengthened our case.

I had been criticized for filing a lawsuit against another physician, for over-reacting, for being unreasonable, too demanding, and too sensitive. Medical colleagues had testified that I was psychiatrically ill. Was I paranoid? Was my judgement skewed by personal involvement?

We were about to spotlight these questions by deposing probably the foremost medical expert in Delaware. The credentials of this physician were unsurpassed: His medical education and training was superb; in addition, he was Board Certified in both internal medicine and nephrology, he had a prestigious private practice, he was the former Editor-in-Chief of the *Delaware Medical Journal*, he was a past president of the Delaware Medical Society, he was a Clinical Professor of Medicine at Jefferson Medical College, and currently he was the Director of the Department of Medicine at the Medical Center of Delaware.

No one in Delaware was better qualified to answer these questions than Dr. Robert B. Flinn.

8
The Professor

The issues that I was brought into the case on had nothing to do with the abortion.

Dr. Russell J. Labowitz

I was there to medically clear this patient for the abortion.

Dr. Russell J. Labowitz

It was a warm sunny day in early May; the pink and white dogwoods were in full bloom. I was driving to Connolly, Bove, Lodge & Hutz to pick up Jim. My father, now seventy-nine years old and still working more than seventy hours a week, had just completed the construction of a ten-story, 106,000-square-foot building at 1220 Market Street, in the heart of corporate Wilmington. His law firm occupied the top few floors of the new building.

As I drove up, Jim was waiting. In a short time, at 1:30, he would be taking Flinn's deposition at the Medical Center's new $145 million dollar hospital just south of Wilmington on Interstate-95.

We arrived at the huge dark-brick 780-bed hospital, and as we took the elevator to an upper floor, I asked Jim, "Is Flinn going to admit that he told me the Medical Code of Ethics is meaningless?"

Jim smiled, "He's going to tell us soon." The elevator door opened and we walked down the hall. Entering Flinn's office, we met Roth and a court reporter. A secretary ushered us in, and Dr. Robert Flinn—in a spotless white lab coat, distinguished in appearance—stood up from behind his desk, and greeted us.

"Dr. Flinn," the court reporter said, "Do you swear to tell the truth, the whole truth, and nothing but the truth, so help you God?"

"I do."

And the deposition proceeded.

Green: Doctor, the reporter has handed you Deposition Exhibit Flinn No. 2, which is captioned "Attachment To Medical/Dental Staff Bylaws, Principles of Medical Ethics of the American Medical Association."

[The one-and-a-half-page code included such statements as, "The principal objective of the medical profession is to render service to humanity with full respect for the dignity of man. . . . The medical profession should safeguard the public and itself against physicians deficient in moral character or professional competence. . . . They should expose, without hesitation, illegal or unethical conduct of fellow members of the profession . . . . [A physician's] fee should be commensurate with the services rendered and the patient's ability to pay."]

Flinn: I see it.

Green: . . . Does that . . . appear to be an accurate statement of the Principles of Medical Ethics of the American Medical Association?

Flinn: Oh, I can't answer that. As you see, the medical ethics thing is a very long type of thing. And I assume since it has their name on it that that's what it is. But I'm not going to be in [a] position of making any statement about it.

Green: Do you know if The Medical Center of Delaware, the Wilmington Medical Center before that, subscribes to the Principles of Medical Ethics of the American Medical Association?

Flinn: I guess what you're asking is whether or not there was something in the Medical Center's official bylaws or documents that says that they do or that they don't. And I don't know whether that's true or not.

Green: Are those principles something which you personally subscribe to?

Flinn: I'd have to read the whole thing. In general, most of them are for motherhood and what-have-you. But most of the Principles of Medical Ethics outlined by the American Medical Association are straightforward and I would agree with them.

[Later:]

Green: Did you tell Dr. Connolly that the Code of Ethics was meaningless, Doctor?

Flinn: No, I don't think I—I am confident I didn't say that a Code of Ethics is meaningless.

Green: Doctor . . . [this Exhibit] is a letter from Dr. Connolly to you dated February 10, 1983, which is characterized as a formal complaint against Dr. Labowitz . . . .

Flinn: Yes. . . .

Green: When you received that, that was turned over to the Credentials Committee?

Flinn: Yes.

Green: How did you do that? Is there a procedure whereby you forward things to the Credentials Committee?

Flinn: Yes. . . . We've never had this kind of complaint. And I can't recall, but it was of the nature where they would want to have a special meeting of the committee so that they had proper time to hear it. So Dr. Lee Reese was at that time head of the Credentials Committee, so I forwarded this to them. And then I left it in their hands as to how to attack the—as to how to develop the formal hearings, which they had so that they could evaluate the complaint.

[And:]

Green: Did you talk to Dr. Lazarus [about my complaint that he had denied me membership in the American College of Physicians based on Labowitz's reports to the Credentials Committee at the Wilmington Medical Center], do you recall?

Flinn: . . . I think I did not talk to Dr. Lazarus because the Dr. Lazarus complaint, as I recall, was basically about the American College of Physicians, which . . . wasn't within the peer review process of the Medical Center.

Green: Did one of Dr. Connolly's complaints involve a Mrs. Boone, if you recall, a patient referred by Dr. Labowitz to Dr. Connolly?

Flinn: Yes, I remember reading that description.

Green: Did you talk to the patient?

Flinn: No. You've got to remember that those actions were not within the Medical Center and I did not get involved directly on those actions that did not relate to the Medical Center.

[Later, Flinn was asked about his April 29, 1983 letter to me, in which he had stated: "it is the Committee's opinion and mine that Dr. Labowitz has behaved in a very ethical fashion and we simply do not agree with your interpretation."]

Green: You say, "We simply do not agree with your interpretation." And isn't that the basis upon which you say that Dr. Connolly needs psychiatric help, because he has a different interpretation of the facts than you?

Flinn: If you look out a window and you see the sky is blue and Dr. Connolly looks out the window and says it's black, we do have a difference of interpretation, but the sky is blue. . . . So that if you get into a discussion with Dr. Connolly, all these facts come up and he feels that we don't understand him. By saying that I disagreed with his interpretation of the facts means . . . that further discussion with me about the facts and that people didn't understand them is really inappropriate. We looked at all the facts. We looked at all his evidence and find that his interpretation is flawed. And it's not only that I disagree with his interpretation but everybody else. (#29)

Green: I think you've answered my question.

Flinn's deposition was then recessed and resumed a few weeks later.

Green: Do you recall if Dr. Connolly discussed with you an incident which occurred in 1979, in which he was criticized for patient abandonment, and [it] had to do with failure or refusal to participate in an abortion?

Flinn: He probably discussed that or he alluded to it. . . .

Green: How did you become aware of it and what did you know about the incident?

Flinn: . . . .There are about 50 different routes where I heard about this. As being a very senior person in the department of medicine, and this occurred within The Medical Center, I knew about it then. Wilmington is a relatively small place and I knew all of the people involved and still do, except for the patient who is deceased. The patient was the daughter of one of our leading [doctors] who I know well, and he frequently consulted me about the patient [who died of kidney failure], so that I was aware of it from many different angles.

[In 1979 I had assumed that Levinson's complaint of patient abandonment to the Professional Conduct Committee was confidential; yet Flinn had heard of it from "about 50 different routes."]

[Later:]

Green: Is it your understanding that membership in the [American College of Physicians] for a board-certified internist is something which is relatively routine, the qualifications having been met?

Flinn: Yes. . . . but you still have to be a person in good standing.

Green: Have you ever heard of anyone being denied membership in the ACP?

Flinn: Well, I wouldn't know. I mean to say no. Just because I've never heard of it doesn't mean that it doesn't occur. But most of the time [applications] that I'm involved in—and I'm involved in a lot of them in running the [residency] program—that really with my recommendation they'll probably get in.

[Later:]

Green: Dr. Connolly had asked you to call [Mrs. Boone] and talk to her. You didn't do that, did you?

Flinn: No. I thought that was inappropriate.

[And later:]

Green: Did you have any discussions with Dr. Reese . . . about the abortion incident?

Flinn: No, not that I recall . . . . The abortion issue was outside the Medical Center. [Flinn had just testified that the abortion "occurred within the Medical Center."]

[And:]

Green: Dr. Flinn, it was shown in the letter . . from Dr. Reese [reporting the Credentials Committee conclusions] to yourself and your letter . . . to Dr. Connolly that the committee concluded that Dr. Labowitz was blameless. Is that right?

Flinn: Yes.

Green: You agreed with that conclusion of the committee?

Flinn: Yes.

Green: Do you base your concurrence upon the review of the documents that Dr. Connolly provided you and the investigation that you've described?

Flinn: We've been over these same facts fifty million times. . . . I based my conclusion . . . on everything I know, what they thought and what I thought and what everybody else thought. . . . I obviously looked at all the data and talked to Dr. Connolly at length on a number of occasions and had done my own independent investigation.

[Later, while Flinn was being cross-examined, we received unintended help from the defendant's own attorney, Ms. Roth.]

Roth: Dr. Flinn, have you had occasion with the complaint and the communications that you have received from Dr. Connolly to have them reviewed by any psychiatrist?

Flinn: . . . .Yes, I did review with—I did have psychiatric evaluation of, I believe, this letter [my 2/1/83 letter to Flinn, in which I urged him to interview Madeline Boone and then concluded by saying that the "problem with the world today lies . . . with people who are free and have an opportunity to make a difference"] and the general information that Ron brought to me with his original complaint. . . . I did have psychiatric consultation on.

Roth: And what was the result that you received of that psychiatric consultation? What was the opinion?

Flinn: . . . .The opinion was that this had the markings of a person who was mentally ill and that I should do what I could to get the individual to have psychiatric evaluation. And I did attempt to.

A short time later, Jim requested the psychiatrist's name, but Flinn and Roth refused to disclose it.

The deposition recessed for the day. Jim then asked the Court to require our opponents to identify the psychiatrist: Flinn and Roth had inserted the psychiatrist's testimony into the record, his identity should also be inserted.

Three days later, Jim was notified by Roth that the psychiatrist was none other than the Director of Psychiatry at The Medical Center of Delaware—Dr. David E. Raskin! The same psychiatrist that Roth, in her initial psychiatric motion, had submitted to the Court in order "to determine [Dr. Connolly's] competency to maintain this action." (Until now, the Court, as well as us, had assumed that our opponents had submitted Raskin as an uninvolved, neutral expert; we had not known that Raskin had already rendered an opinion to Flinn that I was mentally ill!)

In addition, Flinn admitted in his deposition that he had reviewed my complaints with Dr. Raskin *prior* to Reese's and the Credentials Committee's deliberations, and that he, Dr. Raskin, Dr. Morris, and the hospital lawyer—William Wade, also of Richards, Layton and Finger—had had a meeting in 1984, as the Medical Center was considering my hospital privileges.

In the meantime, Jane Roth was not to be dissuaded by the Court's December, 1984 decision striking her Affirmative Defense and awarding us attorney fees. On May 29 she renewed the defendants' motion to the Court for an Order that:

> . . . plaintiff Ronald G. Connolly, M.D., submit to a psychiatric examination to determine his capacity to maintain this action and further to determine whether the failure of his professional practice has been caused or affected by his mental illness, rather than by any action or conspiracy on the part of defendants.

Roth's renewed motion concluded by asking the Court for ". . . an Order, directing Dr. Connolly to undergo psychiatric evaluation by a psychiatrist to be designated by defendants, at such time and place as shall be mutually agreeable to the parties." The motion was co-signed by a younger attorney in her firm—John A. Parkins, Jr.

What new information did Jane Roth rely upon to renew her psychiatric motion? She relied on Flinn's recent deposition testimony, and on two recent letters from Dr. David Raskin to her, one of which said:

> . . . . It appears to me Dr. Connolly does have some strong unchangeable ideas about the

> motivations of Dr. Labowitz. It appears as if the data base for this is minimal, it appears as if Dr. Connolly is unwilling to consider any other explanations . . . . I originally discussed some of the problems of Dr. Connolly's with Dr. Flinn about 2 years ago and after my examination of letters and the taping [referring to the Credentials Committee's tape recording of their meeting with me], I believe are consistent with the person who has a fixed delusional system about the motivations of Dr. Labowitz and perhaps other physicians. (#30)

The psychiatric attack by Roth and my opponents had now, for twenty-one months, been in the forefront of a lawsuit in which Labowitz was the defendant. It had dissipated huge quantities of our time, energy, and finances. Flinn and the medical profession, as well as Roth and her associates, were still unwilling to acknowledge the slightest impropriety, the slightest misconduct. They had damaged my career in a way that Labowitz and Lazarus never could have accomplished by themselves. I had never met and would not recognize Raskin, Bronheim, or Parkins; I had met Levinson for the first time at his deposition. Yet, with no evident restraint, each of them had publicly supported Roth's psychiatric motion.

But my opponents' actions reconfirmed my conviction that I must have struck a nerve center. Reflecting over the past months and years, I never regretted my decision to file the lawsuit. I had quietly tolerated my opponents' tactics, accusations, criticisms, and obstructions for four years, until Lazarus's Christmas Eve letter. Then, for seven months, I had implored the medical community to resolve these problems. Finally, as a last resort, when I asked the Court to address and resolve my complaints, Roth had attacked my capacity to be a party to the lawsuit.

Jim Green, working with Dad and C.J. Seitz, replied to Roth's latest attack by submitting a memorandum to the Court:

At the outset of this action, defendants were offering Raskin to the Court as an independent medical expert who could assist the Court in making a psychiatric examination. We now learn that Raskin had already formed an opinion even before the Motion was submitted, based upon a conversation with Dr. Robert E. Flinn . . . and a review of certain documents provided to him by Flinn . . . .

. . . .The purported support for the renewed motion is even more incredible than the material which the Court earlier rejected as totally inadequate. The support consists of the deposition testimony of Flinn, a nephrologist, and two letters by Raskin, a [psychiatrist] with an already expressed bias against Connolly.

It should be emphasized that the opinions of these two men, such as they are, were formed in or about February 1983—six months before the lawsuit was commenced . . . and therefore were available for defendants to use when their Motion was first filed, or even a year later during the briefing of the Omnibus Motion. So, it was "evidence" available to defendants when the Motion was filed in September, 1983. The only possible reason for withholding it until now is to prolong their harassment of Connolly.

. . . [It] should be noted that throughout this litigation, defendants' attorneys have also represented the Wilmington Medical Center ("WMC"). Flinn is the Director of the Department of Medicine of the WMC and Raskin is the Director of the Department of Psychiatry of the WMC. Therefore, not only were their so-called opinions formed well before defendants began the travesty of using the Court process as a pretext for their malicious attacks against Connolly, they were easily and readily accessible to defendants' counsel. Defendants should not be permitted to

> renew their misguided Motion on the basis of evidence already in their possession or, at a minimum, readily discoverable at the time the original Motion was filed . . . .
>
> This Motion should be denied with prejudice. Defendants and their attorneys should be ordered to pay plaintiffs' attorneys' fees incurred in connection with their opposition to this Motion. Finally, the Court should enter an Order forbidding defendants from renewing this Motion for the duration of this litigation.

John Parkins then submitted the defendants' memorandum, urging the Court to order the mental examination, and he also included a footnote which said:

> The transcript of a . . . [recent] office conference reports Mrs. Roth, attorney for defendants, as stating that a committee "felt he [Dr. Connolly] was a manifest nut." . . . . That statement is a reporter's error. Defendants' counsel believes Mrs. Roth stated that the committee "felt he was, ah, manifesting." It is defendants' position that plaintiff's mental state can best be determined by a psychiatric examination as opposed to simply examining the outward manifestations of Dr. Connolly's mental status.

Besides Parkins' helpful clarification of the reporter's error, he bolstered his memorandum with an affidavit from Raskin, and also with an affidavit from Flinn, which said:

> [Dr. Flinn] has testified at his deposition that in his opinion plaintiff, Ronald G. Connolly, M.D., suffers from a significant psychiatric problem. This opinion is based upon his own observations and investigations, as well as the . . . letter to him from Dr. Charles L. Reese, Chairman of the Credentials Committee. In addition this

> affiant's opinion and his observations of lack of judgment on Dr. Connolly's part and lack of substance to the charges Dr. Connolly is making against Dr. Labowitz have been corroborated by the dismissal by the Board of Medical Practice of Dr. Connolly's 1984 complaint to it re Dr. Labowitz (Tikellis letter) and by the finding by the Professional Conduct Committee of the New Castle County Medical Society in December, 1979 that Dr. Connolly did not act prudently and in the best interest of his patient in refusing to make arrangements for another physician to see that patient if he . . . was not willing to do so. (Syrovatka letter of December 26, 1979).

This time, like every time that I finished reading my opponents pleadings, my anger was mixed with disbelief. I showed each of the pleadings to my support, Sieglinde. I wanted her to understand me and also to understand the issues. Together we shared the torment as each submission by our opponents was filed with the Court.

It was next to impossible for me to get my mind off the lawsuit. As much as I tried, when I was jogging, at Mass, or trying to sleep, my mind focused on the confrontation. Repeatedly I was surprised that even after months and years of litigation, new insights sprang from the most elementary issues in the lawsuit.

A few days after the defendants' memorandum, Judge Clarence W. Taylor, the current judge on our case, ordered:

> Defendants' motion to have plaintiff Ronald G. Connolly, M.D., examined by a psychiatrist to determine his capacity to maintain this action is denied with prejudice, since defendants have not shown good cause for such examination and have not alleged or produced any evidence putting such matters in controversy.

Meanwhile, Roth's judicial nomination was still pending. With help, we could block it.

The youngest of my three brothers, Tom, after graduating from Yale and Oxford, had worked for six years on the staff of the U.S. Senate Select Committee on Intelligence, and he was now studying at Stanford Law School. Roth's judicial confirmation hearing before the Senate Judiciary Committee was still a few months away. At this time (in early June, 1985), if we hoped to block the confirmation, we needed support from the media. Tom, bright and articulate, contacted Howard Kurtz of the *Washington Post*, Philip Shenon of the *New York Times*, and Fred Fielding, Counsel to the President at the White House, concerning Roth's nomination.

In the meantime, Dr. Labowitz, still under oath, had resumed his deposition. In attendance with Roth was John Parkins, a young bespectacled associate at Richards, Layton and Finger.

Green:	Doctor, on the nursing chart . . . it says "Upset and crying, says she does not want to have the abortion." Were you aware that the patient had those feelings?
Labowitz:	No.
Green:	Did you review the nursing charts, the nursing notes, if you recall?
Labowitz:	No, I don't think I did.
Green:	The next entry [on the nursing note]... says "Dr. Labowitz visited on consult." That's the very next entry. . . . Did you consult with the patient at all about her feelings?
Roth:	About what?
Green:	About the abortion.
Labowitz:	I don't specifically recall talking to her about her feelings about the abortion. Most of the information was on the chart through other consultations of

the other physicians who were more intimately involved with her care up to that point. And the husband and the family were aware of it and my understanding was that it was a feeling shared by the entire family. I think you have to remember in interpreting statements from the chart like this that this was a very stressful and trying time for this patient. She had obvious severe psychiatric problems, and I think to have ambivalent feelings at a time like this would be very natural. . . .

Green: You indicated that . . . her family or her husband and family was aware of her situation.

Labowitz: That's my understanding.

Green: Was that gained through other physicians or did you talk with her?

Labowitz: No. The scenario doesn't seem to be clear in your head even though it's been discussed many times. The scenario was that Dr. Levinson was concerned about the medical problems associated with this abortion. The issues that I was brought into the case on had nothing to do with the abortion. He asked me my medical opinion and to watch the patient post-operatively because of the method of termination of the pregnancy and to follow her medically. The issue of abortion was not a concern of mine because it had already been decided that the abortion was to take place. So no one brought this to my attention. . . .

Green: Did you give a medical opinion as to the method of abortion?

Labowitz: No. [Labowitz had written in his consultation in response to Levinson's query whether there was any contraindication to intrauterine saline for the abortion: "See no contraindication to use of saline."]

[A few minutes later, my attorney asked Labowitz whether he had talked with Levinson about the patient and discussed my lack of involvement.]

Labowitz: I would assume because of the lateness of the hour and his concerns that I must have had some contact with him regarding what my feelings were, because she was scheduled for the abortion the next day. Now, whether I talked to him about Dr. Connolly, I wouldn't think so at this point because it wasn't relevant to why I was there. I was there to medically clear this patient for the abortion. [Incredible! A few minutes earlier he had said that the issues he was brought into the case on had nothing to do with the abortion.]

[And:]

Green: Did you make any attempts to talk to Dr. Connolly about this situation?

Roth: About what situation?

Green: The situation involving this patient who was scheduled for an abortion that Dr. Levinson indicated that Dr. Connolly abandoned. . . .

Labowitz: No.

Green: Did you make any attempt to learn Dr. Connolly's position or reasoning?

Labowitz: It was irrelevant to my being there. Whether Dr. Connolly disagreed or agreed with the abortion, he did not come in to assist Dr. Levinson in caring for this patient. And I came in to assist medically. What his philosophy was regarding abortion was not relevant at the time. . . .

Green: You were chief of the rheumatology section at the Wilmington Medical Center at that time?

Labowitz: Yes.

Green: Did you think it not wise to find out what Dr. Connolly's position was in this whole matter?

Roth: For what reason?

Green: Because one of the members of his section was being charged with patient abandonment or accused of patient abandonment.

Labowitz: I did not discuss this with Dr. Connolly.

Green: My question was: Did you not think it something that you should do or find out his side of it?

Labowitz: Obviously I didn't.

[Later:]

Green: Have you told anyone that in your opinion Dr. Connolly has psychiatric problems?

Labowitz: I testified to that effect in committees.

Green: What kind of committees?

Labowitz: Peer review committee.

Green: On more than one occasion?

Labowitz: Yes.

Green: How many occasions?

Labowitz: I don't recall. Probably two.

[A minute later:]

Green: Were those appearances pursuant to a complaint you had made against Dr. Connolly?

Roth: I don't know that that is a proper question, in that that would open up to physicians who make complaints that they could subsequently be embarrassed. I think that that is a proper area to be protected by the statute [#1768], and I will direct you not to answer.

[Later:]

Green: Would you ever instruct a patient that you could not see them until their bill was paid?

Labowitz: No.

Green: Would your staff ever be instructed to tell anyone that?

Labowitz: They are instructed not to say that. We try to work with the patients as best we can. . . .

Green: Was it not standard operating procedure for your office to sue patients who did not pay their bills in the fashion that your office felt timely?

Labowitz: I can't give an answer to that question because of the phraseology. I don't like the term "standard operating procedure." Because we don't have a standard operating procedure. Each patient is looked at individually. Their problems are looked at individually and they are discussed individually with them if they're responsive to inquiries by telephone or by mail. . . .

Roth: So it was not a standard operating procedure. All right.

Green: Isn't it a fact that at least forty-eight patients, former patients, were sued by your office during the period 1980 to 1983 for unpaid medical bills?

Labowitz: I don't know that number.

[Green told Labowitz that the record from the Common Pleas Court documented his lawsuits against his patients. Now an exhibit was made of Labowitz's billing record on Madeline Boone, which had the notation written by his secretary: "Called pt. & she said she sent it — I gave her one week to make payment & told her we cannot see her until acct is pd in full." The patient's billing record showed that her balance had been $121.00 and that the day after the secretary's phone call Labowitz received on account $121.00 from Mrs. Boone.]

[And, a minute later:]

Green: Mrs. Roth, I would like to call for the production at this time of the reevaluation form or reappointment form which Dr. Labowitz prepared relating to Dr. Connolly which was discussed by Dr. Labowitz at his deposition and was discussed also by Dr. Lazarus.

Roth: Well, of course, we won't produce it because that is credentials committee documentation and protected by the privilege.

Green: Our position is that it as been used for purposes beyond any possible purpose of the credentials committee, namely, it was used by Dr. Lazarus [to deny me membership in the American College of Physicians].

Roth: It was not used by Dr. Lazarus.

Green: He has testified that it was.

Roth: Dr. Lazarus saw it in the credentials committee. Now, if you want to get it through him, fine. I don't think you can. But that's the avenue.

A short time later Labowitz's deposition concluded; this had been the fifth and final day, over an eighteen-month period.

Several weeks after Labowitz's interrogation, Jim and I were ready to resume Flinn's deposition. Why had this esteemed physician and his associates at The Medical Center of Delaware not protected the public by informing the four other Delaware hospitals where I practiced, and also the Delaware Board of Medical Practice, of their opinion that I was psychiatrically ill?

When Jim and I walked into Flinn's office, Roth and Parkins were accompanied by a third lawyer, representing The Medical Center of Delaware—William J. Wade, also of Richards, Layton and Finger. A short time later, the deposition was in process.

Green: . . . [There's] a letter of June 15, 1984 . . . from Dr. Connolly to yourself in which he states, "I accept the position in the Section of Internal Medicine." [In response to Flinn's letter of June 5, in which he had offered me the alternative of accepting this position or being "dropped from the staff."] You received that letter on or about June 15?

Flinn: Yes.

Green: You testified you fired a letter back, I think was your term. Is that the letter of July 25, 1984?

Flinn: . . . Yes.

Green: You say that "The Credentials Committee has reiterated to me its feeling that before giving its final approval that a psychiatric evaluation be made." Are you referring to the recommendation in Dr. Reese's letter of March 23, 1983?

Flinn: Yes.

Green: "Therefore, in keeping with the Credentials Committee's request, if you are to have an appointment at the Wilmington Medical Center, it will be necessary for you to have a psychiatric evaluation by a mutually agreeable psychiatrist." The next-to-the-last paragraph concludes, "Should you choose not to go along with this request by the first of September, we will be forced to consider that you have resigned from our staff." Doctor, is it usual to have a psychiatric evaluation as a condition of an appointment at The Medical Center?

Flinn: For all people with psychiatric problems.

[A minute later:]

Green: Did you discuss this letter or your course of action with Dr. Labowitz?

Flinn: No.

Green: Did you discuss it with his attorney?

Flinn: No. I discussed it with Dr. Morris and The Medical Center's attorney.

Green: Mr. Wade?

Flinn: Yes. I think he was—[Flinn looked at Wade.] I'm not sure about that but I think I did bounce it off of you to find out whether you thought—

Wade: Before you go any further, you should not testify at all about what our conversations might have been. It's protected by the attorney-client privilege.

[And, a short time later:]

Green: Did Dr. Connolly submit a letter of resignation?

Flinn: I guess the technical answer to that is no, he didn't. . . .

Green: On June 5, 1984 you told him that [he] will be dropped from the staff . . . if he did not accept the position in the Section of Internal Medicine.

Wade: I'm sorry. What date was that letter?

Green: That's June 5, 1984.

Roth: Is this another sermon or is this a question?

Green: There is no question.

Roth: No.

Green: Do you see that, Doctor?

Flinn: Oh, I see it. I don't think I have to explain it.

Green: . . . Why did you tell him in one letter that he would be dropped from the staff if he didn't do something and in another letter that he would be considered to have resigned if he didn't do something?

Flinn: I did this to protect Dr. Connolly. If he was dropped from the staff I would have to report that to all the licensing bureaus. If he resigns from the staff, I simply report that he resigned. And in all these actions over the years we have bent over backwards to try to protect Dr. Connolly and that's the reason I chose to do it in this fashion. He has a psychiatric problem and I didn't want to make it worse.

[A short time later:]

Green: You did not consider that Dr. Connolly's psychiatric problem affected his ability to practice medicine, did you?

Flinn: I most certainly did.

Green: You did not consider that it adversely affected his ability to practice medicine to the point where you thought you should notify, for example, other hospitals where he might be on the staff?

Flinn: I can't give you a yes or no answer to that for the following reason. We have considered notifying other hospitals. That's a very damaging thing to do. He has not actually had a psychiatric evaluation so I'm very loath to tell another hospital or another organization that this person has a bona fide psychiatric problem without first having a psychiatric evaluation. So in trying to get a psychiatric evaluation, we finally got to the point where our hospital took the position that it would be incorrect to have him taking care of hospitalized patients without first having a psychiatric evaluation. I'm still trying to get him to have a psychiatric evaluation and as of yet I've been unsuccessful. But I have grave doubts about his ability to practice. Doubts are one thing. Action are others.

By August, 1985, discovery was almost complete, and my attorneys had requested a pretrial hearing with the Court.

In the meantime, Dad had met with two psychiatrists in Boston: One of them, James E. Groves, a staff psychiatrist at Harvard Medical School, was joining our team as an expert witness.

In mid-August Sieglinde, the children, and I, joining Mom and Dad, and my brothers and sisters with their spouses and children, took a week's vacation on Sebago Lake in Maine, not far from the site of old Camp Minnewawa, which now had been closed for more than thirty years. The solitude of the pine, birch, and hemlock forest surrounding the deep blue lake was refreshing. Miles across the lake could be seen the White Mountains of New Hampshire, and at night the Milky Way dazzled in the clear sky. We had a few days to swim, sail, and play tennis, and then, at night, to sit in our cabin by a warm crackling fire.

That Tuesday afternoon, as I was sitting on our cabin porch, I received a telephone message to call Florence at my office.

"The lawyer from the Federal Judiciary Committee in New York just called," Florence said. "He'll be in his office for another hour, and he wants you to call him."

I had earlier contacted the American Bar Association concerning Roth's nomination. I immediately called the attorney, and we spent the next ten or fifteen minutes discussing Ms. Roth. I emphasized to him that my complaints against Ms. Roth were not an isolated instance of misconduct, but a continual pattern over almost two years of what I felt was seriously inappropriate conduct. After we had discussed my various complaints, the official from the American Bar Association informed me that his investigation was almost complete. He then concluded, saying, "If she's a district judge, then she no longer will be a problem for you."

"There's going to be a lot of public discussion," I replied, "before Ms. Roth becomes a federal judge."

When I returned to Wilmington a few days later, my office was dead quiet. There was no work on which to catch up; it was as though I had never left. I only had one and a half days of medical work each week. Days would pass without one patient entering the office; hours would pass without a phone ring, and the mailman daily brought a few bills, a few lab results, and a few advertisements.

Patient referrals from other doctors consisted of a slight trickle, perhaps one or two patients per month. More commonly, a doctor would refer his or her patient to Dr. Newman or Dr. Labowitz and the patient would be told that there was a four-to six-weeks' wait for an appointment; then, finding my name in the telephone book, the patient would phone my office for an appointment, and I would see him or her the next day.

Sometimes, a patient of mine would be admitted by another doctor to The Medical Center of Delaware for a nonrheumatologic condition, such as gall bladder surgery. Often the patient, or occasionally the admitting doctor, would ask me to determine if the patient's rheumatologic condition was a factor in their current problem.

The first time I was asked to consult on such a patient, I explained that I no longer had privileges at the hospital but I would ask Dr. Flinn for temporary privileges in order to see my own patient. It was about 9:30 in the morning when I telephoned Dr. Flinn's office. His secretary said that he was in a conference but that he would be back shortly and would return my call. By 3:15 that afternoon I still had not heard from Flinn. Again, I telephoned his secretary. She reported that Dr. Flinn had left the office but that he had been given the message. Again she said she would ask him to return my call. Finally, at 4:30, the unit clerk from the hospital floor telephoned saying that Dr. Flinn had cancelled the consult to me, explaining to the private physician that I did not have hospital privileges, and the private physician had then called Dr. Newman for the consultation.

We were now preparing for trial. Over the years several doctors with whom I had been friends had vehemently criticized Labowitz to me; two of them had encouraged me to file the lawsuit. I now asked them to testify at trial.

One of these doctors, who within a few months of my 1978 arrival in Wilmington had repeatedly decried the throttle grip that Labowitz and a small number of other physicians held on Wilmington medicine, now frantically told me that he had changed his mind. If he was forced to testify, then he would testify for Dr. Labowitz!

Other doctors who had privately spoken to me of their disdain for Labowitz's style of medicine now denied their statements.

Meanwhile, almost daily, I wondered what my family and I would do after the trial was over. Where would I work? The question was bothersome, as well as ironic: I had started premed at Georgetown when I was 19; medicine had been an opportunity to fulfill my interest in working with people, and it had also promised reasonable independence. But now at the age of

45 I was a medical outcast with only a few patients to treat, and I was almost completely dependent on others: My future was in the hands of embarrassed doctors on the one side and lawyers on the other; I was unable to cover either office or home expenses and was financially dependent on my father.

If we won the lawsuit, I mused, it still would have cost us several years of litigation and hundreds of thousands of dollars in legal expenses. But I was lucky. My father was the senior partner of a successful law firm that was willing to spend large sums of money on my plight. And he also had the financial reserves to support me and my family. I wondered what I would have done without this exceptional support.

I was also fortunate that our discovery, which should have gone well, had gone extremely well. How could the facts be any clearer? Medical administrators had professed Dr. Labowitz blameless, while we had volumes of sworn testimony documenting the conduct of both Labowitz and the medical administrators.

I was also learning that my experience with medical administrators was not unique. Medical peer review—doctors reviewing and disciplining doctors—is a major *national* problem. What I was experiencing was unique in its scope, depth, blatancy, and documentation, but daily I was being educated on the magnitude of the problem. On September 2-3, 1985, the *New York Times* had a two-part front-page article by Joel Brinkley, comprehensively reviewing the problems with medical discipline nationwide. The article included a compilation from each of the state medical boards throughout the country, listing the number of disciplinary actions per one thousand doctors in the year 1984. There were major problems throughout the country, but Delaware was dead last on the list, with no disciplinary actions at all.

The March 21, 1985 issue of the *New England Journal of Medicine* had had a similar article and an editorial including statistics for the year 1982. Delaware was again at the bottom of the list, along with Arkansas, North Dakota, the District of Columbia, and Puerto Rico—none of which had any disciplinary actions.

A short time later, the *New England Journal of Medicine* published a letter to the editor from a forthright physician in Florida, who noted that although the Florida Board of Medical Examiners had the best rate—although still not a satisfactory one—of disciplinary action in the country, he believed that the data reflected "the courage" of their Board "in dealing with physicians impaired by alcohol and drug abuse, violators of prescription laws, and convicted felons," but other incompetent physicians were *not* being addressed.

At about the same time, the Delaware Board of Medical Practice had finally developed enough gumption to take action against a physician. A *News-Journal* article said that the Board had suspended a female physician's license, and that charges against the physician included selling street-drugs to one of her patients, and injecting herself with narcotics and other drugs while rendering care to the patient.

In the meantime, we were ready for trial! My attorneys requested a pretrial conference with the Court. The public—represented by the jury—would soon have the opportunity to express their expectations about the medical profession. They would be considering the facts and rendering their verdict.

But Jane Roth was not thinking about going to trial. September 19 she filed a Motion before the Court:

> Defendants hereby move for Summary Judgment in their favor on the ground that there is no dispute of material fact and they are entitled to summary judgment as a matter of law.

My lawyers translated the legal jargon: Roth is telling the judge to throw your case out of Court, not to permit it to go to trial.

Dad and Jim assured me that a Motion for Summary Judgment was a common ploy; Roth's motion had no chance.

While they responded to the Court, however, I was going to Washington. It was time to testify at Roth's confirmation hearing before the Senate Judiciary Committee.

9
The Senate Judiciary Committee

> I have, at all times, conformed to the code of professional ethics required of all attorneys, in the Delaware Bar.
>
> Jane R. Roth, Esq.
> Nominee, U.S. Federal Court

President Reagan officially nominated Jane Roth for the U.S. District Court in Delaware on Friday, October 11, 1985. I would be testifying at Roth's Senate Judiciary hearing in less than three weeks. I needed help in blocking Roth's approval. The issues were significant: Are there any restrictions on an attorney's charging a party to a lawsuit with being psychiatrically ill? Are there any restrictions on an attorney's charging that a citizen "lacks the capacity to sue due to mental illness?" Can an attorney support psychiatric accusations by giving the court his or her personal medical opinion? Can an attorney submit testimony that a doctor or other medical personnel is psychiatrically ill, when on religious grounds that person chooses not to participate in an abortion? Was Ms. Roth "perfectly entitled to annoy, embarrass and oppress" a litigant?

In the meantime, the circumstances surrounding Ms. Roth's nomination were illuminated by a May 24, 1985 *Washington Post* article:

> President Reagan has decided to nominate Jane Richards Roth, the wife of Sen. William V. Roth, Jr. (R-Del.), as a federal judge after a period of maneuvering in which the senator suggested her name to then-Attorney General William French Smith . . . .
>
> Roth's wife initially promoted herself with Justice Department officials for a seat on the 3rd

> U.S. Circuit Court of Appeals, but was passed over in favor of the chief district court judge in Wilmington. The senator said he then asked Smith to consider her for the district court vacancy. . . .
>
> Roth said she told Justice Department officials on several occasions that she wanted to be a judge. She said she made her case to Smith at a diplomatic breakfast in London last year while accompanying her husband on Senate business.

I now prepared for the hearing. If a critical level of public opposition could be achieved, then the process would become self-perpetuating, and the Senate Judiciary Committee—out of common sense, or common fear of political repercussions—would deny approval.

On Monday, October 14, I wrote to the chairman of the Senate Judiciary Committee, Republican Senator Strom Thurmond, and to the ranking Democrat, Senator Biden, requesting to testify.

The next day my brother, Tom, who had worked on the staff of the Senate for six years, called from Palo Alto. He had arranged Friday meetings for me with staff members from six of the eighteen senators on the committee: East, Metzenbaum, Simon, Kennedy, Biden, and Leahy, and while I was in Washington, I could arrange meetings with the remaining twelve.

Urgently, I began work on a two-and-a-half-page cover letter and an indexed file, documented from the public record, summarizing my complaints against Roth. Florence and I worked late into the night. By early Friday, at 2:30 a.m., my complaints had been drafted, written, rewritten, edited, printed, copied, arranged, punched, and inserted into files, and I was ready for the 7:37 a.m. train to Washington.

I had a copy of the complaints for each of the members of the Senate Judiciary Committee, as well as President Reagan (he had nominated Roth, and I hoped that someone on his staff would inform him of my complaints), the president of March for Life (Nellie Gray), the chief legislative counsel of the American Civil Liberties Union, the president of the Vietnam Veterans of

America, and the executive director of the American Association of Retired Persons.

I had additional copies for the press, and for anyone else who could help.

Arriving at Union Station, I walked the few blocks to Capitol Hill. I went from the Dirksen Senate Building, to the Hart, to the Russell, and back again, and again, and again, keeping the appointments that Tom had made and working on additional appointments.

Staff members with Senators East, Metzenbaum, and Biden seemed particularly responsive, particularly concerned.

Returning to Wilmington that evening, I spent the weekend and the next few days working further on the complaints and making more appointments in Washington.

Wednesday, October 23, I drove to Washington for a 1:30 appointment with Nellie Gray. Her small, crowded office was located in a southeast row-house several blocks from the Capitol, on Pennsylvania Avenue. An amiable, middle-aged woman, tall and slim, she was a constitutional lawyer who had sacrificed her law career to speak up for the unborn child in this national controversy.

As we discussed my complaints, Nellie was concerned about Roth's use of the abortion incident in my litigation, and she also questioned the propriety of a U.S. senator being involved in the appointment of his wife to a lucrative, lifetime federal position. She said that she might testify with me at the hearing; she would begin work on her testimony.

After leaving Nellie's office I contacted Joel Brinkley, who only a month before had written the *New York Times* article on the nationwide difficulties with medical peer review. He said he was interested in my story and asked me to call back in ten days.

I drove back to Wilmington that evening, but the next morning returned to Washington for a 10:30 meeting with a special assistant to the President, Carl Anderson, in the Old Executive Office Building. At the meeting he expressed pessimism about any chance of stopping Roth's confirmation.

Afterwards, I checked into the Hyatt on Capitol Hill. This was to be my headquarters. I spent hours on the telephone, following up previous contacts and working on new ones: the Leadership Conference on Civil Rights, the Conservative Caucus, the People for the American Way, the Alliance for Justice, the American Life League, and Susan Liss, the director of the Judiciary Selection Project (a coalition of civil-rights and public-interest organizations), who told me she had just learned that Roth's hearing was scheduled for the next Wednesday, October 30.

Staff members from Senators DeConcini, Hatch, Laxalt, and Simpson were interested in my complaints. I handed my complaints to Stephen Wermiel, who covered the judiciary for the *Wall Street Journal*, and I called the *Christian Science Monitor*.

Around noon on Friday, Brad Bumsted of Gannett News Service called me. "Are you going to be testifying against Mrs. Roth at her hearing?" he asked. Telling him that I would, I reviewed my testimony with him. As we concluded the conversation, he said that he would send a runner over to pick up a copy of my complaints.

Al Kamen, who covered the judiciary for the *Washington Post*, was interested. He asked for a copy of the complaints. As I was leaving the Washington Post Building to look for a sidewalk pay phone in order to call the *Washington Times*, my mind was flooded by a wave of oppressively dark thoughts: Could Roth sue me for libel? What a time to think of this—I had already spoken to every newspaper and public official that would listen to me. What would this do to my lawsuit?

Struggling, I reassured myself that my complaints were true; they were documented from the public record and everyone has a right to express his or her convictions—and after the events of the past years, I had nothing to lose!

I took a taxi out New York Avenue for an interview with the *Washington Times*; Chris Simpson and another reporter were interested. An hour later, the interview being over, I took another cab back to Capitol Hill, where I had a meeting with Biden's Minority Counsel, Chip Reid.

That evening I returned to Wilmington, and the next morning, Saturday, I picked up the *News-Journal*. Gannett's

Brad Bumsted had completed his interviews. His story was on the front page:

BIDEN EXPECTS SENATE TO OK JANE ROTH AS JUDGE

> Delaware Sen. Joseph R. Biden Jr., ranking Democrat on the Senate Judiciary Committee, says he believes that Wilmington attorney Jane Roth will be confirmed as a federal judge—short of major revelations by a doctor who has asked to testify against her . . . .
>
> A committee spokesman said Dr. Ronald G. Connolly of Wilmington is tentatively scheduled to testify. In a letter that Connolly says was sent to Sen. Strom Thurmond, R-S.C., Judiciary Chairman, he said, "she [Jane Roth] has engaged in consistent conduct which, in my opinion, raises serious questions concerning Mrs. Roth's professional ethics and qualifications."
>
> . . . . [Jane Roth] said a similar complaint by Connolly had been made to the Delaware Bar and was found to have been without merit . . . .
>
> Biden indicated that the confrontation presents an awkward situation for him . . . . "I wish I could step back from it; it's a little bit like the Hatfields and the McCoys."

Roth's hearing was scheduled for Wednesday, October 30 at 2:00 p.m. in Room 226 of the Dirksen Building. Tuesday morning I went to the office, discussed several patients with Florence, and placed a box with multiple copies of my indexed complaints in the car. I was ready for the trip to Washington. Shortly before noon I went home and picked up Sieglinde; we went to 12:05 Mass at St. Joseph's and returned home for a quick lunch, and by 1:15 I was on the road.

Throughout the two-hour car ride I reviewed my decision to testify against Roth: It had been easy. When Sieglinde and I had come to Wilmington more than six years ago, I had been reluctant to stand up and confront my opponents. Not because of fear or intimidation, but because I had wanted to be accepted, liked, and successful; I did not want a fight. But every passing year had diminished my acceptance, my success, and my hope of working within the medical community.

Tomorrow's hearing was now an important opportunity. But I was nervous; I did not want to choke. I was experienced in treating patients, and I was comfortable hitting a tennis ball, but not in testifying before the Senate Judiciary Committee. Yet at the same time I knew that I was right, I was well prepared, and I had nothing to lose. I reassured myself that it was normal to be nervous; all that I had to do was concentrate, take my time, and speak clearly.

I had also spoken with a vice president from March for Life, Dee Becker, who—along with the president, Nellie Gray—was planning to testify. The news media were going to have something to report.

I checked into the Key Bridge Marriott, unpacked, changed into work-out clothes, and jogged across the bridge, up to Georgetown, past Dahlgren Chapel, and up to the track field adjacent to the hospital. My apprehension lessened as I ran laps in the warm, clear October evening. I was comfortable on an athletic field; the exercise felt good.

As I circled the track I looked up to the hospital windows where Mom had been six months earlier, riddled with cancer, as she underwent an infusion-pump implant. She was a wife and mother, kind, caring, and honest. She had no titles, and was on no corporate boards. My confidence came from Mom, and from Sieglinde, and from people like them. Their faith, love, values, and commitment were my hope of fulfillment, and were a striking contrast to the exceptional wealth, power, and position of those with whom I was fighting.

After I returned to my room at the Marriott, I called Nellie Gray to discuss tomorrow's testimony. Nellie responded that she and Dee Becker would not be testifying!

Surprised and disappointed, I called Sieglinde. I would be the only one testifying in opposition to Jane Roth's approval as a United States district judge.

The next morning I stayed in my hotel room reviewing my testimony, room service brought breakfast, and I called Sieglinde a few times more. Her suggestions were helpful—pertinent and concise, and it was good to talk with her.

I arrived at the Dirksen hearing room at 1:20. It was deserted. There was a grandeur about the dark mahogany-panelled walls, high ceiling, and carpeted floor. At the front of the room was a large semi-circular dais, at which the judiciary members would be sitting, and in front of the dais was a table and chair for the testifying witness. The rest of the room was lined with rows of seats, on both sides of which were several tables for the press.

I took a seat, and as the room quickly filled, I again reviewed my testimony. At 2:05 Senator Thurmond, in a Southern drawl, called the committee to order. I was surprised to see that Senators Biden, Simon, and McConnell were the only other judiciary members present.

Senator Thurmond: We have met this afternoon to hold hearings on three circuit judges and four district judges. And we will take any Senators or Congressmen who want to speak in behalf of these judges, and I suggest you make your remarks brief. We have seven different judges here we have got to hear.

A few moments later the Senator announced: "The able and distinguished Senator from Kentucky has to leave. Would you want to make a comment, Senator?"

Senator McConnell: Yes. Thank you, Mr. Chairman. I just wanted to stop by and commend the nominees for their selection and look forward to supporting them and apologize for having to head on to two more meetings. Thank you, Mr. Chairman.

Senator Thurmond: Thank you.

Senators Hawkins, Moynihan, D'Amato, Wilson, Domenici, Bingaman, Bradley, and Lautenberg then spoke briefly on behalf of the nominees from their states.

Senator William Roth spoke on behalf of his wife and noted that:

> . . . she has enjoyed broad bipartisan support. She has been recommended by the bipartisan Governor Judicial Nominating Committee for appointment to the State judiciary. We are also very pleased and pleasantly surprised when we received a copy of a resolution adopted by the Democratically controlled State senate, which said the following: "Whereas Jane Roth is one of Delaware's most distinguished and competent candidates, and was recognized and applauded not only by the legal community but highly respected by all Delawareans . . . and whereas Jane Roth's impeccable character and credentials, particularly in the legal community, are impervious to criticism, now, therefore, be it resolved by the members of the senate of the 133rd General Assembly of the State of Delaware, that gratification is hereby expressed upon learning that Jane Roth is being considered for a Federal judgeship."

A short time later Senator Thurmond asked the seven nominees to stand and raise their hands to be sworn.

"Will the testimony that you will be giving be the truth, the whole truth and nothing but the truth, so help you, God?"

Each of the nominees responded affirmatively. The hearing then continued with a brief interrogation of the seven nominees, concluding with Mrs. Roth. Thus far, there had been no witnesses opposing any of the prospective judges.

During Mrs. Roth's testimony, she was asked about my complaints.

Senator Simon: . . . Today we will hear testimony from Dr. Ronald Connolly, who alleges misconduct on your part regarding your representation of Dr. Russell Labowitz. Mrs. Roth, would you tell the committee the facts surrounding your representation of Dr. Labowitz, and the reasons that you feel that Dr. Connolly questions your actions in this case?

Mrs. Roth: . . . I represent Dr. Labowitz, the defendant, in this action and the action is presently pending before the Superior Court [of Delaware] and will ultimately be decided on its merits. In my representation of Dr. Labowitz, I have, at all times, conformed to the code of professional ethics required of all attorneys, in the Delaware Bar. Dr. Connolly has submitted his complaints similar to the complaints that he submits here, to the Board on Professional Responsibility, of the Delaware Supreme Court. Those complaints were dismissed as being without merit. [The letter from the assistant disciplinary counsel, Richard Poole, notifying the disciplinary counsel, Susan Faw, that my complaints had been dismissed, was made part of the record.]

A few minutes later Mrs. Roth's testimony concluded.

Senator Thurmond: We want to congratulate you, Mrs. Roth, and wish you well on the bench. I feel confident that you will make an outstanding judge, and we are very proud of you.

Mrs. Roth: Thank you, Mr. Chairman.

Senator Thurmond: Thank you.

Startled by the Chairman's congratulatory comments even before I had had a chance to testify, I glanced over at the press tables. They were empty, with the exception of one reporter from the *Washington Post.*

Senator Thurmond then called me to the witness stand, swore me in, and I presented my complaints. After five minutes, Senator Simon said, "I do not mean to interrupt you, Doctor, but we would like, if you can kind of summarize the balance of your statement, we will enter the full statement in the record."

"Thank you," I replied. "My concern is that Mrs. Roth's legal conduct reflects a consistent mentality, month after month for more than two years, that raises serious questions concerning her professional ethics and qualifications. It is not an isolated instance, it is not a slip of the tongue. Mrs. Roth says that my complaints have been addressed by the Board of Professional Responsibility of the Delaware Bar, yet when I presented my complaints, the Board did not hear my complaints. The board assigned an assistant investigating attorney, one attorney, to review my complaints and he terminated the investigation. . . . I hope that the committee will put a hold on Mrs. Roth's nomination and confirmation until my complaints can be further evaluated."

Before leaving the witness table, I was asked a few questions.

Senator Biden: Do you believe that the Board of Professional Ethics was biased in their judgment or that they did not get all the facts, or that there is just a—is there an area for reasonable men to disagree on this issue?

Dr. Connolly: The Board of Professional Responsibility never addressed my complaints. The complaints were fielded by one attorney, who terminated the study. In addition, as far as Mrs. Roth acting as an advocate, my complaints are that this goes far beyond advocacy, where, in my opinion, Mrs. Roth is repeatedly

> deceiving the court. Her client admitted that he had billed for Medicaid services not rendered. . . . He admitted this in Mrs. Roth's presence under oath. Mrs. Roth presented to the Court that my charges of Medicaid improprieties were without justification and the manifestation of a psychiatric illness. There are millions of elderly and poor people depending on Medicaid. Their funds are being reduced. This was a misrepresentation to the Court, this was not advocacy. She went beyond advocacy and said that my complaints were without merit, and were the manifestation of a psychiatric illness. She knows that that was false and she knows that that was false because her client was sitting beside her, under oath, stating in the public record, that he . . . billed for services not rendered. . . .

Following my testimony, Charles Crompton, the president of the Delaware Bar Association, testified on behalf of Mrs. Roth, saying that he was formerly the chairman of the Board on Professional Responsibility and a member of it for more than 12 years. He testified that he was confident that the complaints had been thoroughly investigated and that the report of the investigating member was fully considered by the full board.

After the meeting, Joe Biden walked me back to his office. He was concerned for my medical career and asked what he could do to help. "Could you investigate," I responded, "or have someone investigate the attorney general's exoneration of Dr. Labowitz from billing the government for Medicaid no-shows?" He answered that he could not investigate this issue.

Leaving the Russell Building, I walked the few blocks to my car and headed home to Sieglinde.

The next morning I called Washington. Although the Judiciary Committee usually is required to wait 24 to 48 hours before voting, Roth had been confirmed by the committee by 9:30 a.m. And by Friday afternoon, two days after her hearing, without debate or objection, she had been confirmed by the full Senate to the U.S. District Court in Delaware: a lifetime appointment with an annual salary of $78,700.

The *News-Journal* headline read: SENATE CONFIRMS JANE ROTH FOR FEDERAL JUDGESHIP. The write-up included Mrs. Roth's reiteration that the Delaware Board on Professional Responsibility had dismissed similar complaints by me.

If ever, I thought, there was a misnomer, it had to be the Delaware Supreme Court's "Board on Professional Responsibility."

Roth had simply deflected my opposition by saying that similar complaints had already been dismissed by the Board.

I wanted more information on the Board of Professional Reponsibility. Legal peer review, it seemed to me, was as much of a sham as medical peer review. Susan Faw and William Poole were, respectively, the disciplinary counsel and assistant disciplinary counsel for the Board, but neither of them was actually a member of the Board. Poole had recommended to Faw that, pursuant to Rule 9(b), my complaints be dismissed. I now obtained a copy of the *Rules of the Board on Professional Responsibility of the Supreme Court of Delaware.*

Rule 9(b) said that the counsel's recommended disposition shall be reviewed by the panel of the preliminary review committee selected in order from the roster established by the Board, which could then approve, disapprove or modify the recommendation.

The disciplinary counsel in my case, however, had reviewed her assistant's report and terminated the matter herself; the counsel's recommendations were not reviewed by any committee.

I then reviewed the assistant's report to Faw, wherein he had systematically dismissed my complaints according to various Disciplinary Rules contained in the *Delaware Lawyer's Code of Professional Responsibility*. After obtaining a copy of the Rules, I noted that the investigator had not even referred to the Disciplinary Rule on "Trial Conduct," nor to that on "Misconduct"!

Poole had referred to other Disciplinary Rules, which seemed to me totally inappropriate to the complaints being addressed. He had then concluded that there were no violations.

Furthermore, the Board's investigator had dismissed Mrs. Roth's statement that she was "perfectly entitled to annoy, embarrass, and oppress [me]," by saying that he was "satisfied that Mrs. Roth did not in fact conduct the deposition and other aspects of the defense to annoy, embarrass and oppress Dr. Connolly, and that her statement was merely one of exasperation."

I telephoned Ms. Faw, who confirmed that no one else besides Poole and herself had considered my complaints. She said that she had not submitted my complaints to the Board's panel of preliminary review committee in accord with Rule 9(b), because—even assuming the facts to be true—there was no violation of a disciplinary rule, and no basis for disciplinary action; therefore, in accord with Rule 9(a), she had dismissed the matter.

The Disciplinary Counsel further told me quite frankly that Mr. Poole had done a more full and thorough investigation than she thought my complaints merited on their face. I asked her if, when she worked at Richards, Layton and Finger, she had been involved in my litigation. She responded that she had not, although she had done "a lot of work with Jane." A few minutes later we concluded our conversation.

My information contradicted what the public had been told by the *News-Journal*, and also what the Senate Judiciary members had been told. I wrote two letters presenting my findings: one to Senator Thurmond with copies going to the other judiciary members, and the other letter going to the Editor of the *News-Journal*, Donald Brandt, with copies going to the Chairman of the Board on Professional Responsibility, Francis Biondi, and to the President of the Delaware Bar Association, Charles Crompton.

Senator Thurmond responded that complaints against a federal judge are not investigated by the Senate Judiciary Committee, but should be filed in writing with the Clerk of the Court of Appeals for the Third Circuit.

I wrote to Philadelphia to the Clerk for the Third Circuit, requesting the necessary forms and format. Promptly, I received a reply stating that my complaints against Judge Roth were for actions prior to her appointment as a federal judge and therefore were not within their jurisdiction. I then wrote to Senator Thurmond informing him of the problem; I received no response.

Donald Brandt at the *News-Journal*, in spite of my request, did not publish my letter to the editor; nor did he explain to the public the truth surrounding the Supreme Court's Board on Professional Responsibility.

However, since I had sent the Chairman of the Board on Professional Responsibility a copy of my letter, I did receive a written response from Susan Faw stating that the "facts alleged did not constitute misconduct, therefore, [my] complaint was not reviewed by a panel of the Preliminary Review Committee," and further stating that she "did not contribute to the contents of the report or influence Mr. Poole's analysis or conclusions in any way."

The disciplinary counsel's letter noted that she had sent a copy to the Chairman of the Board on Professional Responsibility, Francis Biondi.

Rather than argue further with the disciplinary counsel, I wrote to Mr. Biondi:

> Mr. Poole and Ms. Faw have clearly stated and documented their position. Further argument serves no purpose. The positions are clear and the facts speak for themselves.
>
> Is Mr. Poole's and Ms. Faw's handling of my complaints satisfactory to you and the Board on Professional Responsibility?

Mr. Biondi promptly replied concluding that he was "satisfied that [my] complaint has been processed in accordance with the Rules of the Board by Mr. Poole and Ms. Faw."

The legal peer review system had dismissed my complaints against Roth, and the chairman of the Supreme Court's Board on Professional Responsibility had concurred. It was clear to me that legal administrators, like their medical counterparts, were more afraid of their peers than they were of the public.

There was now only one last tribunal to appeal to: It was reasonable and necessary, I felt, to inform the Delaware Supreme Court of their Board's performance.

As I drafted my complaints to the Supreme Court, I hoped that out-of-state news media would help to correct the *News-Journal's* lopsided presentation in Delaware. The issues, such as medical and legal peer review, were of vital public importance. And the publicity had greatly damaged my practice, my reputation, and my chances in the lawsuit.

I spoke with Gil Gaul at the *Philadelphia Inquirer*, who wanted more information and said that he might be interested in doing a short story in the future.

I tried to contact Bob Woodward at the *Washington Post*, and also television's "60 Minutes." I could not get past the receptionist at either office. I sent them letters; weeks passed without an acknowledgement or response. I phoned both offices again and was reassured by both that a reply would be forthcoming, but I never heard from either of them.

With each attempt to vindicate my complaints—to my friends, my peers, and my community—I turned to Sieglinde for support and understanding. And with each failure, Sieglinde shared the disappointment, frustration, and often humiliation. For three years I had been fighting, and for three years we had been battered by some of the most powerful and prestigious people in American society. Our disappointments resulted in parallel reactions: Sieglinde had periods of exhaustion; she wanted me to stop fighting and for us to move. Whereas with each disappointment I was more outraged and more determined to expose my adversaries. Our plight would be vindicated. What more did we have to lose?

Meanwhile, Dr. Gustave Berger—the 1983 chairman of the Peer Review Committee that had "invited" me to attend their meeting while refusing to tell me that Labowitz had filed complaints against me—had received the 1985 President's Award from the Medical Society of Delaware "for service and outstanding contributions to Medicine in the community and State of Delaware."

In Delaware Superior Court, Dad (now eighty years old), Jim, and C.J. Seitz were still fighting with Labowitz's attorneys, who were unrelenting in their efforts to have the Court order a psychiatric examination of me by a psychiatrist whom they would designate.

Judge Clarence W. Taylor, who had now been assigned to our case, had already denied with prejudice the defendants' renewed motion to have me examined by a psychiatrist, but he had permitted memoranda to be submitted on an issue raised by the defendants at an office conference concerning whether psychiatric testimony was permitted in order to address my credibility. The defendants, in response, filed a memorandum stating, "Dr. Labowitz has established that the plaintiff's mental condition is in controversy," and then, referring to the possibility that I had a character disorder, they said, "Indeed, if that character disorder can cause specific instances of conduct, defendants have the right, with the foundation already established by Drs. Reese, Flinn and Raskin, to verify that that character disorder exists."

We replied in our memorandum: "At the outset, it should be noted that no showing whatsoever has been made that Dr. Connolly's credibility is in issue . . . . On the contrary, it is the defendants' credibility as it relates to intent, malice, motive, etc., which is at issue in this case, not plaintiff's."

Then, in a November 5, 1985 decision Judge Taylor ordered: "With respect to admissibility of psychiatric testimony concerning plaintiff's mental status as an adjunct to . . . plaintiff's credibility, [he believed] that this matter should be ruled upon at trial when defendants can make a proffer . . . as to the proposed testimony."

On November 12 the defendants filed a Motion for Reargument of the denial of their Renewed Motion for a Psychiatric Examination, stating that they had "presented three grounds for the Renewed Motion: the question of Dr. Connolly's capacity to maintain this action, the question of whether Dr. Connolly's mental condition is relevant to his apparent inability to maintain a successful medical practice, and the question of whether a party can be compelled to submit to a psychiatric examination if such examination would be relevant to his credibility."

In support of their motion, the defendants noted that they had "filed among other supporting affidavits, the affidavit of a psychiatrist, Dr. David Raskin, establishing that Dr. Connolly's state of mind concerning Dr. Labowitz, is consistent with that of a person suffering from a fixed, delusional system or a paranoid disorder."

Also, by now, pretrial stipulations had been exchanged by both sides, and Roth's Summary Motion had been briefed, considered by the Court, and denied.

As the litigation moved forward, there was a new development: Jane Roth was no longer representing the defendant; she was now on the bench in the U.S. District Court. Replacing her, from powerful Richards, Layton and Finger, was a law partner, the head of the firm, Edmund N. Carpenter II. He was the son of a late chairman of the board of the DuPont Company and had graduated Phi Beta Kappa from Princeton and received his law degree from Harvard.

About forty percent of the Fortune 500 companies are incorporated in Delaware. Mr. Carpenter's law firm acted as local counsel for (among others) General Motors, Shell Oil, Gannett, Aetna Group, Gulf & Western Industries, and Penzoil. The firm was active in major corporate takeover battles, and its clients included T. Boone Pickens, Jr. and Carl Icahn. Also, Delaware's ex-governor, Pierre S. duPont IV, had joined the firm and was preparing to run for the Republican presidential nomination.

Edmund Carpenter, now 64 years old, had a national reputation as a corporate attorney. Previously he had been a campaign manager for "Pete" duPont. *Delaware Today* magazine had featured Mr. Carpenter on the front cover of an issue discussing some of Delaware's most prominent attorneys:

> Dressed in a blue pin-striped suit, a white handkerchief in the breast pocket, his wavy white-gray hair smoothed neatly back, Edmund N. Carpenter II looks every bit the distinguished corporate lawyer . . . .

> Lawyers love to tell the story of how Carpenter once offered a million-dollar settlement to a group suing over the crash of a military helicopter in which five persons were killed. The plaintiffs turned down the offer and Carpenter went to Court and won the case. The plaintiffs got nothing . . . .
>
> [And another note was of interest to me.]
>
> He has served as chairman for committees ranging from the Delaware Supreme Court Advisory Committee on Professional Accountability to the Lawyers Advisory Committee to the Third Circuit Court of Appeals. And, as head of the state Judicial Nominating Commission [from 1977-1983], he played an important role in shaping the courts of Delaware.

As the lawsuit plodded along, from month to month, in its third year of litigation, my greatest consolation was that I was going to accomplish my goal of getting to trial. There would be no token settlement. I had a chance to win with my peers, the jury.

But it had been a disastrous year. After the Court's December 1984 decision on our Omnibus notion, my attorneys and I had thought that the defendants' psychiatric motion had been kicked out of Court and attorney fees assessed against them. Yet now, more than fifteen months later, the issue of psychiatric illness was to be considered at trial, and payment of fees to my attorneys was still pending!

While Labowitz and Newman continued to have thriving practices, and while Roth and her law firm were being paid handsomely by Labowitz's malpractice insurance company, I was talking to Florence about closing the office (we had less than one day of patients per week); Connolly, Bove, Lodge & Hutz had spent more than $150,000 on my behalf; and Dad continued to fund my home expenses, as well as office deficits.

I had paid dearly for my decision to confront my opponents: an incredible amount of time and energy, a torment for my family, and a fortune in expenses and lost income.

Was there anyone who felt that improprieties had not occurred? If improprieties had been acknowledged by just *one* of the people to whom I had appealed—just one: Robert Flinn or Allston Morris or James Harding, or *one* of the doctors from the Credentials Committee, or *one* of the doctors from the Delaware Board of Medical Practice, or the *News-Journal's* Donald Brandt or Harry Themal or Ralph Moyed or Bob Leary or Norman Lockman, or the Attorney General's Office, or one person from the Supreme Court's Board on Professional Responsibility, or *one* member of the Senate Judiciary Committee, or *one* of the doctors who had bitterly complained to me—before the lawsuit was filed—about Labowitz and other manipulative doctors.

At the office, there were only a handful of loyal patients remaining, including LaRaye Thomas (the disabled rheumatoid patient sued by Labowitz), and Madeline Boone (the patient Labowitz had referred for my fibrositic study). Another patient that I was still seeing was an elderly Mother Superior of a convent. The wise, compassionate, nun listened attentively as I reviewed her medical management; then, as our roles reversed, I carefully listened as she made recommendations for my spiritual reading.

By early spring Mom's cancer had steadily progressed to the point where she was bedridden. Sieglinde and Mary, my sister, provided daily nursing care, and my brother, Tom, had interrupted his final year at Stanford Law School to help with Mom's care.

At 3 a.m. on Thursday, April 17, Tom telephoned. Mom's condition had worsened. I quickly dressed and hurried over to School Road. Mom was lying in bed, comatose. Her blood pressure was 100/60. It was quiet; I held Mom's hand and said my rosary. The early morning hour was peaceful. A short time later I checked Mom's blood pressure; it was 80/40, and it continued to slip further. Dad and Tom were at Mom's bedside. I called Sieglinde, Art and Joan, and Mary and Wilson.

At 8:20 a.m. Mom died. She and Dad had been married for 49 years.

Later that afternoon, as a cold, bleak storm battered northern Delaware, Mary and I went to the Lower Brandywine Cemetery in the rolling countryside on the outskirts of Mom's beloved Wilmington, and we selected a grave site.

Saturday morning was sunny and warm, a beautiful spring day. Daffodils stretched towards the sun; the magnolia and cherry blossoms were in full bloom. At St. Joseph's-on-the-Brandywine, our small country church built in 1841 for the Irish immigrants working at the nearby DuPont Powder Mills, Monsignor Paul Schierse celebrated Mom's funeral Mass with family and friends, followed by the burial.

Gerardine Laffey Connolly
January 2, 1910
April 17, 1986
What The Heart Loves It Keeps
And All Is Well.

On April 29 the Court held a pretrial conference, and our trial date was set for October 7.

In the meantime, however, my complaints against Ms. Roth and the Board of Professional Responsibility were now going to the Delaware Supreme Court.

10
Dr. WHO

It is a deprivation for a person not to have known illness, misfortune, or prison.

Emmanuel Mounier

Since filing the lawsuit August 1, 1983, we had been richly rewarded with thirty-four months of productive discovery. My lawsuit against Dr. Labowitz had charged him with defamation, damaging my reputation, and interfering with my professional and business relations. I had also complained that many of the illegal activities had been conducted as part of a conspiracy between Dr. Labowitz and others to improperly monopolize the treatment of patients throughout Delaware, with the result that patient care had been compromised and health care costs substantially increased.

Both sides were now busy with pretrial preparations. In the meantime, I had reviewed the *Rules of the Board on Professional Responsibility of the Supreme Court of Delaware.* Rule 15(j) stated: "Complaints against members of the board shall be submitted directly to the court."

I had completed the work on my complaints against the Board on Professional Responsibility and also against Ms. Roth. It was now time to present them to the Delaware Supreme Court.

As I worked at my desk shortly after noon on a sunny spring day, Thursday, June 5, I glanced out the window. Walking down the sidewalk, smiling at me, was Sieglinde. I kicked my chair back and opened the sliding glass door. Sieglinde and I were going to lunch, but on the way I would deliver my complaints to the Supreme Court chambers, located in the Carvel State Building at 820 French Street in downtown Wilmington.

In a two-page cover letter I respectfully asked the Court whether the Rules of the Board and the *Lawyer's Code of Professional Responsibility* had been violated by the Board's

Disciplinary Counsel, Susan Faw, and Assistant Disciplinary Counsel, Richard Poole, and also by the Board's Chairman, Francis Biondi, and whether Jane Roth had violated the *Lawyer's Code of Professional Responsibility* with a continuum of actions that had been documented both before and after the Board's 1985 decision on my initial complaints.

As Sieglinde and Florence talked, I attached a cover letter to each of five indexed files documenting my complaints: one copy for each of the five justices—Chief Justice Andrew Christie and Justices Horsey, McNeilly, Moore, and Walsh.

The pages of my complaint against Jane Roth were divided into two columns, with the relevant Disciplinary Rule (or Rules) from *The Delaware Lawyer's Code of Professional Responsibility* listed on the left, and on the right a description of the conduct about which I was making complaint. Exhibits, taken from the proceedings and indexed, supported the complaint. In order to avoid the repetitious use of titles, the parties were referred to by their last name. Thus, the first listed complaint and rule (relating to "Trial Conduct") read:

1.

DR 7-106 (C) In appearing in his professional capacity before a tribunal, a lawyer shall not:

(3) Assert his PERSONAL knowledge of facts in issue, except in testifying as a witness. (Emphasis added)

(2) Assert his PERSONAL opinion as to the justness of a cause, as to the credibility of a wit-

- Roth: "I spoke with Dr. Connolly on the telephone, a lengthy conversation, and I became quite concerned about his state of mind from that conversation . . . . Through my own experience, through my discussion with Dr. Reese. . . I have brought this motion." Office Conference, Hon. J. Martin, September 30, 1983 (Exhibit D 3,4)

- Roth: "I was concerned myself from the conversation that Mr. Green mentioned that I had with Dr. Connolly about Dr. Connolly's mental equilibrium. . . . So that the

ness . . . (emphasis added)

complaints that Dr. Connolly is making, my concern is that these are complaints which are directed at his apparent vendetta against Dr. Labowitz, which is without justification. . . . And I am concerned on the basis of Dr. Reese's opinion, on the basis of my own observations, that this complaint, this vendetta against Dr. Labowitz is a manifestation of Dr. Connolly's mental condition." Argument before Hon. V. Bifferato, October 25, 1984 (Exhibit D 8, 10, 11)

- Roth: "I have continued to be of the opinion that Dr. Connolly's complaints are a reflection of a significant psychiatric condition." Letter from Roth to Hon. V. Poppiti, May 6, 1985. (Exhibit D 12)

- Roth refers to Connolly as a "manifest nut." Office Conference, Hon. V. Poppiti, May 7, 1985. (Exhibit D 16)

The outline proceeded to my eleventh and final complaint against Ms. Roth: Disciplinary Rule 1-102, "Misconduct":

11. DR 1-102 (A) A lawyer shall not: (4) Engage in conduct involving dishonesty, fraud, deceit, or misrepresentation. (5) Engage in conduct that is prejudicial to the administration of justice.	- All of the above conduct of Roth.

After citing my complaints against Ms. Roth, I used a similar format to cite my complaints against the Board on Professional Responsibility, including what I believed were conflicts of interests on the part of those who addressed my complaints; the failure to respond to some of my complaints; the dismissal of other complaints via the recitation of an inappropriate Code; the contradictions between Poole's and Faw's conclusions; and, incredibly, the position that even if the allegations were true, they would not constitute misconduct on the part of Ms. Roth.

Sieglinde accompanied me as I drove to the Carvel State Building and parked half a block away.

"I'll be back in a few minutes," I told her as I got out of the car with the complaints under my arm.

"It bothers me, Ron," Sieglinde said. "I'm not sure it's the right thing to do."

"Roth has wiped us out," I responded. "And the Board on Professional Responsibility was a farce. I'm following the Rules of the Supreme Court; they say that complaints against the Board should be submitted to them."

As I walked towards the building and took the elevator to the 11th floor, I thought of all the upset that Sieglinde had been put through. But once I filed the complaint with the Supreme Court, the facts would be in the hands of the proper authorities. I would then have the satisfaction of knowing that I had done my duty; the decision then would be up to the Supreme Court.

Opening the door to the Supreme Court's office chambers, I entered a large, sumptuous reception room with dark mahogany-panelled walls, deep rugs, and portraits of justices from past eras. At the upper end of the room to the right, behind a great desk, sat a receptionist.

"I'm Dr. Connolly," I said. "I would like to file a complaint before the Supreme Court."

"You what?" exclaimed the bewildered receptionist.

"I'm not a lawyer," I explained, "but if a person has a complaint against the Board on Professional Responsibility, it should be filed before the Supreme Court."

The receptionist looked at me in disbelief. With an air of disdain, she stood up, excused herself, turned, and entered a door behind her. A few minutes later she returned with a man, apparently her supervisor. I explained again my business. After a few minutes of conversation, my purpose was finally understood. I handed over the complaints and left.

Joining Sieglinde in the car, I felt better. I had followed the prescribed channels of our society; I had taken my complaints to completion. I had done my duty. What the Court did now was up to them.

One week later, June 12, 1986, the Supreme Court—Chief Justice Christie and Justices Horsey, Moore, and Walsh—had made a decision regarding my complaint:

> . . . Dr. Connolly is again attempting to litigate the complaints that he has made against a member of the Bar of this Court, which were carefully evaluated and screened, found to be without merit, and properly dismissed. . . . There is no provision in the Rules of this Court or the Board for the filing of a complaint against the Board, its Preliminary Review Committee, Disciplinary Counsel, or Assistant Disciplinary Counsel whenever a party is dissatisfied with the dismissal of a complaint.
>
> To the extent Dr. Connolly seeks to invoke our supervisory powers over the Bar to review an alleged failure of the Board to comply with its rules, we are satisfied that there was no impropriety whatever by the Board, Disciplinary Counsel or Assistant Disciplinary Counsel.

> The record filed by Dr. Connolly with the petition fully supports this conclusion. Accordingly, we decline to exercise our supervisory powers in this case.
>
> The action taken in this matter was final on June 4, 1985, and it will not be reopened. The petition is DISMISSED.

As the warm June days sped by, I prepared myself mentally, emotionally, and spiritually for the trial.

Twenty-eight years ago I had started my pre-med studies; twenty years ago I had graduated from medical school. Now my peers in the medical profession had humiliated me, my practice was destroyed, my career wiped out, and—my self-esteem was thriving. To be considered mentally ill under these circumstances was a badge of honor, a source of pride, the sign of a complete physician!

In a few months I would be presenting to the public—the judge and the jury—evidence, not from my mouth but from the sworn testimony of my opponents, documenting the current practices and priorities of these medical leaders.

I now prepared for trial by outlining each of the issues on a five-by-seven inch index card, and I reviewed my testimony, including rebuttal of my opponents' defenses. I also read articles and books on how to testify at trial.

Meanwhile, the attorneys from both sides urgently prepared for trial in a lawsuit that was now running into millions of dollars in damages and legal expenses, not to mention the reputations of attorneys and doctors on both sides.

Dad, Jim, and C.J. were convinced that the psychiatric attack by the defendant and his accomplices was malicious, and they wanted damages. I completely agreed. On June 23, 1986, my attorneys filed the proper motion before the Court.

Carpenter and Parkins objected, stating that the claims relating to statements allegedly made by Dr. Labowitz prior to the instigation of this litigation had come too late. In a motion of their own, filed June 24, they asked the Court not to permit our claim that I was injured by the psychiatric motions filed during the litigation:

> . . . it is settled that an absolute privilege attaches to statements made during the course of litigation. Since the psychiatric motions are privileged, plaintiffs cannot recover damages for injuries they claim were caused by the motions. . . .
>
> It should be emphasized that defendants' argument is not related on the evidence which could be introduced at trial. Because this privilege is absolute, it does not depend on whether the person seeking to exercise it acted in good faith. . . . Hence, Dr. Connolly's repeated assertions that the motion was brought with malice and without justification are meaningless here.

And the fight continued over whether Labowitz's evaluation statements were defamatory. Carpenter and Parkins wrote in a memorandum to the Court:

> In his opening brief, Dr. Labowitz observed that the credentialing of the physician's are matters of obvious public concern. Indeed . . . this Court has previously observed that the General Assembly enacted the immunity statute in order to promote free and open discussion during the credentialing process. This Court concluded [December 17, 1984 decision] that "this is in the general interest of the public."

And a few days later the attorney for the Medical Center of Delaware, William Wade, of Richards, Layton and Finger, sent a memorandum to the Court quoting from the Delaware immunity statute (24 Del. C. #1768), which stated:

> The records and proceedings of . . . [peer review] committees or organizations . . . shall be used by such committees or organizations and the members thereof only in the exercise of the proper functions of the committee or organization and shall not be public records and shall not be available for court subpoena or subject to discovery; and no person in attendance at a

meeting of any such committee or organization shall be required to testify as to what transpired thereat. . . .

Wade then quoted from a previous Court decision:

. . . it is in the interest of the proper administration of standards of professional conduct in this State that the confidentiality of medical committee proceedings be preserved without exception.

Jim responded:

. . . One doctor (Connolly) filed a peer review complaint against another doctor (Labowitz). The intent of the statute is to preserve Connolly's confidentiality in this situation. Yet the Medical Center is using the statute as a shield to prevent Connolly from learning what was said about him in the course of the presentation and consideration of his complaint against Labowitz. As a result of Connolly presenting his complaint against Labowitz, his (Connolly's) privileges at the Medical Center were revoked without even so much as a hearing, let alone any real due process. It stands the statute on its head to say that this is the kind of situation for which the statute was designed . . . .

. . . The immunity contemplated by #1768 is strictly limited to the review of medical care etc. undertaken "in good faith and without malice." 24 Del. C. #1768 . . . mandates that the records and proceedings shall be used "only in the exercise of the proper functions of the Committee . . . ." . . . .

It has been clearly established that the biennial evaluation forms prepared by Labowitz concerning Connolly have been used by Dr. Lazarus (a Credentials Committee member) to deny Connolly membership in the American College of Physicians. Dr. Flinn has admitted that this is not a proper use or function of the records of the Credentials Committee. Moreover, Dr. Labowitz discussed his evaluation of Connolly with Dr.

Lazarus in a hallway of the Medical Center, again not for purposes of the Credentials Committee, but the American College of Physicians. This is a clear waiver of any privilege. That Dr. Lazarus concluded from Labowitz's evaluation that Connolly's performance was among the worst in the Medical Center whereas it was at least as good as Labowitz's, shows conclusively that Labowitz used the evaluation process in bad faith to undermine his competitor. It is important to note that Dr. Labowitz (Connolly's section chief) never addressed any of his purported criticisms to Dr. Connolly—something he surely would have done if the quality of medical care were in issue. It is also important to note, in considering whether the Credentials Committee proceeded in good faith, that Dr. Connolly's privileges at the Medical Center were revoked not because of any suggestion that his patient care or ability was not of the highest caliber, but because he refused to submit to the psychiatric examination concocted by Dr. Flinn and defense counsel as a result of Connolly's temerity in filing a complaint against Labowitz.

Surely, under the circumstances of this case Labowitz's evaluation forms concerning Connolly were never privileged under #1768. If they were, that privilege has been waived.

In spite of our efforts, on August 7 Judge Taylor stated that "based on the material presented, I do not find waiver of privilege as to any of the documents . . . ."

Jim replied with a Motion for Reargument, again asking that we be permitted to examine Labowitz's evaluations of me, and again explaining that clearly they had been used for improper purposes. Again, the judge denied our motion, saying that the immunity had not been waived.

The hot, humid days of August, 1986 in Wilmington had quickly slipped by. It was now early September. The busy pretrial preparations of the last few months had given way to intense preparations during these few remaining weeks before the October 7 trial. Seven days a week, often late into the night, both sides fought for position: pretrial orders, conferences with Judge Taylor, selection of exhibits and witnesses, interrogatories, last-minute motions, amendments, court decisions, jury selection, pre-testimony and post-testimony instructions to the jury, and on and on.

In the Pretrial Order, Labowitz responded to our charges: He denied all wrongdoing, and he denied that injury had occurred as a result of the alleged acts.

And my opponents had still not given up on having me psychiatrically examined. Carpenter filed a motion asking the Court to order that I submit to such an exam because plaintiff was now asking for damages resulting from the psychiatric issue, and the defendant was "entitled to the defense of . . . truth," and also because "Plaintiff Ronald G. Connolly's mental condition may bear on his credibility as a witness," and "may affect his claim for damages, that is, his practice, defendants contend, declined in part because of his mental condition rather than anything these defendants did."

A few days later Judge Taylor denied the defendant's motion, noting: "This is the fourth effort of defendants to obtain an order requiring plaintiff to submit to psychiatric examination." He further noted:

> I find no evidentiary support relating to plaintiff's conduct . . . which could serve as the factual foundation for a determination of good cause to order a psychiatric examination. I point out also . . . defendant's showing of good cause should be supported by an opinion from a psychiatrist that the evidentiary material established a probability that the proposed psychiatric examination would establish the existence of a condition constituting "mental illness."

The next week Carpenter filed a Motion For Reargument, again requesting a psychiatric exam, and the motion was accompanied by a new affidavit by Dr. Raskin, whom I had still not met, stating that it was his opinion that "a psychiatric examination, accompanied by psychological tests, would establish the existence of a condition constituting 'mental illness' in the plaintiff, Ronald G. Connolly."

Jim responded:

> The record reveals that Dr. Raskin has been allied with the defendants and, indeed, [was] one of the originators of the psychiatric allegations which constituted the Medical Center's response to Dr. Connolly's complaint against Dr. Labowitz. His "opinions" are foregone conclusions rather than deliberative medical analyses . . . .
>
> Nowhere have defendants specified any evidence of record which supports Dr. Raskin's "opinion." . . . . Moreover, defense counsel has admitted in open Court that Dr. Connolly is capable of practicing medicine but mentally ill only in his perceptions of Dr. Labowitz's misconduct. As the Court has held [decision on our Omnibus Motion, December 17, 1984] it is these perceptions which are for the jury's determination.

The next day Judge Taylor denied the defendant's Motion For Reargument because of Raskin's earlier involvement. He further stated that "if defendants intend to pursue this subject further, defendants should submit an affidavit by a psychiatrist who has had no prior involvement with the subject matter of this case . . . . "

Meanwhile, we also prepared for another critical aspect of the case. Labowitz had testified under oath that he accepted assignment on patients who had problems paying, or who were on a fixed income, whereas records from the Court of Common Pleas showed that he had sued LaRaye Thomas, the disabled woman on welfare, for $272.50, and the records also documented that he had sued forty-seven other patients over a thirty-month period.

Also, under oath, Green had asked Labowitz: "Is it standard policy to tell patients that you will not see them until they pay their bills?" Labowitz had replied: "No." The next moment Labowitz had been shown his ledger card on Madeline Boone, whose husband worked as a school custodian, documenting that when she owed $121, one of his employees had noted on the ledger card that the patient had been told she had one week to make payment and she could not be seen until her account was paid in full. An entry on the ledger card the next day indicated that Dr. Labowitz had Received On Account $121 from Mrs. Boone.

These facts were pertinent to a central issue in the lawsuit, namely, the *medical performance* of the two opposed physicians, Labowitz and myself. For years Labowitz had criticized my medical performance, and my practice had been devastated. At the same time, in spite of flunking his rheumatology boards, suing his own patients, and charging higher fees than I, he had a thriving and lucrative practice.

These facts also reflected Dr. Labowitz's *credibility* as a witness—as well as the credibility of his attorneys. They would be helpful to us at trial as Labowitz took the witness stand.

Furthermore, the facts were relevant to Dr. Labowitz's *motive:* Was it greed? The consequences of Labowitz's actions had not only affected me; he had not singled me out. Others (such as Madeline Boone, La Raye Thomas and the forty-seven other patients whom he had sued) had also paid the consequences of Labowitz's behavior.

Madeline Boone and LaRaye Thomas were ready to testify, and the Court of Common Pleas records, which documented Labowitz's suits against his own patients, were exhibits that we were going to present to the jury.

Also, there was the issue of Labowitz's billing for Medicaid no-shows; this testimony too would be helpful to us at trial.

Labowitz's nationally renowned lawyer, the past chairman of the Delaware Supreme Court Advisory Committee on Professional Financial Accountability, Edmund Carpenter, was up to the challenge. Speaking at a pretrial conference, he told the Court:

> There are certain contentions which the plaintiffs apparently seek to make which we contend are inadmissible and that the offering of the evidence itself would

presumably result in a mistrial. These are contentions relating to Dr. Labowitz' billing practices, which are unrelated to Dr. Connolly in any way. There was an investigation of Dr. Labowitz in connection with Medicare and Medicaid payments, and I should say that he was found to have acted properly and to be a caring physician, I think was the Attorney General's finding, but the plaintiff seeks to introduce that evidence nonetheless in order to show that Dr. Labowitz is naughty and because of this irrelevant matter should be punished by awarding Dr. Connolly additional damages.

Our opponents also objected to some of our other claims; for example, they held that the letter to the Delaware Medical Journal was an expression of opinion, while the abortion claim was barred by the statute of limitations; the referral of Madeline Boone caused "no cognizable injury," and alleged injuries were also barred by the statute of limitations.

My attorneys argued that there was a continuum or conspiracy of misconduct over the years—which had continued to the present; therefore, the statute of limitations was still running. We argued to the Court that the defendant was involved in the conspiracy:

> . . . Dr. Labowitz has been shown to have acted in concert or combination with others for an unlawful purpose resulting in damage to Dr. Connolly. Persons in positions of authority which would have allowed them to put an end to defendants' wrongdoing instead joined in and actively participated in the wrongful conduct.

The co-conspirators whom we now named for the Court included:

Medical Center of Delaware, Inc.
Robert Flinn, M.D.
Alfred Lazarus, M.D.
John Levinson, M.D.
James Newman, M.D.
David Raskin, M.D.

"If the Court," Dad explained that evening, "permits us to present our conspiracy evidence to the jury, then, as co-conspirators, they don't have a penny of liability themselves, but to the extent that Labowitz conspired with Lazarus or Newman or Flinn, it increases Labowitz's liability; and if the jury decides that Labowitz acted with malice, the jury can add punitive damages which can double or treble the award."

A few days later Jim called; he had good news. Judge Taylor, after having reviewed both parties' submissions, said:

> I have tentatively concluded, subject to hearing the actual testimony, that evidence as to each of the subject areas, if believed, would reasonably contribute to the inference that a conspiracy existed on the part of Dr. Labowitz and one or more of the persons named by Plaintiff as co-conspirators. Accordingly, Defendants' Motion . . . to exclude such testimony is denied.

Super! Now, when Flinn and Lazarus and Levinson and Newman and other Medical Center of Delaware doctors testified at trial, they would be testifying not as uninvolved doctors but as named conspirators.

Over more than three years of confrontation and litigation my emotions had ranged from self-satisfaction and exhilaration for having publicly taken a stand against my opponents, to anxiety and fear that I might choke on the witness stand, thus hurting our chances. These feelings had been part of my daily life since my decision to confront. Now, with only a few days left before trial, my feelings were amplified. I had never doubted my decision to confront, and I was proud of what I had already accomplished, but I also wanted to do well at the trial. I reassured myself that I had done my job; the outcome of the lawsuit was in the hands of numerous people, of which I was only one. I was pleased; I was eager for the trial to start.

There were now only a few days left before trial. For the past 38 months I had invested every ounce of strength in fighting my opponents. And throughout the fight Sieglinde had supported me. But she had suffered more than I; she had not wanted the confrontation, whereas I, finally, had eagerly accepted it.

The trial would start next Tuesday. Both parties now filed joint jury instructions. Thursday morning Jim and I went to Richards, Layton and Finger for a last-minute deposition; Carpenter interrogated me on our recently named co-conspirators. Afterwards, I returned to the office to rehearse my trial testimony.

At 3:30 that afternoon Florence interrupted me; Jim was on the phone.

"Ron, I hate to tell you this, but they're still pushing their psychiatric motion. They're getting an affidavit from Dr. Lawrence Weiss."

"From Dr. WHO?" I responded.

"From Dr. Lawrence Weiss."

"WHO is Dr. Lawrence Weiss?"

"Another psychiatrist . . . they went up to Philadelphia to get him."

"Taylor won't permit a psychiatric exam now, will he? Not three days before trial!"

"I don't think so," Jim responded. "The Court knows they haven't presented one fact to support their motion . . . they just keep adding more doctors."

Jim concluded the conversation, saying that he had a 2 p.m. office conference with Judge Taylor the next day; he would call me when they finished.

The next afternoon, the hours slipped by. I waited . . . and waited . . . for Jim's call. Shortly after 5:00 the phone rang. It was Jim; he was furious.

"The worst has happened! Absolutely the worst! Taylor continued your trial!"

"What do you mean, 'continued' the trial?"

"It means he's called off the trial; it will have to be re-scheduled. He is permitting the defendants to have a psychiatric exam of you! . . . We now have to work out who the examining psychiatrist will be. Carpenter wanted Raskin to do it."

I was numb as I hung up the phone. How could they do this? For three years the Court had thrown out the psychiatric motion. How much longer would Sieglinde and I have to wait for a new trial date? When would we be able to get on with our lives? When was someone going to put an end to this farce?

I called Sieglinde. She was concerned about Dad and the rest of the family; the public ordeal would continue, and we would continue to be a financial burden, dependent on Dad.

I called Dad. He was depressed. He was eighty years old and had spent countless hours on my litigation over the past three years; he had worked with Jim and C.J. seven days a week. And now the Court had added months to our fight.

What had the defendants done that resulted in the Superior Court of Delaware finally granting their psychiatric motion three days before trial? My opponents had obtained affidavits from two Philadelphia psychiatrists, total strangers to me, Dr. Lawrence Weiss and Dr. Robert Sadoff. The affidavit of Dr. Weiss, after being duly sworn, said that he had reviewed pleadings from the lawsuit, and:

> Based on my preliminary review of these documents it is my opinion that this material establishes a probability that a psychiatric examination, accompanied by psychiatric tests, would establish the existence of a condition constituting "mental illness" in the plaintiff, Ronald G. Connolly.

And the "back-up" affidavit which the defendants had obtained from Dr. Robert Sadoff, stated, after being duly sworn, that he had reviewed pleadings from the lawsuit, and:

> Based on my preliminary review of these documents it is my opinion that this material establishes a probability that a psychiatric examination, accompanied by psychiatric and psychological tests, would most likely establish the existence of a condition constituting "mental illness" or mental disorder in the plaintiff, Ronald G. Connolly.

As my attorneys and I tried to adjust to the Court's latest order, I told Dad, Jim, and C.J. that the psychiatric exam should not be done by Raskin! It should be done by an uninvolved psychiatrist, and the exam should be standardized—the kind the federal government routinely gives to an airplane pilot.

"I don't care," I said, "how long the exam takes, or how detailed and comprehensive it is, but it should be a *standardized* exam."

For forty-five months I had been fighting, and now it would be a few months more. The trial had been delayed, but it should not hurt our chances. The psychiatric attack was going to add to our victory!

Yet blood was in the water, and sharks were circling. I awaited the psychiatric exam.

11
The Psychiatrist

There are periods of what perhaps you and I would call remission during which time Dr. Connolly is not climbing the walls or claiming that people are after him and he appears even to a psychiatrist to be in reasonably good shape. And the psychiatrist would need to know how he acted on other occasions.

Edmund N. Carpenter, II, Esq.
Richards, Layton & Finger

Since the day of my opponents' initial response to the lawsuit, more than three years earlier, their position in Superior Court had been that Labowitz was blameless and that I was mentally ill. They had supported their accusations with testimony from Drs. Raskin, Reese, Levinson, Bronheim, Flinn, Weiss, and Sadoff. My attorneys and I had argued that my opponents' psychiatric accusations were malicious, unfounded, and not supported by an iota of objective evidence, but were simply a disgraceful diversionary tactic. We believed that the jury could draw their own conclusions from the abundant evidence which had been accumulated over the past three years. The Superior Court had decided otherwise; I had been ordered to submit to a psychiatric examination. The Court and the lawyers were now in the process of selecting the psychiatrist.

Labowitz, responding to our Supplemental Interrogatories, also had some comments concerning my mental status:

> . . . . Dr. Labowitz denies making any defamatory statements concerning Dr. Connolly's mental state. However, statements that Dr. Connolly had a psychiatric problem or was in need of counselling would have been true.
>
> Dr. Connolly exhibited characteristics of paranoia in his conversations with Medical Center officials and Dr.

> Labowitz. He also demonstrated evidence of paranoia in his complaints to various administrative bodies, his testimony at depositions, his testimony before the Senate Judiciary Committee. . . .

I had always thought that Americans supported freedom of speech. Yet when I had exercised this right, I had paid dearly. My freedom of speech in presenting serious complaints to the appropriate administrative bodies resulted in my opponents' accusing me of being mentally ill.

Freedom of religion granted me, I thought, the right not to participate in actions which for me would have been seriously wrong, such as an abortion, but my opponents said I had abandoned a patient. The results had been devastating to me, my family, and my career.

Free enterprise for me necessitated defending my life's work by presenting complaints to civil authorities, yet for my opponents it had supported their charges of a psychiatric disorder.

Participatory democracy for me meant following prescribed channels as I presented evidence to the Senate Judiciary Committee, but for my opponents it had become further evidence that I was paranoid.

When I had presented my complaints against Dr. Labowitz to the medical profession, the first medical authorities to render a decision decided that he was blameless. This decision, in my mind, had simply been rubber-stamped by subsequent medical authorities. And when I had presented complaints against Ms. Roth to the legal profession, the first legal authorities to render a decision concluded that she was blameless; again, I felt, subsequent authorities had simply rubber-stamped the decision.

Meanwhile, as Labowitz was telling the Court that I was paranoid, the attorneys from both sides battled over which psychiatrist would perform my psychiatric exam. My lawyers and I wanted the exam performed by an independent psychiatrist, preferably at a large, out-of-state university or government hospital or facility.

I was emphatic that Carpenter not select the psychiatrist. My opponents had already stated that absolute privilege attached to statements made during the course of litigation, and

I imagined some of the testimony that a psychiatrist selected by my opponents might give.

Carpenter wanted Raskin to perform the exam; Sadoff was his second choice.

It was an odd experience for me. I was an observer as lawyers, judges, and doctors—most of whom I had never heard of prior to three years ago—argued vehemently about my mental health, while the newspapers headlined the battle.

Yet before I had confronted Drs. Labowitz, Lazarus, and Levinson, no one had questioned my mental health.

A few months ago Sieglinde, the children, and I had thought our ordeal would by now be over, but as the autumn days shortened and as the nights became colder, our greatest ordeal lay ahead. It was now December, 1986. The struggle was in its forty-eighth month—and every month had reaffirmed my decision to confront; I knew that I was right, and every passing day supported my conviction. And, in the process, for four years I had documented the actual performance of leaders of the medical profession—not simply their public pledges.

It seemed to me that before the lawsuit my opponents had been brazen and self-righteous as they attacked me while hiding behind their committees; yet since the lawsuit, their performance had been pathetic.

On Friday, January 2, 1987, as I sat at my desk, a wet, cold snow was falling, partially covering the ground. Cars slushed up and down Pennsylvania Avenue. I reviewed my office financial sheet for the past year; *gross* income for 1986 was down to $38,918. As my receipts steadily declined, my office expenses steadily increased—malpractice insurance premiums, heat and electricity bills, and more. I was in the midst of a financial hemorrhage as Dad pumped more money into my office and home expenses. I hoped that the Court would soon grant relief.

And Connolly, Bove, Lodge and Hutz had now spent $272,945 on my litigation.

Meanwhile, my lawyers had retained Dr. John Stapleford, an economist and the Director of the Bureau of Economic and Business Research at the University of Delaware. Using 1981 as my base year—my best year in practice, when I was operating at 50 percent capacity—and calculating the damages to my practice from 1979 until the year 2004, when I would be sixty-five years old, my attorneys estimated damages of over $3 million.

As the fight continued, the President Judge of the Superior Court gave word that Judge Vincent J. Poppiti was being assigned to our case. A short time later, Judge Poppiti denied the defendants' designation of a psychiatrist; he would make the selection himself. He also selected a new trial date: August 24, 1987.

Meanwhile, Jim reminded Judge Poppiti that among the issues still pending was the Court's December 18, 1984 award of attorneys' fees to us after the affirmative defense raised by the defendants had been struck down.

On Friday, April 3, I called Jim. Six months to the day had passed since the Court had authorized the psychiatric exam, yet the psychiatrist had not even been selected! The snail-like pace of the litigation was a torture for Sieglinde and me. We needed decisive action from the Court. Meanwhile, Labowitz's practice continued to thrive, and his attorneys were well paid.

Finally, on April 6, 1987, Judge Poppiti selected a Board Certified psychiatrist from Baltimore to conduct the examination—Dr. Jonas R. Rappeport.

Dr. Rappeport's curriculum vitae was impressive: Diplomate of the American Board of Psychiatry and Neurology (Psychiatry), Diplomate of the American Board of Forensic Psychiatry, Chief Medical Officer—Medical Service of the Circuit Court for Baltimore, past president of the American Board of Forensic Psychiatry, past president of the American Academy of Psychiatry and the Law, staff appointments at Johns Hopkins University School of Medicine and the University of Maryland School of Medicine, and his distinguished credentials continued over a curriculum vitae of twelve typewritten pages.

Dr. Rappeport's rate was $200 per hour, with a per diem of $2,000, payable by the defendant. After the initial examination Dr. Rappeport would determine whether further psychiatric examination and/or psychological testing would be required. In the event that psychological testing was requested by him and ordered by the Court, the testing would be performed by Dr. James Olsson, a psychologist associated with Dr. Rappeport.

Sieglinde and I wanted the earliest available examination date. My examination was scheduled for Friday, May 22 at 1:00 p.m. in Dr. Rappeport's Baltimore office.

Another controversy, however, had now been ignited; namely, the language by which Judge Poppiti should refer me to Dr. Rappeport, and which, if any, documents from the litigation should be forwarded to him.

My attorneys and I were opposed to sending any documents from the lawsuit. Rappeport, as an independent expert, should determine the manner of the examination, and he should determine what documents, if any, he believed to be relevant. Our opponents, however, wanted to make selections from the pleadings and forward these to the psychiatrist.

On April 16 a conference was held in Judge Poppiti's Chambers. Edmund Carpenter, attorney for the defendant, spoke:

> I really don't know what Dr. Rappeport knows as of today as to why the examination is necessary. I am assuming that, like the other psychiatrist with whom we have conferred, he will want to know what has Dr. Connolly done, what is it that has been regarded by others as aberrant behavior, what has Dr. Connolly said in this and other places, and what are the views of the people around him, which the other psychiatrists tell us is a key. If everybody or everybody in a position to know, for example, other doctors, thinks there is a serious problem, that's something that a psychiatrist weighs in reaching his determination.
>
> It will be necessary for him, therefore, we feel, to do what the other psychiatrists in this case have done. Namely, review the depositions, review the developments in this case where Dr. Connolly has said, "Well, the head of the department of medicine is a conspirator against me. This doctor whom I've never seen is a conspirator against me. That doctor who I've heard mention something about me is a conspirator against me. This doctor with whom I was to consult and confer

but whom I let down and didn't appear is a conspirator against me. There are conspirators against me everywhere and they're after me."....

He needs to read what Dr. Connolly said before the Senate Judiciary Committee as he was raving on there about how people were after him and trying to get him ....

A few moments later Jim Green responded:

Your Honor, my reaction is that if Dr. Rappeport with his impressive resume and experience doesn't know what questions to ask, then something is wrong. He knows what questions to ask in determining whether somebody suffers from a mental illness. He will after performing the examination know what additional information he needs, wants, or desires, to make a complete examination including psychological tests.

I think what Mr. Carpenter would like to do is—well, I'm sure he would like to write the report beforehand. But short of that, he would like to direct those materials to Dr. Rappeport which he believes support his case. And I just don't think that having any confidence in Dr. Rappeport's expertise and ability, that that is the way that an examination should be done ....

A few minutes later Carpenter responded:

If I were the doctor, I would want those materials there .... I would certainly like those documents right there where I or my nurse or assistant could look at them and say "Okay, well, it's true, this guy sees conspirators under every bush."

And, a few minutes later Carpenter continued:

... The necessity of [Dr. Rappeport's] having these materials readily available to him is enhanced not only because we are talking about periods of time that are

> somewhat remote now but also because the nature of this illness as it has been explained to us is that it is, I think the psychiatric term, compensated. Which means that there are periods of what perhaps you and I would call remission during which time Dr. Connolly is not climbing the walls or claiming that people are after him and he appears even to a psychiatrist to be in reasonably good shape. And the psychiatrist would need to know how he acted on other occasions. And that's only available to him through the documentation, including the depositions in this case. (#31)

The Court deliberated and then agreed with our opponents. Documents would be selected by both parties and transmitted to Dr. Rappeport.

Sieglinde and I were eager to proceed at last, but I was disgusted that the Court had ordered me to submit to the humiliation of a psychiatric examination, performed by a stranger, with my medical career in the balance.

I realized that much was riding on the outcome of the examination, but my life of forty-seven years was open to review; I was proud of my performance. The psychiatrist had to be reasonable; he could not draw unsubstantiated conclusions.

I was disgusted also that the Court had denied our discovery into Labowitz's critical evaluations of me, evaluations that had been transmitted behind my back. Was there anyone who though that they had been done in good faith — to improve patient care?

I knew of no one more arrogant than my opponents— when they could strike and hide in the dark—yet more cowardly when it came to standing up publicly for their conduct.

The opposing attorneys, exhibiting their extraordinary intellects and talents, had also contrived a new attack. Dad had seen to it that I had been able to cover my expenses by drawing on savings which he had been setting aside for me since I had been an infant—savings that had been started to ensure my college education. Thus, I had a source of income apart from my medical practice. Because of this income, John Parkins, Carpenter's associate from Richards, Layton and Finger, now argued in a letter to the Court, "Defendants contend that Dr. Connolly's practice failed, at least in part, because he is disinclined to work."

As my scheduled examination approached, my lawyers, to my disappointment, had one last preparatory step for me. My opponents had paraded psychiatrists and other doctors into the lawsuit to attack my mental health, and soon the court-appointed psychiatrist would render his opinion. Now my attorneys wanted Dr. Groves, the Harvard psychiatrist with whom they had been consulting, to examine me.

I had met Dr. Groves—studious, dark-haired, personable—for the first time the previous fall, when he had come to Wilmington for a Saturday-afternoon conference with my attorneys. I dreaded being forced to respond to personal questions, and I hated to have my life judged by opposing psychiatrists.

I was not mentally ill. My past was open for review. My opponents had scrutinized and spotlighted me for more than three years with their charges of mental illness, and their findings, such as they were, were public. I only wished the cowards would shed their reluctance and join me under the spotlight!

Lack of freedom is one sign of mental illness: a given stimulus or situation results in a restricted response; the individual is not free to respond in various ways. I wondered if my opponents were as free as I.

On Saturday, May 2, I took a 7:40 a.m. Eastern flight to Boston, then a cab to Eight Hawthorne Place, near Massachusetts General Hospital. My appointment with Dr. Groves was at 10:00 a.m. Arriving at the modern, high-rise building twenty minutes early, I walked along the sidewalk, passed two tennis courts waiting to be used on this sunny spring morning, and after walking a little further, I came to a Catholic Church, entered, walked up the center isle, and knelt in the pew.

Returning to Dr. Groves' first-floor office, I sat in his empty reception room. After a few minutes, a door opened, and Dr. Groves appeared. He cordially greeted me, then ushered me through a short hallway and into his inner office, where I took a seat.

"CLICK!"

Turning back to the hallway, I saw Dr. Groves lock the door leading back to the reception room and then, taking a step from the hallway into his office, lock the second door. A precaution, I told myself; some patients are angry, they yell and scream—certainly such conversations should be confidential. Unfortunately, my psychiatric exam was going to be discussed publicly at trial.

Groves and Rappeport could ask *any* question, and I had to respond or risk being viewed as uncooperative, hostile, or perhaps worse.

I hoped my examiners were *good* doctors, and I hoped that I would not choke.

A few hours later Dr. Groves had completed his exam; it had not been too painful. He was a gentleman. He now unlocked both doors, and we visited for a while. "Your evaluation was exceptional," he said.

"I was concerned that I was boring you with my story," I replied.

"You did excellent! I intentionally was totally unresponsive to you, giving absolutely no positive or negative feedback, and in effect putting you into an emotional desert so that you'd have to fend for yourself. The entire exam was exceptional. You show a lot of confidence and an unusual ability to survive under stressful circumstances."

Relieved, later that afternoon, I met my brother Chris, a learning-disabilities psychologist who lives in the Boston area. Chris and I had dinner at Quincy Market, and afterwards I took a late evening flight from Logan back to Philadelphia. It had been a big day.

Later, Dr. Groves sent me his office notes:

> Dr. Ron Connolly, examined 2 1/2 hours, structured interview; 1 1/2 hours unstructured, social interactions, 5/2/87 . . . . He presented his legal case fully but relevantly and without inappropriate rancor or blame. He appeared to see his conflict with Dr. Labowitz in the

> round without any sign of delusional or paranoid ideation . . . . On formal mental status testing he appeared relaxed and healthy, tanned and well-dressed . . . . His speech was normal and his thinking was entirely normal in its form and content . . . . His Cole animal and 3 wishes tests were unremarkable, except for an unusually pacifist and altruistic orientation. His mood and affect were normal . . . . Past medical history is unremarkable, past psychiatric history was negative. There was no evidence whatever of any psychopathology or symptomatology of childhood or adulthood, with the possible mild exception of poor studying and easy distraction by sports in 3rd and 4th grades, which was perhaps his way of rebelling, and which was corrected by the time he was in 9th grade . . . . His developmental and social history were elicited in detail, but they were unremarkable and unrevealing of pathology . . . . He was strictly reared, a devout Catholic, and extraordinarily lucky in his upbringing and fortunate in his marital and family situation. In sum, I found no psychiatric disease or illness in this man, no Axis I or Axis II disorders (DSM-III). There is, however, an unusually perfectionistic value system, rooted in an extraordinarily fortunate childhood and unusually stable temperament, so that to the novice or naive observer it might distantly resemble some elements of some personality disorders. But there is nothing here even close to a diagnosable personality disorder.

On May 13, Judge Poppiti wrote to Dr. Rappeport and transmitted the pleadings which both sides had selected. (We were keeping Dr. Groves' examination and its results confidential until he testified as our rebuttal witness at trial.)

May is a beautiful month in Wilmington with warm spring days, a profusion of pink and white dogwood blossoms, and baseball fields bustling with activity. This May was no exception. The days quickly slipped by, and Friday, May 22, the day of my psychiatric exam, arrived.

I drove Christina and Anna to school, then drove home and jogged to Christ Church and back. Sieglinde and I talked for a while; then I showered and dressed and was on my way to Baltimore by 11:00. My appointment with the court-appointed psychiatrist was at his office, 101 Read Street, at 1:00 p.m.

I found Dr. Rappeport's office, on the third floor of an aging Medical Arts Building. Entering the empty reception room, I sat on the well-worn sofa, apprehensively waiting to meet the psychiatrist.

A short time later the door opened and Dr. Jonas Rappeport entered: a short, pleasant-appearing man of about sixty, wearing spectacles, a short-sleeved shirt, and a tie.

"Would you like a soft drink, Dr. Connolly?" he asked, smiling, as we shook hands. "The refrigerator is right there in the corner."

"No, thank you, Dr. Rappeport," I replied.

"Maybe you would prefer a cup of coffee?" Dr. Rappeport asked.

"I'm fine for the time being, thank you."

Dr. Rappeport then ushered me into his office, offered me a chair, locked what I now knew were the customary two doors, and sat down, and the examination began.

It was obvious that the psychiatrist had read the pleadings forwarded by Judge Poppiti. For more than three hours, he questioned me on each of the issues in detail. I told him that I had filed the lawsuit only after five different levels of medical administrative review had refused even to consider most of my complaints and had found Dr. Labowitz blameless of other complaints without investigating basic facts. I told him that I had complained against Dr. Labowitz only after four years of his interference in my practice, culminating with my being denied a customarily routine membership in the American College of Physicians. I told him that the denial was based on derogatory evaluations that Dr. Labowitz had submitted to my peers without his once having discussed them with me. And I said that Dr. Labowitz's major criticism seemed to be in regard to my decision, like that of many doctors, not to use my private patients to teach hospital residents in my office. I noted that there was no hospital requirement to do so, and Dr. Flinn had testified that there was no such requirement. I also mentioned Dr. Labowitz's referral of Madeline Boone with a probable diagnosis of fibrositis even though, at the time of his referral, she clearly was excluded from that diagnosis by the criteria that Dr. Labowitz had publicly proclaimed.

As Dr. Rappeport continued his interrogation, I told him that Dr. Labowitz had testified that he was Board Certified in Rheumatology while in fact he had flunked his certifying exams; he had billed for Medicaid no-shows; and he had sued forty-eight of his patients for non-payment, to which Dr. Rappeport replied, "Well, I guess he isn't perfect, is he?"

Dr. Rappeport also delved into the abortion controversy. I explained that on religious grounds I cannot participate in an abortion. "You weren't asked to participate in the abortion," the psychiatrist responded. "You were asked if intrauterine saline would cause a problem with her scleroderma."

"But for me to give approval to the technique of abortion," I replied, "would be participating in the abortion . . . at least in my mind."

"They just wanted you to treat her scleroderma," Dr. Rappeport replied, "and tell them whether scleroderma patients can have intrauterine saline."

The conversation continued. I mentioned that Dr. Levinson had told my brother a few months after the abortion that there was talk of running me "out of town."

"What does that have to do with your lawsuit against Dr. Labowitz?" Dr. Rappeport, visibly irritated, replied.

"Well, that's exactly what they're trying to do; my practice has been devastated."

"So what if they wanted to run you out of town?" Rappeport snapped. "They were angry at you and disagreed with your conduct!"

As we continued discussing the abortion, I related that the hospital nursing notes shortly before the abortion quoted the patient as saying, "I don't want the abortion."

"Fifty percent of therapeutic abortions are done on women who during the previous twenty-four hours expressed a change of mind," the psychiatrist replied.

A short time later, Dr. Rappeport suggested a break; he had to use the bathroom. Opening the two doors leading back to the reception room, he left the room and returned a few minutes later. "Would you like to use the bathroom, Dr. Connolly? It's right off the reception room. The bathroom has no window and its electricity is out, but there's a flashlight on the back of the toilet so at least you're not in total darkness."

"I'm O.K. for the time being, Dr. Rappeport, thank you," I replied.

Dr. Rappeport then continued the examination until 4:30, when he handed me a Minnesota Multiphasic Personality Inventory test (MMPI) and directed me back to his reception room where I took the 565-question true/false test.

I answered the questions . . . page after page after page after page.

True or false: "Christ will come a second time."

True or false: "Christ actually did change water into wine."

True or false: "I believe in life after death."

In the middle of the test I took a break to use the bathroom. It was pitch black. I stood the flashlight on its end, and, with the weak beam directed towards the ceiling, I was able to hit the target—better not miss, or the doctor would probably think I had some unresolved hostility. The circumstances were ludicrous: the defendants had pleaded to the Court for almost four years to order this psychiatric exam, both sides had spent fortunes arguing the issue, the psychiatrist's opinion could mean the difference between winning and losing, and here I was trying to hit the toilet in semi-darkness.

Finishing in the bathroom, I returned to the last half of the tedious true/false questions. Finally, after an hour more, I had answered the last question. It was 6:15. I had been examined and tested for five hours. Tired, but relieved that it was over, I knocked on Dr. Rappeport's office door. He opened, peering through his spectacles as I handed him the test. "Dr. Connolly," the psychiatrist said, "I want to meet with you again, and I also want you to have psychological testing with Dr. Olsson."

My spirits plummeted. I had assumed that five hours would be sufficient. I knew that Poppiti had given Rappeport latitude in conducting the exam, but I had not expected this. As I left the psychiatrist's office, I had a return appointment for Tuesday, June 2, at 1:00 p.m.

When I returned to Dr. Rappeport's office at the appointed time, the psychiatrist interrogated me further about the abortion. I respected the convictions of others regarding abortion, and I expected them to respect my convictions.

On religious grounds I cannot participate in abortion. Each embryo and fetus is genetically unique and complete, requiring only oxygen, food, water, and reasonable temperature, like every human being. It is my belief that I cannot terminate this life, nor can I ask another doctor to do so.

"If you were in the same position again, Dr. Connolly," the psychiatrist said, "would you still refuse to give medical clearance for the abortion or to get another doctor to take your place?"

"I would have to respond the same way," I replied.

"You mean after being charged with patient abandonment and being reprimanded by your peers," the incredulous psychiatrist replied, "you wouldn't act differently?"

"No." I quietly responded. "I couldn't." The psychiatrist was incensed; his face twisted. "That may make it very difficult for you to practice medicine!"

I told Dr. Rappeport that Delaware state statute clearly gives a doctor the right *not* to participate in an abortion, and that I also had a Constitutional right, not to participate in abortion.

"I don't care!" the psychiatrist angrily replied. "What does the AMA Code of Ethics say?"

Restraining my anger, I simply responded to the question. "Dr. Rappeport, nothing I did compromised the patient's health. My action required Dr. Levinson to make an extra phone call to bring in Dr. Labowitz for the consultation."

"Didn't you think that it would affect your practice?" the psychiatrist shot back.

"I hoped people would be tolerant of my religious beliefs."

"But that did involve a risk; were you aware of that?"

"I didn't think a person would be accused of patient abandonment for following their religious beliefs."

"If you are found to have abandoned a patient," Rappeport snapped, his face red, "then no wonder you don't get referrals from other doctors. Maybe your practice failed, Dr. Connolly, because people just don't like you!"

After pounding me for more than thirty minutes on the abortion issue, Rappeport shifted the focus, interrogating me on my childhood, schooling, interests, and other past history, including my decision after graduating from medical school to sign up with the military's Berry Plan, thereby satisfying my military obligation and enabling me to join the Navy so I could request the Marine Corps in Vietnam.

Rappeport then returned to the lawsuit complaints. As we proceeded, I told the psychiatrist that at the time I filed the lawsuit the medical administrators, including Flinn, had never even responded to some of my complaints, such as the abortion charge, denial of American College of Physicians' membership, and the unfairness of Labowitz's discussing evaluations of me with my peers but never with me.

Flinn had told me, Rappeport insisted, when we met to discuss my complaints in January of 1983, that he concurred with the Professional Conduct Committee's patient-abandonment reprimand. Politely, I told him that that was false. "Obviously Dr. Flinn concurred with the Professional Conduct Committee," Dr. Rappeport snapped. "It seems that no one can get through to you, Dr. Connolly, unless they agree with your viewpoints!"

Struggling, I restrained my anger. Rappeport had not been at my meetings with Flinn, yet now he angrily insisted that he knew what Flinn had told me. But Rappeport was not finished. "No matter how many doctors tell you the same thing, Dr. Connolly, the message just doesn't get through to you. You need it spelled out for you! Even then you don't get the message! If your practice is having difficulty, it's understandable. The doctors find it difficult to work with you. They're afraid you'll sue them!"

Maintaining a civil tone, I said that the woman had retracted her consent *before* the abortion; according to the nursing notes she had said "I don't want the abortion." And, I reminded Rappeport, that before the abortion the woman's scleroderma was stable and there were no signs of internal involvement. Then

Labowitz gave medical clearance, the abortion was done, and within a week the woman's scleroderma had a sudden exacerbation, from which she died three months later. But the psychiatrist continued to berate me.

Finally, at 4:20 p.m., after more than three hours, Rappeport terminated the examination, saying that he had to attend a clinic. But he was still not finished with me. On Friday, June 12, Dr. Olsson, the psychologist with whom Rappeport was associated, would be doing psychological testing on me from 1 to 4 p.m., and afterwards, Rappeport might want to continue his examination.

I walked downstairs, out to the street, and towards my car. I was tired but relieved to be out of Rappeport's office. He had pounded me for almost three hours, and my hands had been tied; if I had vented my anger it could have cost me the lawsuit.

I was not, however, disappointed. These same issues were the crux of the lawsuit. I looked forward to the Court's decision.

As I drove back to Wilmington, I wondered whether Rappeport had intentionally stressed me to test my response, but I doubted it. He had gone far beyond providing a stress. He had taken license with the privilege granted him by the Court.

It was also clear to me that Rappeport knew that I was not psychiatrically ill. I imagined him trying his stunt with various psychiatric patients. He would have been smacked around.

Returning to Wilmington, I talked with Sieglinde and then with Dad and Jim. "Whatever you do, Ron," Jim said "don't get mad. We don't want a hostile witness at trial."

As my lawyers continued pre-trial preparations, we received a setback. At a June 5 pre-trial conference with Judge Poppiti, Carpenter—noting that Dr. Groves was listed as one of our witnesses—had said that he wanted to know whether or not Dr. Groves had examined me and the nature of his testimony at trial. Green responded that our decision to have Dr. Groves testify might depend on Dr. Rappeport's conclusions. Carpenter argued that if Dr. Groves had examined me and was going to testify, then the defendants wanted the opportunity to select a psychiatrist to examine me as well. Judge Poppiti replied:

"What I . . . was doing when I determined that there should be a court-appointed psychiatrist was literally to get their litigation into a posture where it would not be a circus of psychiatrists . . . . I would strongly encourage the parties in this case to leave in place the process that the Court has set in motion . . . . I want . . . a definitive list of the plaintiffs' witnesses. If that includes Dr. Groves, then I will entertain any appropriate application in behalf of the defendants to expand their witness list."

I was furious. The defendants had already paraded Raskin, Bronheim, Weiss, and Sadoff—none of whom I had ever met—as well as Reese, Flinn, and Levinson before the Court; each had rendered his opinion on my mental health. Groves was to be our sole rebuttal witness against the psychiatric attack. Yet the Court would not let us use him in this capacity unless we were willing to let the defendants' psychiatrist—probably Raskin—examine me.

Under these circumstances, my lawyers and I decided that Dr. Groves would not testify on my mental status. There was already an abundance of evidence on the psychiatric issue, and it was hard to imagine how more psychiatric testimony could make it any clearer. The jury's duty should be self-evident.

The next week I was at Dr. James Olsson's office. The pale, middle-aged psychologist ushered me into his office and motioned for me to have a seat next to his desk. Olsson explained that he had already discussed the legal issues with his associate, Dr. Rappeport, but he wanted me also to review the main aspects of the lawsuit. After I summarized my story, the psychologist administered various psychological tests. He showed me several cards, each having a different design, comprising from about five to twenty-five dots, and gave me a blank piece of paper and a pencil, instructing me to copy the designs. If there were only a few dots, I counted them and made an exact copy; if the dots were too numerous, then I just put a representational number of dots for the design.

The psychologist then moved on to other tests: "Draw a picture of a man . . . and now a woman."

He held up pictures depicting different scenes and asked me to make up a story about each. . . .

"These are Rorschach ink blots; when you look at them what is the first image that comes to your mind?"

"Complete the following sentences:

'A man wants a woman who . . . .'
'He felt he could murder a man who . . . .'
'After he made love to her, he . . . .'
'A man would be justified in beating a woman who . . . .'
'Sexual intercourse . . . .'
'Most women act as if they . . . .'

Almost three hours later, I had finished the last psychological test. Saying good-bye to Dr. Olsson, I left, relieved to be out of his office. But I was now on my way to Rappeport's for another session. My appointment was scheduled for 4:30.

When I arrived at Rappeport's office, he greeted me. "Well, Dr. Connolly, did you have fun taking your psychological tests?"

The Court-appointed psychiatrist then wanted to hear about my complaints against Ms. Roth. Not surprisingly, he disapproved. He even objected to my complaint that Ms. Roth had repeatedly played the role of a psychiatrist, rendering to the various Superior Court judges her opinion of my mental health.

Rappeport spent most of the next two hours angrily rehashing the same issues. "Why," he asked, "didn't you pick up the phone a few days after Dr. Levinson called you, and talk over your misunderstanding with him?"

"When Dr. Levinson called," I said, "I *wanted* to talk over the misunderstanding between us, but Dr. Levinson was furious, interrupted as I tried to explain, yelled he was charging me with patient abandonment, and slammed down the phone."

"Nobody," Rappeport angrily replied, "is able to get through to you, Dr. Connolly, unless they agree with you!"

The Court-appointed psychiatrist continued, "If you disagreed with the reprimand you received after the abortion, why didn't you complain at that time? Wouldn't that have been helpful to your Catholic doctor-friends in case the abortion problem came up again?"

Rappeport continued relentlessly to pound me—as unwilling to grant me the slightest concession as he was to acknowledge the slightest fault in my opponents.

Finally, Rappeport modified his behavior; he was finished. His face composed, he said calmly: "I haven't come to any conclusions Dr. Connolly, but are you satisfied with my evaluation? Do you think I have been fair?"

"Since I don't know the results of your evaluation, Dr. Rappeport," I replied, "I can't answer your question. Certainly if your evaluation is favorable, I'll be pleased, and if it's unfavorable I'll be disappointed."

"But do you think you received a fair examination?" Rappeport said.

"You told me that no one can get through to me," I responded, "unless they agree with me. And that's totally false. I don't know whether you were playing the devil's advocate, trying to stress me, or if you believed what you were saying, but I totally disagree with those statements."

"As a forensic psychiatrist," Rappeport replied, "I do have to play the devil's advocate and stress people that I'm evaluating. I don't have a lie detector test."

As Rappeport ushered me towards the door, he again repeated that he had not yet drawn his conclusions.

Rappeport's report was due in Judge Poppiti's office before June 25. As we awaited the report, it seemed that Carpenter and Parkins' confidence in their psychiatric motion was disintegrating: On June 23 they notified Jim and C.J. that they were filing a motion before Judge Poppiti to "renew their application for an examination of Dr. Connolly by a psychiatrist and/or psychologist of their own choosing."

As Sieglinde and I awaited the report, the lawsuit was becoming more burdensome to our children; it had consumed far too much family time. "Daddy," Anna, our seven-year-old, asked, "where will we live if we lose the lawsuit?"

As I arrived at my office on Tuesday, June 29, we were still awaiting Rappeport's report. I called Dad at the law firm to see if he could join Sieglinde and me for dinner the next evening.

Dad sounded depressed. "Rappeport's evaluation was delivered late yesterday afternoon," he said. "The evaluation was not good."

Dad briefly related that Rappeport had concluded I was paranoid. "We certainly want to keep this under wraps," Dad said "and I think Poppiti agrees with us."

"I don't want it under wraps!" I shot back. "Rappeport's evaluation is a farce! I want everyone to have public access to it!"

But Dad was worried. I explained to him that it was not necessary to be a doctor to know that paranoia means *un-reasonable* feelings of persecution: feelings of distrust and suspicion *not* supported by facts. I told Dad that Rappeport could not pull a hocus-pocus diagnosis simply because he was dealing with lay people. The *facts* supporting my complaints were overwhelming.

Dad and I talked for a few more minutes. A messenger from the law firm would hand-deliver the report to me in an hour or two.

I immediately called Sieglinde. She was in full agreement with me: the report should be public. I then called Jim; unable to reach him, I called C.J. "I'm concerned," C.J. said, "because this represents the opinion of the court-appointed expert."

A short time later the messenger came walking down the sidewalk, a white package under her arm. Thanking her, I took the parcel, closed the door to my office, and opened it.

On top was a cover letter from Judge Poppiti notifying the defendants that they owed Drs. Rappeport and Olsson $5,850 for their evaluation. I then read Rappeport's report:

> It is my opinion, within reasonable medical certainty, that Dr. Ronald G. Connolly is suffering from personality disorders of a compulsive and paranoid type. . . . Dr. Connolly is in need of psychiatric treatment of a psychotherapeutic nature. . . . I believe further that from about 1979 through 1984 Dr. Connolly was suffering from the same mental disorders for the same reasons described in this report....I believe that Dr. Connolly suf-

fers from a paranoid personality disorder based on his hypersensitivity to criticism from those around him. . . .

The diagnostic criteria for paranoid personality disorder (p. 309) [referring to page 309 of a text: the *Diagnostic and Statistical Manual of Mental Disorders, Third Edition*—usually called *DSM III* for short—which the psychiatrist was quoting from in order to support his diagnosis]:

"A. Pervasive, unwarranted suspiciousness and mistrust of people as indicated by at least three of the following: (Those that Dr. Connolly clearly shows are at least:)

(1) Expectation of trickery or harm. (Madeline Boone referred from Dr. Labowitz)
(4) Avoidance of accepting blame when warranted. (1979 abortion issue, no residents in private office, etc.)
(6) Intense, narrowly focussed searching for confirmation of bias, with loss of appreciation of total context. (1979 abortion issue)
(7) Overconcern with hidden motives and special meanings. (Madeline Boone referral. . . .)

B. Hypersensitivity as indicated by at least two of the following:

(1) Tendency to be easily slighted and quick to take offense. (Letter to editor)
(2) Exaggeration of difficulties, e.g., 'making mountains out of molehills.' (Residents in office, Mrs. Roth's judicial appointment)
(3) Readiness to counterattack when any threat is perceived. (Mrs. Roth. . .etc.)

C. Restricted affectivity as indicated by at least two of the following:

(1) Appearance of being 'cold' and unemotional. (My evaluation and Dr. Olsson's, 1979 abortion issue)
(3) Lack of a true sense of humor. (My evaluation and Dr. Olsson's)

D. Not due to another mental disorder such as schizophrenia or a paranoid disorder." (No other mental disorder evidenced). . . .

The diagnostic criteria for compulsive personality disorder that applied to Dr. Connolly are: (p. 327, DSM III)

(1) restricted ability to express warm and tender emotions. (Dr. Connolly's behavior during my interview and that of Dr. Olsson)
(2) perfectionism that interferes with the ability to grasp "the big picture," e.g. preoccupation with trivial details, rules, order, organization, schedules and lists (1979 abortion issue, Madeline Boone, interview and deposition behavior)
(3) insistence that others submit to his or her way of doing things, and lack of awareness of the feelings elicited by this behavior. (1979 abortion issue, no residents in the office, his testimony with reference to Mrs. Roth's appointment to the bench, etc.)
(5) indecisiveness. (Behavior with Dr. Olsson, although more evidence would be desirable.) (#32)

Clearly three of the five items listed in DSM III are met by Dr. Connolly based on the evidence that I have. [The DSM III diagnostic criteria for Compulsive Personality Disorder required that at least four out of five enumerated characteristics be present.] However, reading between the lines and using clinical judgement as well as psychological test results, I believe that Dr. Connolly fits that definition. (As Chief Justice Potter Stewart once said with reference to the definition of pornography, "I shall not today attempt to further define the kind of materials I understand to be embraced within

> that shorthand definition and perhaps I could never succeed in doing so . . . but I know it when I see it.") (#33)
>
> During my interviews with Dr. Connolly, he represented the epitome of total coldness, humorlessness and lack of any apparent feeling except for the frequent flushing of his face and a minimal expression of some anger towards Dr. Labowitz. Of the thousands of patients that I have examined, I believe that he represents one of the most controlled, expressionless persons that I have seen. He practically did not move throughout the interviews. He refused anything to drink, and if my recollection is correct did not even use the bathroom, despite the fact that I found it necessary to take a couple of breaks during our interviews . . . . (#34)
>
> . . . Throughout the course of Dr. Connolly's career in Wilmington it would appear that he was not willing to "pay his dues." This is seen in repeated instances of his complaint . . . .

[The Court-appointed psychiatrist then elaborated on various issues of the lawsuit, including my complaints against Roth to the Senate Judiciary Committee.]

> Here Dr. Connolly acts in a most inappropriate fashion for one who is supposed to be a sophisticated physician . . . . As I read the depositions I did not see anything about Mrs. Roth's behavior which appeared to be extraordinary. This represents Dr. Connolly's hypersensitivity, vindictiveness and inability to recognize other people's roles and responsibilities. Further it represents a moderately severe impairment in his judgment of what is an appropriate complaint and what is appropriate behavior for someone in his position. When this is discussed with him, he accepts no criticism [for] the inappropriateness of his "vindictive" behavior. (Rigidity, inability to accept criticism, his rules, etc.)

[And Rappeport even expressed his opinion on my Naval service in Cam Ranh Bay, Vietnam]

> . . . . it is apparent that it was to his benefit to sign up for the Berry Plan and that his decision to go to Vietnam was also to his benefit in that he could take care of his military obligation at that time and select the Navy and an essentially non-dangerous situation . . . .

After finishing Rappeport's thirty-five-page, single-lined, report I telephoned C.J.. "They can fly Rappeport's evaluation from the top of a flagpole!" I exclaimed. "It's pathetic! Short of a glowing report, this is the next best thing."

As we discussed the report I said it was obvious to me that Rappeport had not done a psychiatric evaluation but had simply judged the lawsuit: He was grossly unfair; it means that in courtrooms across the country, one party can simply accuse the other of being psychiatrically ill. Why are they ill? They are ill because they filed a lawsuit.

I further explained to C.J. that Rappeport had not acknowledged a *single* incidence of wrongdoing by Labowitz; his conclusions completely supported Flinn and the medical profession's position that Labowitz was blameless, and I was paranoid. At the same time, the Court-appointed expert had not found a single favorable trait in me.

(During these years, while I was accused of being psychiatrically ill—for not participating in an abortion, for submitting complaints against a doctor, for filing a lawsuit, for testifying before the Senate Judiciary Committee—I often thought of the political dissidents in the Soviet Union who had been imprisoned in psychiatric hospitals. Perhaps I should feel lucky.)

The Superior Court had given Rappeport exceptional authority and had seen to it that he was handsomely paid. His response to this public trust was now documented in the public record.

As Dad, Jim, C.J., and I prepared for the quickly approaching trial we dissected Rappeport's report. I was encouraged; the report was going to help us. Of all the diagnoses that

Rappeport could have chosen, he had chosen paranoid and compulsive, the two easiest diagnoses to puncture. Lay persons on the jury would have no difficulty understanding these popularly used terms. Other diagnoses might have been cloaked in mystery and involved esoteric terms.

Rappeport also had helpfully limited his data base to the issues of the lawsuit. The jury could make their own decision whether Rappeport's criteria for the diagnosis of "paranoia" and "compulsive" had been fulfilled. The jury could decide whether my complaints reflected unreasonable feelings of persecution, distrust and suspiciousness, or whether my complaints were reasonable and appropriate. If my perceptions were accurate, then my opponents were frauds.

Similarly, the jury could readily decide whether they agreed with the diagnosis of "compulsive," or whether striving for perfection in some areas of life is desirable in healthy men and women whether they be athletes or airplane pilots, bridge engineers or musicians, doctors or lawyers, mothers or fathers.

I found the situation preposterous. Both sides were concluding four years of litigation and discovery. Numerous doctors and lawyers—extremely well paid—had submitted diametrically opposed testimony concerning the same issues while under oath to tell the truth.

My understanding of American democracy, the Holy Bible, the American flag, and the black robes of the judiciary was the antithesis of what I had been witnessing day after day, year after year. Did anyone gave a damn?

I was convinced that we had volumes of sworn testimony and exhibits documenting that my opponents were frauds and hypocrites: Publicly they pledged good medical care and a judicial system of justice, law, and order; but in action they systematically perverted the most basic foundations of society—while making themselves rich.

We were ready for trial. The polarized views were ripe for the jury.

12
The Trial

> Beware of false prophets who come to you disguised as sheep but underneath are ravenous wolves. You will be able to tell them by their fruits. Can people pick grapes from thorns, or figs from thistles? In the same way, a sound tree produces good fruit but a rotten tree bad fruit. A sound tree cannot bear bad fruit, nor a rotten tree bear good fruit. Any tree that does not produce good fruit is cut down and thrown on the fire. I repeat, you will be able to tell them by their fruits.
>
> Saint Matthew 7:15-20

Thus far, I had been the scapegoat. My opponents had been declared blameless—from Labowitz to Roth, from the Board of Medical Practice to the lawyers' Board of Professional Responsibility—and my complaints without merit.

It was now the first week of July, 1987, and I eagerly awaited August 24, the date our trial would start. Just being among the ten percent of cases that went to trial would be a significant victory: I would have a chance to win, and the public—the jury—would have a chance to render its verdict on health care standards.

I interrupted my trial preparations to attend a five-day Alumni College at Georgetown University. It was a combination of school, vacation, and spiritual retreat—lectures in literature and art, history and government, philosophy and theology. Late in the afternoon on Tuesday, having finished the last lecture for the day, I returned to my campus dorm room to change into running shorts and sneakers. I jogged up to the track, adjacent to the hospital, and as I ran in the hot Washington sun I thought of Sieglinde, Mom, the courtroom climax which was quickly approaching, and also of Teilhard de Chardin.

As an anthropologist, Teilhard researched the evolution of life over the millennia. He believed that all of our human endeavors participate in this evolution—matter is in the process of "complexifying," the physical world and human life is EVOLVING, our consciousness is expanding, and ascending from matter to spirit. In Christ, God become man, matter and spirit reconciled. At Mass, our work and labor share in the Eucharistic Bread—the actual Body of Christ; our sufferings, separations, and death share in the Eucharistic Wine—the actual Blood of Christ. Thus, we actively meet and are united with the living Christ *today*. And by sharing in Christ's life, we believe, we also share in his death, his atonement for our sins, and his resurrection to eternal life—in fulfilled love and perfect truth, goodness, beauty, and glory.

That evening, I ended my day in Dahlgren Chapel where I joined five to ten other men and women as we participated in an 11:15 p.m. Mass said by one of the Jesuits, a theologian, Father Thomas King. The chapel was dark, with the exception of a few flickering candles on the altar, which sent silent shadows dancing up the walls. Father King replaced his homily with a reading from Thomas Merton's *Seeds of Contemplation*. In the candlelight the priest slowly and movingly intoned:

> People who know nothing of God and whose lives are centered on themselves, imagine that they can only find themselves by asserting their own desires and ambitions and appetites in a struggle with the rest of the world. They try to become real by imposing themselves on other people, by appropriating for themselves some share of the limited supply of created goods and thus emphasizing the difference between themselves and the other men who have less than they, or nothing at all.
>
> They can only conceive one way of becoming real: cutting themselves off from other people and building a barrier of contrast and distinction between themselves and other men.
>
> I have what you have not. I am what you are not. I have taken what you have failed to take and I have

> seized what you could never get. Therefore you suffer and I am happy, you are despised and I am praised, you die and I live: you are nothing and I am something and I am all the more something because you are nothing. And thus I spend my life admiring the distance between you and me; at times this even helps me to forget the other men who have what I have not and who have taken what I was too slow to take and who have seized what was beyond my reach, who are praised as I cannot be praised and who live on my death . . . .

At the end of the week I returned to Wilmington and was greeted by a shocking development. Judge Poppiti and the lawyers from both sides were discussing a settlement! I assured Dad and Jim that there would be no settlement unless it was reasonable; avoidance of embarrassment to me and to the medical profession was *not* cause for settlement. Edmund N. Carpenter summarized the defendants' settlement proposal in a letter to my father, who was now eighty-one years old, had spent his lifetime becoming a respected member of the community, had worked harder than anyone to extricate me from my dilemma, and was embarrassed by the repeated public assertions that I was a mentally ill physician.

Carpenter wrote to my father, "Dear Art: . . . We continue to desire to settle the case as expeditiously as possible, and hopefully before there is any further publicity or even any further dissemination of information relating to it." Carpenter then summarized his settlement proposal, suggesting that I give a full and complete general release to Labowitz; Labowitz would give a full and complete release to me ("This is to protect Ron against any suit for attorneys' fees which, as you know, our clients have indicated they would otherwise file"); each party would bear all of its own costs expended in this litigation; the action would be dismissed with prejudice; neither side would publicize the settlement in any way or make any further comment on the case, and the Dr. Rappeport report would be kept confidential.

The next day Dad rejected the proposal, saying, "Settlement at this stage is out of the question, and the remaining three weeks should be devoted entirely to trial preparations."

A few days later Rappeport's deposition was taken in his Baltimore office.

Green:	Doctor, would you tell me if you have any knowledge or acquaintanceship either on a social or a professional basis with any of the following individuals: Dr. Russell Labowitz?
Rappeport:	None . . . .
Green:	Dr. Robert Sadoff? [Dr. Sadoff was one of the two Philadelphia psychiatrists who had submitted affidavits the previous October which had resulted in the Court ordering me to submit to a psychiatric exam.]
Rappeport:	I know him very well. We're close professional colleagues.
Green:	How do you know Dr. Sadoff?
Rappeport:	I was the first president of the American Academy of Psychiatry and the Law; he was the second president. I was the second president of the American Board of Forensic Psychiatry; he was the third president. I was at his daughter's wedding; he was at my daughter's wedding. So we're very close friends. . . .
Green:	You were provided, were you not, Doctor, with certain materials which had been authored by Dr. Sadoff and specifically an affidavit in this case?
Rappeport:	Yes, mm-hmm.
Green:	Did you at any time advise Judge Poppiti that you had a close professional tie with Dr. Sadoff?

Rappeport:	No, I didn't.
Green:	Is that something that you considered doing?
Rappeport:	No, I wouldn't.
Green:	When is the last time, to the best of your recollection, that you had a discussion or meeting with Dr. Sadoff?
Rappeport:	I spoke with him on the telephone Sunday evening.
Green:	Of this past week?
Rappeport:	Yes, sir, yesterday—or Monday. . . .
Green:	Have you discussed the particulars of this case or of your examination of Dr. Connolly—
Rappeport:	Oh, no, indeed.
Green:	—with Dr. Sadoff?
Rappeport:	Absolutely not. Absolutely not.
Green:	Did he discuss it with you in any respect?
Rappeport:	Absolutely not. To my knowledge, he has no awareness that I'm involved in the case.
[Later:]	
Green:	Would it be fair to say, Doctor, that personally you do not approve of Dr. Connolly's lawsuit against Dr. Labowitz?
Rappeport:	I don't have any personal opinion about it one way or the other. . . .
Green:	Would you say that you do not approve of Dr. Connolly's moral or religious position on abortion?
Rappeport:	No. I respect Dr. Connolly's right to have his own moral and religious beliefs.
Green:	Doctor, do you believe that a doctor should, quote, pay his dues to other doctors who have been in practice longer than he has?

Rappeport: I believe that is the accepted policy of the medical profession and of every other profession, including the legal profession, et cetera, and I have no problem with it.

The following week Olsson, whose two-and-a-half-page report had accompanied and supported Rappeport's, had his deposition taken.

Green: Do you have a professional relationship with Jonas Rappeport, M.D.?

Olsson: Yes. My relationship is that he is the chief medical officer of the Circuit Court for Baltimore City and I am the chief psychologist in that office. I might say that we also do some of our private work, we collaborate and form a team to evaluate individuals.

Green: Could you explain to me how that collaboration or team work would, in a typical situation, work?

Olsson: In a typical situation, Dr. Rappeport may get a referral for an evaluation and wish to have a psychological evaluation as part of his psychiatric evaluation, so he will request that I see the individual. I will obtain from him initially a reason for referral, usually a brief statement, either verbal or written, as to the purpose of the evaluation and then I will set up an appointment with the individual, perform the evaluation and submit to him a written report.

Green: Was your evaluation of Dr. Connolly one of these, as you put it, collaborative efforts with Dr. Rappeport?

Olsson: Yes, it was. . . .

Green: Doctor, do you have an estimation of the percentage of cases in which you evaluate a person and find no psychological or psychiatric problems in that individual?

Olsson: I would have to say that the number of individuals we see with absolutely no psychological problems would be probably nil for the population that we are referred.

[Later:]

Green: Prior to your meeting with Dr. Connolly on June 12, did you obtain any background information on either Dr. Connolly or the matter for which this evaluation was done?

Olsson: I obtained some verbal background information from Dr. Rappeport which essentially outlined the difficulties that Dr. Connolly stated that he had experienced with Dr. Labowitz.

Judge Poppiti, in the meantime, responding to one of our motions, had ordered Labowitz to disclose his income tax returns from his rheumatology practice. Jim studied the returns with our economics expert, Dr. John Stapleford, the Director of the Bureau of Economic and Business Research at the University of Delaware, and with my accountant, Kenneth Stewart.

Afterwards, Jim telephoned me. In comparing my tax returns with Labowitz's, and noting that in a regional market with a limited number of suppliers of a service, he found a "classic" example of Labowitz having a monopoly and maintaining it by running out the opposition. Jim continued, saying that during my first fiscal year I had acquired a significant fraction of the market, which represented good-quality work. Soon thereafter my practice plateaued, and in 1983 it started to decline rapidly. During these years Labowitz's income was a mirror-image of mine. When I started practice, Labowitz's income plateaued out, dipped for a year, and then rose rapidly. Furthermore, my income curve was significant in that it was rising during the first year (when the population of our area was actually declining), but over the last few years, while the population of the area was increasing, my income curve had decreased.

My attorneys notified Judge Poppiti and our opponents of their claim for my economic loss. The damages, over the past years and projected until shortly before I reached the age of sixty-five, were calculated at $3,049,843.

My life's work of the past thirty years was smashed, and my reputation, upon which my future work depended, was shattered. Maybe the jury would triple the award by granting us punitive damages!

Meanwhile, the law firm of Connolly, Bove, Lodge & Hutz now had expenses of over $350,000 for my litigation. There was a limit to how much more money they could spend. My father, who had put in more time than any of the attorneys, had been paid nothing.

At the same time, my gross office income for the past twelve months, from which I had to pay my office expenses, was $36,300. Over the past few years I had received referrals from approximately five doctors.

The start of the six-week trial was now only one week away. Judge Poppiti was in the process of deciding whether or not we could tell the jury that Dr. Labowitz had filed lawsuits against forty-eight of his patients, billed Medicaid for office visits which had not occurred, and refused to see patients whose bills were in arrears. Thirty-three of the forty-eight lawsuits were cited by Jim and C.J. to Carpenter as ones that they intended to offer into evidence. My attorneys submitted a memorandum to the Court arguing our position:

> How these two physicians [Labowitz and Connolly] practice medicine is central to this lawsuit. The evidence will show that Dr. Labowitz failed to become Board Certified in his specialty, misrepresented his qualifications, sued indigent patients and billed Medicaid for nonexistent office visits. The Affidavits of . . . former employees of Dr. Labowitz . . . highlight the unscrupulous conduct of the defendants in the practice of medicine.
>
> [Delaware Rules of Evidence] 404 (b) provides that evidence of a defendant's other crimes, wrongs or acts

is admissible to prove motive, opportunity, intent and absence of mistake. Dr. Labowitz's motive in this case is simple greed. Evidence of his unscrupulous billing practices and treatment of indigent patients is consistent with the greed motive, and will provide the jury with a basis for understanding Dr. Labowitz's conduct towards Dr. Connolly. Furthermore, Dr. Labowitz has claimed that the misdiagnosis of a patient, Madeline Boone, was a mistake. The foregoing evidence rebuts this contention, and instead supports the alternate and more plausible explanation that he intended to sabotage Dr. Connolly's research project and interfere with his practice.

Carpenter and Parkins replied with a memorandum in opposition, arguing:

. . . Even if this Court were to determine that the proffered evidence is somehow admissible, it should be excluded under [Delaware Rules of Evidence] 403 since its minimal probative value is substantially outweighed by the danger of unfair prejudice and confusion of the issues . . . .

. . . plaintiffs have sought to introduce evidence of a suit brought against Laraye Thomas [the crippled indigent black woman who was on Medicare] for fees she did not pay. . . .

If this Court were to allow evidence of this suit, then defendants would be forced to present evidence that it was justified. This evidence would include evidence of the services rendered to Ms. Thomas, as well as an exploration into Ms. Thomas' financial state and her ability to pay. In addition, Dr. Labowitz would produce substantial and necessarily time consuming, evidence that he forgave bills when patients explained to him that they were unable to pay.

. . . plaintiffs provided counsel with 33 other complaints which they intend to offer into evidence....It is appropriate for Dr. Labowitz to demonstrate to the jury that each and every one of these suits was justified. Needless to say, this undertaking would be difficult since some of the events took place 12 years ago. Perhaps more importantly, the seemingly endless trek of witnesses necessary to establish that each of these suits was justified and reasonable would inevitably confuse the jury and distract from the real issues in this case.

Carpenter and Parkins then addressed the alleged Medicaid fraud:

Here, under the guise of establishing motive, Dr. Connolly seeks to try Dr. Labowitz for a criminal offense in this civil proceeding. . . .

Dr. Labowitz has once before been required to defend himself against these charges. He was the subject of an intense investigation by the Department of Justice headed by a seasoned prosecutor who had the assistance of an experienced auditor skilled in investigative techniques. The investigators interviewed the witnesses whom Dr. Connolly will offer in support of their "Medicaid Fraud" theory. Moreover, those investigators had an opportunity for an unhurried study of Dr. Labowitz's books and records (something the jury will not have). At the conclusion of this prolonged investigation, the Department of Justice absolved Dr. Labowitz of any wrongdoing. . . .

. . . . Under these circumstances it is incomprehensible that the jury will be in a position to make a more accurate determination than the Department of Justice.

Judge Poppiti, during an August 21 conference in his chambers, ordered that we would *not* be permitted to present evidence to the jury concerning Labowitz's billing practices, the collection suits he had brought, or his alleged Medicaid fraud. The order said further that the Court believed that this evidence was relevant to establishing that Dr. Labowitz was motivated by greed; it was, however, excluded because the Court found that its probative value was substantially outweighed by the danger of unfair prejudice, confusion of the issues and misleading the jury.

Angrily, I wondered how time-consuming and confusing could it have been to determine that LaRaye Thomas—who had lost her job because of crippling arthritis and who had now, at the age of thirty-nine, already been qualified for Medicare—should not have been sued for $272.50 by Dr. Labowitz, who had been driving a Jaguar and a Cadillac.

To hell with the "intense investigation by the Department of Justice headed by a seasoned prosecutor." Labowitz's sworn testimony on Pg. 337 of his deposition was: "To my knowledge there was a period of time, a short period of time where office policy was that if a patient did not show, whether they're Medicaid, private or whatever, that they were billed for it. Now, I'm not sure whether Medicaid was billed for that. But I know that there was a time when my practice was very busy and I resented the fact that people did not have the courtesy to call me to cancel their appointments . . . ." And two of his ex-secretaries had signed sworn affidavits regarding Labowitz's office policy of billing medicaid for no-shows. One of them, Phyllis Morenco, swore in her affidavit that she had worked for Labowitz for approximately six years. She said, "I recall many instances of Medicaid abuse by Dr. Labowitz. . . . Dr. Labowitz would see approximately six Medicaid individuals per day. Approximately ten of the individuals scheduled per week would not appear for their appointments. For approximately half of these individuals, about five patients per week, Dr. Labowitz would bill Medicaid as if they <u>had</u> appeared for their appointments. This was improper and could be done because there was no form for the patient to sign verifying that services were actually rendered." The other ex-secretary, Mary Malloy, who was employed by Labowitz for twelve months, swore in her affidavit, "He often billed Medicaid for an office visit when a Medicaid patient failed to appear for an appointment."

It was now Saturday; the trial would be starting on Monday. Fortunately, our case revolved around multiple issues, not a single incident. The jury had plenty of facts from which to determine whether Labowitz had defamed me and interfered with my professional and business relations.

Saturday evening I met with Jim and C.J. at the law offices. They had met with Dad earlier in the day, as well as with two younger attorneys who were supplying Jim and C.J. with logistical support. We had carefully reviewed my direct-exam and anticipated Carpenter's cross-exam.

They reviewed the trial schedule with me. We had been assigned to courtroom 204, where I would be meeting Jim and C.J. on Monday morning, shortly before 10 a.m.

Well-wishing friends called Sieglinde and me; some of them would be attending the trial. We telephoned Mutti and Papa, Sieglinde's parents, in Aschaffenburg; they would be praying for us. Dad would be reviewing the daily transcripts and would be meeting with Jim and C.J. throughout the trial; he would not, however, be in the courtroom. Mary and Wilson, and my brother, Tom, would be at trial. Sieglinde also would attend the trial, but she did not want to be present while I was testifying.

Sunday night I slept well for four hours, but then I was wide awake. Today was trial day. At last the Court, capping four years of my work and the work of my attorneys, was ready to hear the complaints of unethical medical practice. I was proud of my accomplishments, apprehensive about what was to come, and optimistic about our possibilities; we had everything to gain and nothing to lose. With the help of my lawyers, I had gotten the case to trial. It was hard for me to imagine how discovery could have gone better. Our position, I felt, was supported by flagrant admissions and contradictions on the part of my opponents.

I shaved and showered, dressed in a dark suit, white shirt and red tie, had orange juice and a small bowl of cold cereal for breakfast, and kissed the children good-bye.

"Good luck, Ron," Sieglinde said as she gave me a hug. "I'll be praying for us. It'll be nice to soon have this behind us." I gave Sieglinde a kiss and was on my way.

It was a clear, warm and comfortable August morning. I drove to within a few blocks of the courthouse and parked my car in a drive-up garage. As I walked down the stairs, my briefcase in hand, another surge of nervous anticipation and apprehension swept through me. The future of me and my family was in the balance.

I intentionally walked slowly and deliberately up the sidewalk towards the courthouse. I reminded myself that I had already accomplished my primary goal: I had gotten to trial documented evidence of what I believed was serious medical fraud, including the refusal of the Board of Medical Practice even to consider complaints of unethical medical conduct. It was now up to the lawyers and the judge and the jury. I should be satisfied; I should not worry about what might happen at trial; it was out of my hands. I would do my best on the witness stand; I would concentrate and set my own pace, confident in my position and in my instincts.

I continued towards the courthouse, bombarded by a combination of fear and exhilaration. My anxiety was assuaged as I thought of my communion of saints: Francis of Assisi, Ignatius of Loyola, Francis de Sales, Teilhard de Chardin, John Paul II, Mother Teresa, Mother Mary Raphaelle, Mom, Mutti, Sieglinde, and more. I thought of Christ. Everything was in order!

"Ron, Carpenter and his witnesses are going to attack you throughout the trial," Jim said. "Don't get angry. If the jury sees you upset, we won't have a chance."

"I understand," I responded. Over the past four years I had become fully accustomed to legal procedure.

We walked up to the third floor and entered a cavernous chamber where within a few minutes our jury selection would take place. Jim, C.J. and I sat at a table to the left of the dais. At the table to our right sat Carpenter, Labowitz, and Parkins. Behind us were rows of perhaps fifty to a hundred prospective jurors who had been preselected.

"Judge Vincent Poppiti presiding!" announced the Clerk of the Court. Following Jim, C.J., and everyone else, I stood up. Judge Poppiti—wearing judicial black robes and tanned, reminded me of a 40-year-old Paul Newman. He strode to the dais and warmly greeted the two parties and the assembled prospective jurors.

As the jurors' names were drawn at random, each left his or her seat, walked forward to the jury box to the left of Judge Poppiti, and took a seat. Soon twelve jurors and four alternates had been selected. The judge announced that in a few minutes we would reconvene downstairs in courtroom 204 to start the trial.

Downstairs, a crowd of bipartisan supporters and interested observers milled in the hallway. Jim, C.J. and I picked our way through the crowd and entered the courtroom. To the left, spectators, including interested attorneys, were quickly filling up rows of benches. A waist-high wooden partition with a swinging gate gave us entry into the center of the courtroom. We had the counsel's table to the left, our opponents the one to the right. At the front of the courtroom was a large dais, upon which the judge would sit; to his right was the witness seat, behind which stood the American flag, and to its right was the door from which the jury would enter to take their seats in the jury box. Between the counsels' tables was a podium with a microphone, and between the podium and the judge's dais was the prothonotary's table, where a clerk would be recording the exhibits used at trial.

Jim told me to take the left seat at our table, so that I would be immediately next to the jury, separated by another waist-high wooden partition. C.J. was to my right, and Jim had the seat closest to the podium. At our opponents' table, Carpenter sat closest to the podium, then Labowitz, and then Parkins. A court reporter set up her tripod and chair in front of the witness stand. Jim and C.J. were getting their files organized at our table.

"Mr. Green!" I turned to see a smiling old man, with a stubbled beard, wearing an old sport jacket, lean over the wooden partition to hand Jim some cellophane-wrapped hard peppermint candy. "Who's that?" I asked.

"That's our court-watcher," C.J. replied. I learned that the old man's hobby was attending trials—studying witnesses, lawyers, judges, and juries, then predicting the winners and losers. "It beats sitting home and watching the 'soaps'," C.J. added.

A bailiff suddenly appeared behind the dais on the right and announced: "The Honorable Vincent J. Poppiti presiding!"

All those assembled in the crowded courtroom stood, and a moment later Judge Poppiti entered. Taking his seat, he made a few comments to the attorneys and then announced: "The jury, please." The bailiff opened the door for the jury, and in single file they entered and took their assigned seats in the jury box. I studied them; they represented a cross-section of American society—young and old, black, white, and Hispanic; professionals, retirees, clerks, and housewives—seven men and five women. In spite of their diversity, they shared a common pledge—none of them knew anything about Connolly vs. Labowitz. And they shared a common goal—to analyze the facts and then render a verdict. The victor would need a unanimous vote from the jury; a split vote, even eleven to one, would mean a mistrial. I looked from one juror's face to the next: the first, the jury foreman, was a fifty-year-old youth-counselor; another was a thirty-seven-year-old bespectacled chemical engineer from the DuPont Company; a thirty-two-year-old black secretary, an elderly widow, a young Hispanic secretary . . . I wondered which ones were the leaders.

Judge Poppiti, in his black robes, swiveled his chair towards the jury to address them.

"Ladies and gentlemen . . . before testimony is introduced in this case, I am going to give you some initial instructions, in order to assist you better to understand the evidence which is about to be presented to you. After I have finished, counsel for each side will have an opportunity to make an opening statement to you. Then you will begin hearing testimony from the witnesses. At the end of the case, after you have heard all of the testimony, I will instruct you on the law which is applicable to the facts of the case.

"You are the sole and exclusive judges of the facts of this case, of the credibility, that is, the believability of the witnesses and of the weight and value to be given to their testimony. It is your sworn duty to determine the facts and to determine them only from the evidence that will be presented to you during the course of this trial. Later, the attorneys will be permitted to comment on the evidence. However, you should understand that nothing the attorneys say is evidence. Although you should consider the arguments of counsel in evaluating the evidence you have heard, you must decide the facts of this case on the evidence alone.

"Now, this case involves two physicians, Dr. Ronald G. Connolly, plaintiff, and Dr. Russell J. Labowitz, defendant. Physicians often incorporate their practices, and those corporations are known as professional associations. Both Dr. Connolly and Dr. Labowitz practice through professional associations . . . .

"Dr. Connolly's professional association is a plaintiff in this action, and Dr. Labowitz's professional association has been named as a defendant. However, for simplicity, the lawyers, witnesses and the Court may directly refer to plaintiffs simply as Dr. Connolly and defendants as Dr. Labowitz.

"Now, plaintiffs charge that defendants have defamed and libeled them, wrongfully interfered with their professional and business relations and practice, unfairly competed with them and conspired with others to irreparably damage their practice and prevent legitimate competition in the practice of rheumatology in Delaware.

"Plaintiffs also contend that both before and throughout the course of this litigation, defendants and their accomplices have actively participated in a continuing scheme of misconduct, defamation and libel. Plaintiffs allege that all of the defendants' actions have been undertaken in bad faith and with malice and that they have virtually destroyed Dr. Connolly's reputation and practice.

"Defendants deny all charges of wrongdoing. In addition, they assert that any statements they have made about Dr. Connolly are true. They also contend that those statements were made to persons with a need to know, and are therefore privileged under the law.

"Finally, defendants contend that it is Dr. Connolly, himself, who has ruined his medical practice. Dr. Connolly must prove his case by a preponderance of the evidence. He must prove . . . that Dr. Labowitz committed wrongful acts and that those wrongful acts caused, that is, proximately caused him injury . . . .

"In light of certain issues raised in this case, I have determined that it may be helpful for you to hear the testimony from a medical expert who has examined Dr. Connolly. Ordinarily, expert witnesses are selected and retained by the parties themselves, but in this case, I wanted to ensure that the psychiatric expert who examined Dr. Connolly had no prior contact with the parties, their counsel or the witnesses in this case. Therefore, I selected a Baltimore psychiatrist, Dr. Jonas R. Rappeport, and arranged for him to examine Dr. Connolly.

"During the trial, I will call Dr. Rappeport as the Court's witness and both sides will be able to cross-examine him. Now, in this regard, you are instructed that the testimony of any expert is to be considered like any other testimony and is tried by the same tests and should receive just so much or as little weight and credit as you the jury may deem it entitled to, viewed in connection with all of the evidence in this case. The fact that I have appointed an expert witness does not in any way mean that the witness' testimony is entitled to any greater or lesser weight than any other witness' testimony.

"You are to understand that no favoritism or partisan meaning should be inferred from the witness' Court-appointed status. Furthermore, you must not view the fact of Court appointment as any expression of opinion by the Court.

"Remember, I have told you that you are the sole judges of the facts and of the credibility of the witnesses and of the weight and value to be given to their testimony . . . ."

And the Superior Court Judge, continuing to read from prepared notes, instructed the jury on another aspect of the trial. "This will likely be a long trial. There may be publicity concerning this case in the newspapers, radio, and perhaps other electronic media. It's important that you decide this case only on the basis of what you hear in this courtroom. Therefore, you should not listen to or read any media discussions of this case.

"Likewise, you should not discuss this case with anyone. You may not discuss the evidence of this case among yourselves until you have heard all of the evidence that is going to be presented to you during the course of this trial and I have instructed you on the law of the case at the conclusion of the trial.

"If anyone attempts to discuss this case with you, or if you hear or read any media discussions of this case, you must immediately advise the bailiff or me of that fact.

"Now, under our legal system, plaintiff, Dr. Connolly, will first present his case. Defendant, Dr. Labowitz, will then respond.

"I have already indicated to you that this will probably be a long trial and it's therefore important that I remind you to keep an open mind and withhold judgment until all of the evidence has been presented to you.

"I am confident that you will do your duty, your sworn duty, in this regard . . . ."

As Judge Poppiti concluded his address to the jury, he turned toward Jim. "Counsel, you may address the jury. Mr. Green."

The crowded courtroom was silent. Jim calmly arose, walked to the podium, arranged a few notes, and eloquently began his opening arguments.

"Thank you, your Honor. May it please the Court, ladies and gentlemen of the jury . . . . [Jim then explained defamation, unfair competition, interference with professional and business relations, and then continued.]

"Finally . . . we've alleged and we believe the evidence will show you that Dr. Labowitz engaged in a conspiracy . . . with one or more other individuals or entities, to accomplish an unlawful purpose; namely, the unfair competition and/or the interference with professional relations which I just described.

"We believe the evidence will show you at the conclusion of the case that each of the following persons . . . conspired or combined with Dr. Labowitz to cause the [harm] which we've discussed . . . .

"Those persons or entities are the Medical Center of Delaware, Dr. John Levinson, Dr. James Newman, Dr. Alfred Lazarus, Dr. Robert Flinn, and Dr. David Raskin . . . .

"During the course of my opening and during the course of the next several weeks, I'm going to ask you to accept and consider certain propositions in this case which you may never have thought about, and you may not want to necessarily accept.

"The first concept which I'm going to ask you to accept is that the practice of medicine is a business, and indeed it is a very big business. But it is a business.

"Second, while most physicians are highly competent, extremely dedicated, overworked, caring men and women . . . as in many walks of life, there are good and bad people. And given the number of physicians who practice medicine in one specialty . . . or another, I suggest that it is not at all unreasonable to conclude that some of those physicians may not be completely ethical and that some may have more of an interest in financial matters and money than in other matters pertinent to health care and patient care.

"One theme that I think the evidence will show . . . and we submit is instrumental in the damage and destruction to Dr. Connolly's practice . . . relates to the control or administration, if you will, of the practice of medicine.

"When Dr. Connolly joined the Medical Center of Delaware, which was then called the Wilmington Medical Center, in 1979, he was handed—and I have the exact documents right here [Jim held them up for the jury to see] . . . some detailed, explicitly detailed books which are specifically the Rules and Regulations of the Medical-Dental Staff of the Wilmington Medical Center, covering more than forty pages, [and] the By-Laws of the Medical-Dental Staff of the Wilmington Medical Center, which cover thirty-eight pages and have an appendix at the end which are the Principles of Medical Ethics of the American Medical Association and the Wilmington Medical Center . . . [and] Bylaws of the Department of Medicine, which are seventeen pages long.

"These are the rules, as I mentioned, that were given to Dr. Connolly when he was admitted to the staff of the Medical Center. They include an outline of appointment and promotion procedure, as I mentioned, the code of medical ethics which all doctors are to follow, staff responsibilities, et cetera, et cetera.

"The evidence, I believe, will show you that these rules and codes and regulations are largely ignored in the day-to-day operations of the Medical Center, and the practice of medicine in general. There are certain unwritten rules, however, which are used to govern what a physician is supposed to do and how he gets promoted and has his reputation enhanced. They are unwritten rules. It's hard to find them and even harder to define them, but if you will permit me, I will take a stab at writing what these two rules are."

[Jim took a few steps to a large blackboard which faced the jury in the middle of the room and, as he movingly addressed the jury, he wrote the two rules.]

"The first is pay your dues. And the second is—maybe this is the first time these were even written, ladies and gentlemen—don't make waves.

"If you violate those two rules, you are an outcast in the medical profession, a pariah, if you will; [Tears suddenly welled up in my eyes; months had often passed without one doctor speaking to me; most of my patients had left me; and my practice was bankrupt—I looked straight ahead, not wanting to be noticed by the jurors on my left or by Poppiti on my right]; and in the case of Dr. Connolly, his violation of those unwritten rules led to charges by defendants that he was mentally ill and ultimately led to the termination of his privileges at the Medical Center of Delaware.

"Ironically, Dr. Connolly to this day is a member of the staff of the Medical Department at St. Francis Hospital in Wilmington, at Riverside Hospital in Wilmington, at Nanticoke Hospital in Seaford, and at Milford Hospital in Milford. But his privileges have been terminated at the Medical Center of Delaware, and we submit that they were terminated because he violated [these] two unwritten rules.

"Finally, ladies and gentlemen, because Dr. Connolly, 'bucked the system,' if you will, and made charges against another physician, not surprisingly, a court of physicians have not run to his side to aid us in this case. Many of the witnesses that we call will be . . . adverse or hostile witnesses, including each of the co-conspirators which I named at the outset. Therefore, much of our case will be unusual in that we will in part be attempting to prove our case to your satisfaction out of our opponents' mouths . . . .

"Prior to coming to Delaware to set up his office, Dr. Connolly talked with Dr. Labowitz over the telephone and by correspondence to determine that indeed there was a need for additional rheumatological services in Delaware, and, at that time, Dr. Connolly will testify that Dr. Labowitz asked him to join . . . his office. Dr. Connolly preferred to open his own office and told Dr. Labowitz that, and indeed . . . in January of 1979 did open his office . . . .

"We suggest, ladies and gentlemen, that Dr. Labowitz wanted Dr. Connolly to join his office when he returned to Wilmington to prevent Dr. Connolly from becoming a competitor, a competitor in the practice of rheumatology, competing for the patients, and, as I indicated, the practice of medicine is a business.

"We suggest that Dr. Labowitz is one of those physicians who practiced medicine as a business and his business did very well, and we suggest he did not want to see someone coming into town and making inroads into that business.

"We suggest, further, that he especially did not want to see someone such as Dr. Connolly come into town to try to make inroads into that business because Dr. Connolly was better qualified. Dr. Connolly was board-certified in rheumatology, whereas Dr. Labowitz was not board-certified in rheumatology. He'd not passed his boards to become a certified specialist in rheumatology; indeed, Dr. Labowitz had twice failed the examination for certification in rheumatology.

"You are going to hear testimony that he took every pain to keep that fact from people. His partner didn't know that.

"In fact, ladies and gentlemen, you will hear testimony that Dr. Labowitz testified in a deposition . . . in a case in this court that he was board-certified.

"We submit that Dr. Labowitz's greed and his unrelenting desire to maintain his corner on the market for rheumatological services in Delaware caused him to do everything in his power to undermine and destroy Dr. Connolly as a source of competition.

"As the senior member and the section chief of rheumatology both at the Medical Center and at St. Francis Hospital, Dr. Labowitz had a unique opportunity to do so, and he had a unique opportunity to enlist others or to influence others to assist him.

"Dr. Labowitz criticized continuously . . . Dr. Connolly's performance at the Medical Center to his superiors. He told people that Dr. Connolly had abandoned a patient. He referred a patient to Dr. Connolly with a different diagnosis than [she] really had, we submit, for the purpose of jeopardizing an important study that Dr. Connolly was undertaking.

"He accused Dr. Connolly of being psychiatrically ill. He publicly criticized Dr. Connolly on an article which Dr. Connolly published, although before that he'd reviewed the article and never said one word to Dr. Connolly about any criticisms that he might harbor.

"Ladies and gentleman, even though he was Dr. Connolly's boss, in effect, his section chief, he never once, to this day, has come to Dr. Connolly or did go to Dr. Connolly and say, 'You ought to do this differently.' . . . . He criticized him behind his back, but he never once came to his face and said, 'Here's my criticism . . . .'

"Of course, he preferred to do it behind his back because that way it would help him and not help Dr. Connolly.

"Dr. Connolly, when he opened his office, did most of the things, maybe even more of the things that new doctors and new professionals do when they open an office. He did everything that he thought possible and manageable to build up his practice to get his name around town.

". . . In short, ladies and gentlemen, he played by the rules, he'd paid his dues and he didn't make waves. Despite his efforts of corresponding with doctors, of doing volunteer work at the hospital, and doing research and studies and publishing articles, his practice didn't grow the way that he would have expected it to grow, given the enormous need for rheumatologists in Wilmington.

"Nevertheless, the practice did grow in those first . . . years, to the point where it had made inroads on Dr. Labowitz's practice. For the first time Dr. Labowitz's income dipped and this provided whatever further incentive, we suggest, that Dr. Labowitz needed to continue his practice of dirty tricks and unfair competition, which eventually led to the almost utter destruction of Dr. Connolly's reputation and practice.

"We suggest that after Dr. Connolly opened his office, Dr. Labowitz took every possible opportunity to undermine that practice and to undermine Dr. Connolly's reputation in his research, his publication, his professional associations, Medical Center activities, patient relations. As a result, Dr. Connolly's practice, as I indicated, which is very dependent on referrals from other physicians, since most people first go to a family physician, and if they are in need of rheumatologists, the family physician will refer the patient. Because of that need for referrals and the damage to his reputation, those doctors stopped or certainly slowed significantly in their referrals to Dr. Connolly . . . ."

[Jim then focused and explained the various individual issues.]

As he concluded his opening remarks, he cautioned the jury that no matter what they decided after listening to Drs. Rappeport and Olsson, "it cannot and it does not excuse or defend or in any way limit the evidence on unfair competition, on interference with professional relations and on defamation, which we believe the evidence will show you has been perpetrated since Dr. Connolly set foot in town by Dr. Labowitz and those co-conspirators . . . .

"I appreciate your attention and I know that you will give Mr. Carpenter . . . that same attention and that when you retire at the end of this case, you will do your best to do whatever is fair and impartial to the parties to this case.

"Thank you."

The Court: Thank you, Mr. Green.

A few minutes later, Judge Poppiti announced the lunch recess. The Court was to reconvene at 2:10, when Mr. Carpenter would present the defendants' opening remarks.

As we walked the three blocks back to Connolly, Bove, Lodge and Hutz, C.J. and I congratulated Jim. His opening argument had been masterful: a moving account of the issues, delivered to the jury in a polished yet personable manner. As we came to 1220 Market Street, the building that my father had proudly constructed a few years earlier, we took the elevator to Jim's ninth-floor office overlooking Wilmington and the Delaware River. "How did things go?" Dad said as he walked into the office. He was pleased with our account of the morning session. Other lawyers and secretaries stopped by and wished us luck for the afternoon session.

A secretary brought Jim and C.J. sandwiches. Sieglinde had made me a brown-bag lunch—four peanut-butter crackers and a small apple. I wasn't hungry; my stomach felt tight, my mouth dry: I would start my testimony during the afternoon session.

For the first time in four years I would finally have the opportunity to tell my story. I was eager, yet nervous.

Before I took the witness stand, however, our opponents would be firing their opening salvo at us—more specifically, at me. Edmund Carpenter would be delivering his opening remarks to the jury. The nationally-renowned sixty-six-year-old attorney—the son of a late Chairman of the Board of the DuPont Company, a senior partner at Richards, Layton and Finger—was a formidable opponent.

The tactics of Jane Roth, Carpenter's predecessor, flashed through my mind. Roth had said she was "perfectly entitled to annoy, embarrass, and oppress" me. She had told the Court that I was a "manifest nut." She had repeatedly given the court *her* medical opinion that I was mentally ill, on the basis of a conversation with me when I was looking for an attorney. Then, after publicly accusing me of being mentally ill, she had claimed immunity for Reese when he was interrogated on the facts, if any, for his affidavit.

And yet Carpenter, in my opinion, had been just as unconscionable as Roth.

A short time later, as Jim, C.J., and I walked back to the courthouse, my anxiety was mixed with self-satisfaction. I had nothing to lose and everything to gain; all I had to do was concentrate on my facts. The morning session had gone well; we were right on target.

The courtroom, filled to capacity, hummed with activity. The court-watcher, with his stubbled beard, sitting in the first bench on the right, smiled and offered more hard candy to the lawyers, to the prothonotary clerk, Vince, and to Labowitz and me. I talked to the court-watcher; he showed me the tattered pencil-written notebook in which he had logged past trials. Today he had started a new page.

"The Honorable Vincent J. Poppiti presiding!" the bailiff announced. Judge Poppiti, pulling at the collar of his judicial black robes, strode to his seat, turned to the bailiff, and announced, "Jury, please." The bailiff, standing beside the American flag, opened the door, and the jury filed into the courtroom, taking their seats in the jury box.

Turning towards the defense counsel, Judge Poppiti announced, "Mr. Carpenter, you may make your opening statement to the jury, please."

Edmund Carpenter—wavy silver hair smoothed neatly back, wearing a dark blue pin-striped suit with a white handkerchief in his breast pocket—solemnly moved to the podium. The courtroom was silent as the defense counsel began his address.

"With deference to your Honor, ladies and gentlemen of the jury, my name is Ned Carpenter . . . . Before I start to say anything about the case itself, let me re-emphasize certain principles of procedure which Mr. Green has touched upon, but as to which I totally agree with him.

"As you have already observed, it's our privilege as attorneys in this case to come before you at the beginning of the case and tell you what we expect the testimony will show. Our remarks at this time are not intended to be argument.

"At the conclusion of the case we'll again be privileged to come before you and then argue what our positions are in the case . . . .

"What about this case? I suppose all of us have a tendency from time to time to blame or to try to blame our mistakes, our defenses, our failures on others. This is the sad case of a person who had that tendency to a pathological, a sick extreme.

"Dr. Connolly, the testimony will show, is not a very successful doctor, although he had every advantage. As was mentioned, he went to private schools, an advantage my client did not have; as was mentioned, he's board-certified, an advantage my client does not have.

"These things alone were not enough to make him a successful doctor. While he is the son of a very successful lawyer and a brother of another very successful lawyer, success has eluded him and he tends to be bothered perhaps more than the average person by that fact.

"And, most of all, he tends to blame every failure on other people. Contrary to popular views, all doctors are not successful. Further, Dr. Connolly, I assume, from what Mr. Green has told you, is going to rely very heavily on the fact that he is board certified, as though that were a guarantee of success, and he's going to try to make a big point of the fact that Dr. Labowitz, a practicing doctor, is not board certified, and try to make a big point of the fact that Dr. Labowitz, who in fact is board certified in internal medicine, got mixed up on a deposition between his board certification in internal medicine, and his claim, alleged by Mr. Green as to a certification in rheumatology, and misstated what his credentials were, though he had in mind his board certification in internal medicine.

"But that board certification is not a guarantee of success. Doctors fail for many reasons. Some of them fail because they simply do not want or are not willing to perform their minimum obligations to their patients, to their hospitals, or to their own training and you will hear about that in this case . . . .

"Some of them fail because they simply don't have the personality or may even have a more deep-seated deficiency.

"This is a story of a doctor whose practice appears to be failing, Dr. Connolly, and he has a delusion that people all around him are out to get him, and that that is the reason he's failing.

"Further, the testimony will show that this has always been Dr. Connolly's way of dealing with problems in life that other people deal with in a much more normal fashion.

"He has always blamed others and Dr. Labowitz is not the first, nor the last, to be blamed. In fact, many of the instances that Mr. Green has referred to were originally blamed on other people. In some cases, Dr. Connolly even filed written charges against others.

"For example, the testimony will show . . . that in fact Dr. Connolly was charged back in 1979 with abandoning a seriously ill patient who needed his care and guidance. Dr. Connolly originally blamed this on a Dr. Levinson . . . .

"You probably won't be surprised, based on what I've told you so far, that the testimony will also show that Dr. Connolly filed charges against Dr. Labowitz's previous attorney, Jane Roth, who later had to withdraw from the case because she's become a United States District Court judge, a federal judge, and he brought charges before the Delaware Board on Professional Responsibility, a board made up of distinguished attorneys who weigh charges of this kind and reach a conclusion. Those charges were dismissed, and what did Dr. Connolly do then? Well, you can imagine from what I told you so far what he did then. He filed charges against the Delaware Board on Professional Responsibility . . . and the Disciplinary Counsel and the Assistant Disciplinary Counsel and petitioned the Supreme Court of Delaware. He tried to denounce them there. The Supreme Court found that effort entirely without merit and they dismissed it.

"You will be interested to know, Mr. Green has hinted on this, and you will be interested to know that while these few days or weeks we are going to be talking about Dr. Labowitz, that Dr. Connolly has named in this case many others who he says are conspiring against him. There are, in his view, conspirators under every bush, behind every tree. He has named Dr. Robert Flinn, the distinguished head of the Department of Medicine at the Delaware Medical Center, the largest department. He's a conspirator, he says. . . ." [As Carpenter spoke, tears welled up in his eyes; unabated he continued, tears and all, to look straight at the jurors, citing named conspirators.]

"He's named Dr. James Newman, Dr. David Raskin, Dr. Lester Bronheim, in addition to Dr. Lazarus, Dr. Levinson and Dr. Labowitz, and there are others which Mr. Green hasn't mentioned who have also been named. [Carpenter named members of the Department of Medicine Credentials Committee.] . . . . I won't recite more, but you can see that Dr. Connolly is blaming everybody for conspiring against him, distinguished physicians, leaders in this community.

"I could go on, but I think I've suggested enough of the theme of this case, so you will understand the specific charges to which Mr. Green has referred. But let me stress one more point before I turn to those specific charges, and this is an important point.

"The testimony will show that the real victim in this case, the man who has been persecuted by irresponsible and wild charges, the man who has been dragged through vilification, through all kinds of name-calling, the man who has suffered is not Dr. Connolly, but Dr. Labowitz." [Carpenter's eyes again filled with tears; his lips quivered as he eloquently addressed the jury.] "He's the one who is being dragged in by this man and his attorneys [Carpenter, his left arm outstretched, jabbed his finger at me], who are making these wild claims."

[Carpenter then explained to the jury the defendants' position on the various issues.]

He continued:

"Now, Mr. Green has told you that Dr. Connolly is also going to complain about alleged remarks by Dr. Labowitz about his, Dr. Connolly's, mental condition. The evidence will show, however, that Dr. Labowitz did not make any practice of circulating rumors; Dr. Labowitz spoke only to those who shared his concern, other doctors who needed to know that there was a problem here that had to be addressed or had to be considered in connection with their duties.

"You, as jurors, will recognize the need for doctors to communicate among themselves about the situation with respect to other members of their profession, so as to protect you and me when we are patients and so that a doctor who has a disability will not make mistakes with us or abandon us.

"Thus, you will understand why Dr. Labowitz had to communicate concerning potential problems and actual problems, which Dr. Connolly was involved in, since Dr. Connolly was in the section headed by Dr. Labowitz and was Dr. Labowitz's responsibility. Such communications, I repeat, protect you and me as patients and all of us in this courtroom.

"The testimony will show, furthermore, that others in the hospital had a concern about Dr. Connolly's mental health, a real concern. The Credentials Committee, composed of distinguished doctors who had been selected because of their positions and because of their abilities, found . . . that Dr. Connolly needed psychiatric evaluation. There may be some argument that they weren't all psychiatrists; in fact, [Dr.] Lee Reese, the head of the Credentials Committee, was, I believe, board certified in both psychiatry and neurology, but that's not an important point because, as the doctors will tell you, doctors are trained, and I guess to a certain extent all of us, but particularly doctors are trained to identify psychiatric problems which need a reference to an expert in their ordinary practice.

"The Credentials Committee, as I say, reached this conclusion. Dr. Robert Flinn, after talking with Dr. Connolly and after receiving a rather bizarre letter from Dr. Connolly, concluded that there was a problem here and consulted with the head of the Psychiatry Department about it. The head of the Psychiatry Department felt the problem was so obvious, he concluded that it did exist even though he was not able to examine and evaluate Dr. Connolly.

"The Delaware Medical Center later took the position that Dr. Connolly could not continue to practice there unless he obtained a satisfactory psychiatric evaluation, which he did not do.

"There were other psychiatrists also involved. Dr. Connolly, they felt, was so disturbed that his condition was apparent even before a detailed examination.

"Further, as your Honor, Judge Poppiti has told you, an independent psychiatrist with a national reputation, selected by the Court, without any input either from Mr. Green or me or any of the attorneys for the plaintiff or any of the attorneys for the defendant or any of the parties, a forensic psychiatrist, who has no connection with any of the parties, did make an evaluation of Dr. Connolly, and as Mr. Green very candidly had to concede to you, found that he had a paranoid personality disorder and a compulsive personality disorder. He does indeed have mental problems. . . .

"In short, as this case unfolds, you're going to find that Dr. Connolly felt he was persecuted by this person and that person and the other person. He looks about for somebody to blame his deficiencies on. He sought conspirators everywhere, as I said, behind every tree, under every bush, all threatening him, and so he singled out one doctor, whom he competes with, Dr. Labowitz, and he's tried to make him the scapegoat, the person on whom he heaps all of his problems. . . .

"I say again that the testimony will show that the real item in this case is not Dr. Connolly; it's Dr. Labowitz, who has had to endure all of this vilification, all of this denunciation, time and time again, and now once more before you.

"At the conclusion of this case I will come before you again and urge that based on the testimony you have heard and the documents you have read, you return a verdict in favor of the defendant, Dr. Labowitz, and against the plaintiff, Dr. Connolly.

"Thank you."

As Carpenter left the podium, Jim stood and requested that the four attorneys have a sidebar conference with the judge, out of hearing of the rest of the Court. A few minutes later, the attorneys having returned to their seats, the judge announced: "Mr. Green, you may call your first witness, please."

"Thank you, Your Honor. I would call Dr. Ronald Connolly to the stand."

13
Some Testimony

As political philosophy derives its sanction from ethics, and ethics from the truth of religion, it is only by returning to the eternal source of truth that we can hope for any social organization which will not, to its ultimate destruction, ignore some essential aspect of reality. The term 'democracy,' as I have said again and again, does not contain enough positive content to stand alone against the forces you dislike—it can be easily transformed by them. If you will not have God (and He is a jealous God), you should pay your respects to Hitler and Stalin.

T. S. Eliot

As I pushed my chair back to take the witness stand, my apprehension was mild compared to my sense of opportunity at finally being able to tell my story. With head high, I walked past the jury, stepped up to the dais, and remained standing as the bailiff came forward to administer the oath. In a voice easily heard in the last row of the courtroom, I responded, "I do." Then, as I took my seat, Jim began the direct-examination.

Jim oriented the jury by interrogating me on my personal background, education, training, and experience. As we continued, I looked at the jury and calmly explained my story.

I explained that upon my return to Wilmington to open my practice Dr. Labowitz had repeatedly urged me to consider joining his practice, and he was disappointed when I opened my own office. I described carefully to the jury my efforts in establishing my office. I also explained that although the Medical Center is a large hospital, its rheumatology section had only three full-time rheumatologists (Dr. Labowitz, his associate Dr. Newman, and me) plus one part-time rheumatologist. I explained that for a subspecialist such as a rheumatologist, referrals from other physicians and a good reputation in the medical community were essential.

Soon, the hours of the afternoon having sped by, Judge Poppiti, in his distinguished black robes, announced the evening recess. "Ladies and gentlemen . . . as I indicated to you, [we'll] begin taking testimony again tomorrow morning at 10:00 o'clock. Between now and then you are instructed that you may not discuss the case with anyone. You may not read anything about the case in the printed media, view or listen to anything about the case in the electronic media. If any information regarding this case comes to your attention over the course of the evening recess, you must bring that to my attention when we reconvene tomorrow morning. Once again, you may not discuss the case among yourselves until you have heard all of the evidence that's going to be presented to you during the course of this trial, and I have had an opportunity to instruct you on the law of the case."

By the time I returned to the witness stand the next morning, I was fully familiar with the routine whereby Jim would hand me a document to identify as he handed a copy of the same document to the defendant's attorney and another copy to the prothonotary clerk—Vince, a young man wearing a dark sports jacket and dark slacks, who carefully filed the exhibits.

Jim interrogated me about the abortion incident. I calmly explained to the jury, that Dr. Levinson had accused me of patient abandonment after I had elected not to participate in the abortion because of my religious convictions. I told the jury that Dr. Levinson had said that the consultation in no way requested my "opinion as to the advisability of abortion but only that [I] would observe and treat as need be [the patient's] scleroderma." I then identified, the hospital consult Dr. Levinson had written to me, in which he had noted that the patient was hospitalized for an abortion and had then asked me: "Any contraindication to intrauterine saline for abortion?"

My attorney asked me what that meant.

Connolly: In second-trimester abortions, abortions done between three and six months, commonly these are done by sticking a needle into the uterus through the abdominal wall and instil-

	ling 120 cc's of concentrated salt solution, which is an irritant to the pregnancy and induces labor and expels the pregnancy. So intrauterine saline is a method of abortion. In the first trimester, often suction curettage will be done.
Green:	So, Dr. Connolly, is Dr. Levinson asking you to give an opinion as to how to do the abortion?
Connolly:	Yes.

My testimony continued; more exhibits were filed with the prothonotary clerk, followed in each case by a careful explanation to the jury, as we proceeded through the various issues of the lawsuit. Occasionally the proceedings were interrupted for a "sidebar" conference, out of hearing of the jury and the rest of the courtroom, while the attorneys and the judge briefly discussed procedures.

I told the jury about the $5,000 grant I had received to study fibrositis, Dr. Labowitz's review of my fibrositic manuscript for the *Delaware Medical Journal,* and his inquiry whether all of my study patients had normal sedimentation rates, followed a few weeks later by his referral of Madeline Boone as a fibrositic patient, and how only later I had learned that Mrs. Boone's last three sedimentation rates while under Dr. Labowitz's care had all been abnormal. I told the jury that Mrs. Boone now had a confirmed diagnosis of lupus.

I carefully explained to the jury that my publication in the Medical Journal had met with approval everywhere—including requests for reprints from foreign countries—with the exception of Dr. Labowitz, my section chief, and his associate, Dr. Newman. They had criticized my use of a particular medication, even though Dr. Labowitz had referred his own patient to me so that I could use this medication.

Jim continued my direct-exam. More testimony. More exhibits. More sidebar conferences. And more testimony.

I told the jury that I had applied for membership to the American College of Physicians on May 6, 1982, when I had submitted my application to the college's governor for Delaware, Dr. Alfred Lazarus. I explained that on May 28, 1982, Dr. Lazarus wrote to the American College of Physicians endorsing my proposal for membership "without hesitation." But then, on September 1, he withdrew his endorsement as a result of communications from Dr. Labowitz. Dr. Lazarus then waited until the day of Christmas Eve to notify me that he was deferring my ACP application.

I explained to the jury that I had tolerated these actions for four years, but with the arrival of the Christmas Eve letter it had become clear to me that I had no alternative but to confront my opponents. I continued, telling them that I had then presented my complaints to the President of the Medical Center, who referred me to the Vice-President for Medical Affairs, who referred me to the Chairman of the Department of Medicine, Dr. Robert Flinn. With deliberation, I told the jury that as I sat in Dr. Flinn's office I quoted from Section 4 of the American Medical Association Code of Ethics, as adopted by the Medical/Dental Staff of the Medical Center, which said that physicians have a duty to "expose without hesitation illegal or unethical conduct of fellow members of the profession." As I finished reading, I looked at the members of the jury and told them that Dr. Flinn's response to me was that the Medical Code of Ethics was "meaningless!"

I carefully explained to the jury, that in hopes of finally getting the Medical Center to respond to at least *one* of my complaints, I had then singled out Dr. Labowitz's referral of Madeline Boone and presented this to the Credentials Committee of the Department of Medicine; failing there, I had presented all of my complaints to the state Board of Medical Practice.

The jury listened with rapt attention.

Green:	What's the Delaware Board of Medical Practice? . . . .
Connolly:	The Delaware Board of Medical Practice is set up by the legislators in Dover to supervise and monitor and ensure the health and welfare of every citizen in the state of Delaware. . . .

Green: And you did file a complaint with the State Board of Medical Practice?

Connolly: Yes, I filed a formal complaint before them.

Green: Dr. Connolly, I'm handing you what has previously been admitted as Plaintiffs' Exhibit 9-B and ask you to identify that document.

Connolly: This is a letter from the State Board of Medical Practice, dated May 4th, 1983, addressed to me, Dr. Connolly, from Vincent G. Lobo, Jr., the president of the Delaware Board of Medical Practice.

Green: Would you read the letter, please?

Connolly: Dear Dr. Connolly: The Delaware Board of Medical Practice wishes to inform you that after considerable review of your complaint, dated March 15, 1983, against Dr. Russell Labowitz and Dr. Alfred Lazarus, that your complaint does not come under the jurisdiction of the Board. Sincerely, Vincent G. Lobo, President, Delaware Board of Medical Practice.

Green: You indicated it was your understanding that matters such as this were delegated to the State Board of Medical Practice; is that right?

Connolly: Absolutely.

Green: When you received that letter, what did you determine to do?

Connolly: At that point I had exhausted five different levels of medical and administrative review. This was the top governing and supervisory board in the State of Delaware, and my practice was being destroyed. . . .I realized at this point that the problem did not just

	involve Dr. Connolly and Dr. Labowitz, but it also involved the public. It also involved the people of Delaware.
Green:	And what did you do?
Connolly:	I had two alternatives. One was to take my family and leave the state and try to start a practice elsewhere. The other alternative was to take my complaints before a different tribunal in hopes that they would address and resolve my complaints, so I chose to do that.
Green:	And what tribunal was that?
Connolly:	I filed a complaint in Superior Court of Delaware. I filed a lawsuit.
Green:	When did you do that?
Connolly:	August 1, 1983.

I then explained the various instances of flagrant misconduct by Jane Roth and my formal complaints against her.

This was followed by Jim interrogating me on the Medical Center's demand that I submit to a psychiatric exam or lose my hospital privileges.

Jim then concluded my interrogation by asking about those patients of mine who had been admitted to the Medical Center of Delaware and wanted me to see them. I responded that I had to tell them that I no longer had hospital privileges; they would have to be seen by another doctor.

Green:	And who most likely . . . would that be?
Connolly:	It's Dr. Newman and Dr. Labowitz.

My attorney turned to the Judge: "I have no further questions. Thank you, Dr. Connolly."

"Counsel, approach the bench, please," Judge Poppiti said.

A sidebar conference was held, and then the Judge turned to me: "The witness may step from the witness box, please."

As I walked back to my counsel's table, I was pleased. I felt that Jim and I had hit homeruns. We had coordinated the presentation and had carefully explained each of the complaints to the jury.

As Judge Poppiti began to dismiss the jury, he again instructed them: "[You] may not discuss the case with anyone, you may not read anything about the case in the printed media, view or listen to anything about the case in the electronic media."

The next morning I was back on the witness stand, this time for cross-examination. As Carpenter attacked me on the various issues, calmly I explained again the facts to the jury. Hour after hour my cross-examination continued, and by the end of the day, as the jury was being dismissed, again I felt pleased.

A few minutes later, Judge Poppiti recessed the Court. "You did great," Jim commented.

"Carpenter isn't scoring," C.J. added.

For two and a half days Carpenter attacked my credibility, my competence, my performance, and my ethics. I calmly responded to his questions as I repeated the basic facts for the jury.

After Carpenter completed his cross-examination, Jim had a brief re-direct exam in which I concluded by telling the jury that if Dr. Labowitz, my section chief, was truly concerned about patient care and my professional performance, he would have presented his criticisms to me. Yet over more than eight and a half years, I had never been permitted to see the criticisms. I had not even known that they existed until after the lawsuit had been filed!

The next day an attorney-friend, who had been a spectator at the trial, wrote a note to me: "You have been an outstanding witness—clear, articulate, thoughtful, honest, and compassionate. Defendant's counsel, in my opinion, has made no inroads. . . . There are few witnesses that could be so successful in using cross-examination as an effective re-enactment of direct-examination."

My testimony was done. It was now time for my opponents, prestigious doctors in the community, to take the witness stand.

It was their turn to explain their actions publicly to my attorneys, to the Judge, and to the jury.

C.J. walked to the podium: "Your Honor, the plaintiffs call Dr. Alfred Lazarus."

The ex-governor of the American College of Physicians for Delaware, currently section chief of gastroenterology at the Medical Center of Delaware, demurely walked to the witness stand, placed his right hand on the Bible, was sworn in, and took his seat. After a few introductory questions, C.J. asked whether there was any business relationship between the witness and Dr. Labowitz.

Seitz:	Have you referred patients to Dr. Labowitz?
Lazarus:	Yes.
Seitz:	And has he referred patients to you?
Lazarus:	Yes.

[Lazarus, after reviewing Labowitz's evaluations of me, had concluded that I was the worst physician at the medical center. He was asked to read to the jury his letter to the ACP, whereby he withdrew his recommendation for my membership because he had "subsequently learned that [Dr. Connolly] has failed to meet his obligations for teaching at the Medical Center and his Chief of Section has found him deficient in this area." C.J. then continued:]

Seitz:	What were the teaching requirements that Dr. Connolly failed to meet?
Lazarus:	I do not recall the exact details. . . .

Interrogated further on the subject, Lazarus again responded, "I do not at this time recall any details."

Later, Carpenter cross-examined the witness.

Carpenter:	Let me start by asking you if you know that you have been named by Dr. Connolly as one of the conspirators in this case. Did you know that?

Lazarus:	Yes, I did.
Carpenter:	Have you conspired with Dr. Labowitz to harm Dr. Connolly?
Lazarus:	I did not conspire with Dr. Labowitz.
Carpenter:	Did you conspire with Dr. Levinson to harm Dr. Connolly?
Lazarus:	I did not conspire with Dr. Levinson.
Carpenter:	Did you conspire with anybody to hire—to harm Dr. Connolly?
Lazarus:	I did not conspire with anyone to harm Dr. Connolly.
Carpenter:	Do you know of any conspiracy to harm Dr. Connolly apart what—apart from what may exist in Dr. Connolly's mind?
Lazarus:	I know of no such conspiracy.

Day after day the fight continued. Every morning, at about 10:00 a.m., the bailiff would announce the arrival of Judge Poppiti, everyone would stand, a few housekeeping matters would be discussed between the judge and the attorneys, the jury would be ushered into the jury box, and the testimony would resume. Direct-exam. Cross-exam. Re-direct. Re-cross. More exhibits for the prothonotary clerk. More sidebar conferences.

Morning sessions went from 10:00 a.m. to 1:00 p.m., followed by a one-hour lunch recess, with the afternoon sessions continuing from 2:00 p.m. to 5:00 p.m. During lunch break Jim, C.J., and I went back to the office, where we reviewed the morning testimony and discussed the upcoming afternoon session.

And at the end of each day Judge Poppiti concluded by warning the members of the jury not to discuss the evidence with anyone, not to read anything in the printed media or view or listen to anything about the case in the electronic media.

Each day, throughout the proceedings, spectators came and went—acquaintances, supporters of both sides, family, friends, strangers, and the old stubble-bearded court-watcher, with a smile and an offer of peppermint candy.

Sieglinde, Florence, Mary and Wilson, and Tom often were present. I also came to recognize Dr. Labowitz's wife, his parents, a handsome, elderly couple, and a reporter from Gannett's *News-Journal*, Tom Greer, who followed the trial for the public.

The morning after Lazarus's testimony, a central figure in the litigation—comparable, in my mind, to Labowitz, Roth, Carpenter, and Rappeport—was called to the witness stand.

I believed that there were numerous persons, committees, and institutions, who, by performing their minimal professional duty, could have prevented this conflict from escalating. I felt that the next witness epitomized the calculated refusal of those in authority to do their duty. He felt that I was mentally ill.

The packed courtroom was silent. "Mr. Green," Judge Poppiti announced, "would you call your next witness, please."

"If it please the Court," Jim responded, "we would like to call Robert Flinn."

From the spectator section, the distinguished-appearing doctor walked past the swinging gate and up to the witness stand.

"Doctor," Judge Poppiti said, "would you remain standing at the witness stand, please, and place your right hand on the Bible." Dr. Flinn swore to tell the truth, the whole truth, and nothing but the truth, and then took his seat. After responding to a few introductory questions, the Chairman of the Department of Medicine at the Medical Center of Delaware acknowledged that I had presented to him my complaints against Dr. Labowitz and Dr. Lazarus.

Green: During the course of that meeting, did you tell him that—and I'm quoting—"the Code of Ethics was meaningless"?

Flinn: No.

Green: You thought for a moment. Are you sure?

Flinn: Yes.

Green: Dr. Connolly presented several issues to you for his complaint, did he not?

Flinn: Yes.

Green: And would it be fair to say that you assured him that you would investigate those issues or those complaints?

Flinn: As I recall, we discussed them in great depth. I was trying to understand them. Some I disagreed with, some I couldn't understand. But as I recall, the complaints at that time were for conduct that did not take place in the Medical Center. . . .

Green: Did you tell [Dr. Connolly] that you would look into the matters that you thought did involve the Medical Center? . . . or were there none that involved the Medical Center?

Flinn: There really, as I recall, were none that I thought really involved the Medical Center per se from his original complaints . . . .

Green: Did he raise to you in that meeting a matter involving his application for membership in the American College of Physicians?

Flinn: . . . I think he did bring that up.

Green: And that involved Dr. Alfred Lazarus, did it not?

Flinn: Yes.

Green: Did you talk to Dr. Lazarus?

Flinn: The American College of Physicians has nothing to do with the Medical Center. So I did not pursue something that was not in my domain.

Green: Dr. Lazarus is a member of the Department of Medicine, isn't he?

Flinn: Yes.

Green: And a member of the Credentials Committee, at the time, of the Department of Medicine?

Flinn: He was, yes. . . .

A few minutes later the witness acknowledged that he did investigate some of my complaints, and my attorney continued.

Green: As part of your investigation, you talked to Dr. Labowitz, didn't you?
Flinn: Yes, yes, I did.
Green: And did you tell Dr. Labowitz about what Dr. Connolly was complaining?
Flinn: Yes. . . .
Green: Well, he told you there was no truth to Dr. Connolly's complaints, didn't he?
Flinn: Yes.
Green: And you believed him, didn't you?
Flinn: Yes.
Green: And that was well before the Credentials Committee hearing of . . . March 14, 1983, wasn't it?
Flinn: Yes.
Green: And you assumed on the basis that Dr. Labowitz told you there was no truth to any of Dr. Connolly's complaints that Dr. Connolly's complaints therefore had no merit or no basis in fact, isn't that true?
Flinn: I had talked with Dr. Connolly in depth. I had talked to Dr. Labowitz, but in less depth. I had my own opinions. I referred the matter to the Credentials Committee for their opinion without comment.
Green: And your opinion was that Dr. Connolly's complaints did not have any merit, was it not?
Flinn: I think my opinion at that time is confidential. I was Chairman of the Department. I was not making a judgment on a situation. I referred it to the Credentials Committee. And I at that time also realized that Dr. Connolly was mentally ill.
Green: Now, you made that determination—let me interject here . . . . You are a nephrologist?
Flinn: I'm an internist and a professor of medicine...

The interrogation now focused on the letter I had written to Flinn the day after he told me that the Medical Code of Ethics was "meaningless," when I had realized that my efforts at the Medical Center were futile and my future in Delaware was non-existent. Harding, Morris, and Flinn had shown no support for my complaints. Then, I had urged Flinn in my letter to investigate the complaints and had concluded by saying: "The problem with the world today lies not with Russia, Poland, Afghanistan, Iran, Central America, etc., but here. The problem lies with people who are free and have an opportunity to make a difference."

Green: But you had a conversation with Dr. Connolly in late January, 1983, and based on that conversation you concluded that Dr. Connolly was mentally ill; is that right?

Flinn: No. It was—I was concerned. I was very concerned. It was after the subsequent letters that came in and subsequent conversations, but before the matter went—had an opportunity to go to the Credentials Committee that I became quite—that it became quite obvious to me that there was a problem.

[Later:]

Green: Dr. Flinn, after you made your conclusions... that Dr. Connolly was mentally ill, you went and talked to Dr. Raskin; is that right?

Flinn: Yes.

Green: And that was before the Credentials Committee met; is that right?

Flinn: Yes.

Green: And Dr. Raskin, for the benefit of the ladies and gentlemen and the rest of us here, was the newly appointed director of the Psychiatry Department at the Medical Center; isn't that right?

Flinn: Correct . . . .

Green: And you told Dr. Raskin your feelings and conclusions about Dr. Connolly, did you not?

Flinn: As I recall, I took the letter to him, had him read the letter, asked his opinion, and then I told him the story.

Green: And you told him what your feelings and opinions were before—

Flinn: No. I told him that I thought we had a real problem after he concurred that this letter was—well, I don't want to use his words, but in a nutshell, he thought that the person who wrote this letter had some significant psychiatric problems and that we should be concerned. And then the question arose . . . how to deal with the problem. And his recommendation in a nutshell was that he needed to be seen by a psychiatrist.

Green: So Dr. Raskin agreed with you; is that right?

Flinn: Yes. . . .

Green: You went to Dr. Labowitz . . . and you told Dr. Labowitz, not only, as you told us before, that Dr. Connolly had made a complaint against him and was it true or untrue, but that you concluded that Dr. Connolly had a mental problem; you told that to Dr. Labowitz, didn't you?

Flinn: I really can't state that I said that. I really don't know that I did say that.

My attorney then handed the witness the transcript of his deposition, taken May 22, 1985, and referred him to page 177.

Green: I asked you the question: "Did you express to Dr. Labowitz your opinion that Dr. Connolly had exhibited a psychiatric illness?" Answer: "Yes. Dr. Labowitz was head of the section and after talking with him I said something to the effect that 'I think that Dr. Connolly has a psychiatric problem and we had better try to deal with that by defusing the situation so that it doesn't get out of hand.'" Was that your answer under oath?

Flinn: Yes.

[A minute later:]

Green: Does that refresh your recollection whether you talked to Dr. Labowitz about your conclusions that Dr. Connolly had a mental illness?

Flinn: It's very helpful.

[Jim slowly walked from the podium and standing directly in front of the jury, he turned to Flinn.]

Green: He agreed with you, didn't he?

Flinn: I assume he did . . . .

Green: I understand [from] the deposition testimony we reviewed a minute ago . . . you not only told Dr. Labowitz about your conclusion that Dr. Connolly had a mental illness, but you solicited Dr. Labowitz' help in defusing the situation; is that right?

Flinn: It was pretty—I think I stated that, that I was concerned that the problem was going to boil up into what it has boiled-up into, and I don't think that that has been helpful, particularly when you're dealing with a person you believe has a psychiatric problem.

Green: So you went to the person against whom the complaint was brought, asked him if it was true, and then tried to get him to help you to deal with Dr. Connolly; is that correct?

Flinn: Well, I don't think he could do much about the dealing with Dr. Connolly.

Green: After you talked to Dr. Labowitz, or perhaps before, you told Dr. Morris, the Vice-President of . . . Medical Affairs for the hospital, that you had concluded that Dr. Connolly had a psychiatric illness, didn't you?

Flinn: Yes.

Green: Do you know how many discussions you had with Dr. Morris?

Flinn: No, but over the course of intervening years, a number.

Green: And your original or initial discussions with Dr. Morris in which you conveyed your psychiatric analysis was before the Credentials Committee had a hearing about Dr. Connolly's complaints against Dr. Labowitz, was it not?

Flinn: Yes . . . .

Green: . . . You communicated your conclusions that Dr. Connolly was psychiatrically ill to Dr. Labowitz, Dr. Morris, Dr. Raskin; correct?

Flinn: Yes.

Green: Is there anybody else that we should know about that you discussed that subject with prior to the Credentials Committee hearing of March 14, 1983?

Flinn: I don't believe there would have been any other—this was all—the people that I was conferring with obviously were people in official capacities. And I talked to no one else.

Green: So, in other words, what you mean, it was in an official capacity, you were confident nobody would repeat that. Is that fair?

Flinn: Yes.

Green: Isn't it a fact, though, that the subject matter that Dr. Connolly had a mental illness or psychiatric condition was widespread throughout the Medical Center after you had made that conclusion?

Flinn: I—I don't know what was widespread. I knew what I knew.

[Jim left his position in front of the jury and walked back to the podium.]

Green: In fact, Dr. Flinn, when the Credentials Committee met on March 14 and then issued an opinion on March 23, 1983, which is Plaintiffs' Exhibit 7-C in this case, their conclusion was essentially the same as yours, was it not, that Dr. Connolly's complaint had no merit and therefore he ought to seek psychiatric help?

Flinn: That's correct . . . .

Green: You never had a complaint such as Dr. Connolly had presented . . . against a section head before, did you?

Flinn: No.

Green: Your main concern was how to defuse the situation, was it not?

Flinn: Actually, my main concern was about Dr. Connolly and what could be done for him and to get him to have psychiatric help.

Green: Is it your usual procedure when you have a complaint at the Department of Medicine to go to the person against whom the complaint is made, ask him whether it is true or false?

Flinn: Yes.

Green: And then believe them irrespective of what they say?

Flinn: I make my judgment based on the information that I can gather from both parties.

Green: Would it be fair to say, Doctor, that the basic assumption underlying your opinion and the Credentials Committee's opinion is that Dr. Labowitz was blameless in the matters in which Dr. Connolly complained?

Flinn: Yes.

My attorney was not yet finished with Flinn. After the Superior Court had denied the defendants' motion to have me psychiatrically examined, Flinn and the Medical Center had demanded that I submit to a psychiatric exam upon being transferred to the Section of Internal Medicine or lose my hospital privileges.

My attorney handed the witness plaintiffs' Exhibit 8-L. "If you'll take a moment, Doctor, and I'd like to ask you to read that out loud. It is a letter from you to Dr. Connolly, is it not?"

Flinn: Yes. "The Department of Medicine's Credential Committee has reviewed your request to be made a consultant to the Wilmington Medical Center. They reviewed this in great care, but find that you do not meet the criteria for being a consultant.

"Since the Credentials Committee of the Department of Medicine has now reviewed three different requests in trying to arrive at a proper appointment which would be acceptable to both you and the Medical Center, our Credentials Committee has reaffirmed their original recommendation that you be offered a position as an assistant in the Section of Internal Medicine and a member of the active staff. I am therefore offering you that appointment which I hope you will accept understanding all the duties and obligations as well as privileges that go with the appointment. If this is acceptable to you, please let me know in writing within two weeks of the receipt of this letter. If I have not heard from you within two weeks, I will assume that you are not interested in an appointment at the Wilmington Medical Center, and you will be dropped from the staff."

Green: This is June 5, 1984; is that right?

Flinn: Correct.

Green: That is about a year and a half after Dr. Connolly came to you with the complaint about Dr. Labowitz; is that right?

Flinn: Correct.

Green: And I gather from this letter that he was still on the active staff at the Medical Center; is that right?

Flinn: We had carried him all that time trying to resolve the problem.

Green: And, as you state in this letter, "I am therefore offering you that appointment, which I hope you will accept, understanding all the duties and obligations as well as privileges that go with that appointment." Did you write that?

Flinn: Yes.

[And:]

Green: Dr. Connolly sent you a letter within two weeks so that he beat the deadline for you dropping him from the staff. Is that right?

Flinn: Yes.

Green: Ten days later, June 15, 1984, he sent you a letter, "Dear Dr. Flinn, I received your letter of June 5, 1984." That is the one we just talked about, where he was offered a position in the Section of Internal Medicine, and I'm back to Dr. Connolly's letter. "I accept the position in the Section of Internal Medicine. I could work during the months of September, October, November, February, March or April if two of these months would work into your schedule. Sincerely, Ronald G. Connolly, M.D." Did you receive that letter?

Flinn: Yes.

Green: And Dr. Connolly indicated in that that he accepted a position in the Section of Internal Medicine, did he not?

Flinn: Yes.

Green: And he clearly offered to work any two of a number of months which he indicated were available?

Flinn: Yes . . .

Green: You did not reply to Dr. Connolly's letter until July 25, forty days later, did you?

Flinn: That's correct.

Green: But you did reply then; is that correct?

Flinn: I think that that is when the next letter went out. You probably have a copy of it.

Green: Yes, sir, I do. It is Plaintiffs' Exhibit 8-N. You sent that letter to Dr. Connolly?

Flinn: Yes.

Green: Would you read it, please?

Flinn: "Dear Dr. Connolly: After receiving your letter that you would be willing to accept an appointment in the Section of Internal Medicine, thus transferring out of [the] Rheumatology Section, I forwarded this change in appointment back through normal channels. Appointment changes go through the Department's Credentials Committee and then over my desk; then on to the Central Credentials Committee and through Staff Council to the Board.

"The Department of Medicine's Credentials Committee has agreed in principle with your change in status, but has reiterated to me its feeling that before giving its final approval that a psychiatric evaluation be made. As you recall, some months ago, I told you that we were concerned about you, and that the Credentials Committee of the Department of Medicine had recommended that you seek psychiatric attention. Therefore, in keeping with the Credentials Committee's request, if you are to have an appointment at the Wilmington Medical Center, it will be necessary for you to have a psychiatric evaluation by a mutually agreeable psychiatrist. If the psychiatric evaluation finds you in good mental health and recommends continued staff privileges, I will be happy to forward your application on to the Central Credentials Committee.

"In an attempt to come to a conclusion on this matter, I would like to request that the evaluation be completed before the first of September. Should you choose not to go along with this request by the first of September, we will be forced to consider that you have resigned from our staff.

"If there are any questions about this or if I can help you in any way, please feel free to contact me."

Green: This psychiatric examination had not been mentioned in any correspondence from you to Dr. Connolly since a year and a half earlier when you were talking about Dr. Labowitz's complaints; is that fair?

Flinn: That's correct.

Flinn was asked about a subpoena from my attorneys, requesting the production of documents on the Credentials Committee's deliberations on my privileges.

Jim continued, "Do you remember receiving such a subpoena?"

Flinn: Not in specific, but I'm sure we did, and it was referred to counsel.

Green: And you identified your counsel as William Wade. Is that right?

Flinn: Correct.

Green: And Mr. Wade is a partner in the law firm of Richards, Layton & Finger, is he not?

Flinn: Correct.

Green: And that is the law firm in which Doctor Labowitz's attorney, Mr. Carpenter is also a partner. Is it not? If you know.

Flinn: I assume so.

[A short time later:]

Green: You did meet with your attorneys between June 15 and July 25 . . . though, did you not, to discuss this matter of Doctor Connolly's privileges?

Flinn: I—I can't recall whether I met with the attorney or whether I discussed it just with Doctor Morris, who discussed it with the attorney. But I was—they were—the attorneys were aware of the steps that I had chosen to take.

Green: Doctor Flinn, at your deposition—I'm referring you to the deposition of July 16, 1985 at page 266 of the transcript. I asked you the question, "Did you discuss this letter..." —and I'm referring to the letter of July 25, 1984, Plaintiff's Exhibit 8-N, that we have just been discussing for sometime—"Did you discuss this letter or your course of action with Doctor Labowitz." And your answer was, "No." Was that question and answer asked and given?

Flinn: Yes. That's correct.

Green: Question: "Did you discuss it with his attorney?" Answer: "No. I discussed it with Doctor Morris and the Medical Center's attorney."

Flinn: Then you have already clarified—

Green: Question: "Mr. Wade?" Answer: "Yes." So you discussed it with Mr. Wade, is that right?

Flinn: Yes, I did.

Green: And subsequently to discussing with Mr. Wade, you sent the letter of July 25, advising Doctor Connolly as a condition of continued privileges at the Medical Center, he had to submit to a psychiatric examination. Is that right, Doctor?

Flinn: Yes.

Green: Doctor Flinn, I'm handing you plaintiff's 8-O and plaintiff's 8-P. Do you have them?

Flinn: Yes, I do.

Green: When I asked you earlier was it not true that Doctor Connolly's privileges were taken away as of September of 1984, you said he resigned. Would you please take a moment and read Plaintiffs' Exhibits 8-O to the jury....

Flinn: You want me to read them?

Green: Would you, please.

Flinn: This is exhibit 8-O, September the 7th, "Dear Doctor Connolly: As you will recall, I wrote you on July 25th, 1984 requesting that a psychiatric evaluation be carried out before the 1st of September, 1984. It also stated in the letter that you—that should you choose not to go along with our request for psychiatric evaluation to be completed by the 1st of September, we would consider that you were resigning from the staff.

"In follow-up of that letter, I note that we have not heard from you and, therefore, it was with some regret that I accept your resignation from the staff of the Wilmington Medical Center. Your resignation will be effective as of September 21st, 1984."

Green: And as of September 21st, 1984, did you consider that he had, indeed, resigned?

Flinn: Yes.

Green: Doctor Connolly didn't submit any letter of resignation or anything like that , did he?

Flinn: No.

[And:]

Green: Had anyone ever in the history of the Medical Center, as far as you're concerned, been resigned from the staff of the Medical Center for refusing to submit for a psychiatric evaluation?

Flinn: I don't know. I don't know that. I don't know yes or no. . . .

Green: Dr. Connolly was the first and only one that you know of under this type of circumstance. Isn't that right?

Flinn: Yes.

Green: In the course of this litigation . . . Doctor Labowitz's attorneys filed a motion in the case which alleged that Doctor Connolly was mentally ill and you filed an affidavit in support of that; did you not?

Flinn: I filed an affidavit with my feeling on his mental condition, yes.

Green: And did you discuss that affidavit with Doctor Labowitz's attorney before you signed it?
Flinn: Doctor—
Green: Doctor Labowitz's attorney.
Flinn: I think—
Green: Mrs. Roth.
Flinn: Yes.
Green: And did you work with her in preparing the affidavit?
Flinn: She asked me my opinion on a series of questions. I gave them to her. She wrote them up. I reviewed them and concurred that those indeed—that indeed was my opinion.
Green: One moment, please, Doctor. [Jim turned from the podium and quietly asked C.J. if there was anything else; agreeing that everything had been covered, he turned back to the judge.] No further questions, Your Honor. Thank you.

As Jim sat down, Carpenter walked to the podium and began his cross-examination.

Carpenter: Does that continue to be your opinion Dr. Flinn that Dr. Connolly, at that time, was in need of a psychiatric evaluation?
Flinn: Yes.
Carpenter: Doctor Flinn, have you been told by anyone that you are on a list of people that Doctor Connolly and his attorneys have identified as conspirators in this matter?
Flinn: Yes.
Carpenter: Let me ask you in your own terms, as distinguished from a legalistic definition, whether or not you conspired with Doctor Labowitz . . . to harm Doctor Connolly?
Flinn: Certainly not. On the contrary, my motives were to try to get Doctor Connolly

to have a psychiatric evaluation, because I thought that that was the problem.

After Carpenter and Flinn had presented their view of the problem, and the cross-examination was completed, Jim followed with his re-direct.

Green: . . . When you later offered [Dr. Connolly] the position in internal medicine, he gave you a list of six months that he would be happy to work in the clinic, didn't he?

Flinn: Yes.

Green: And at that time, which was in the summer of 1984, I believe you told us that you understood that the litigation in this case was ongoing; is that right?

Flinn: Yes. I know the litigation was, yes.

Green: All right. And at that point Dr. Reese, the chairman of your Credentials Committee, had submitted an affidavit in support of a motion by Dr. Labowitz, did he not? Do you know that?

Flinn: I'm—I don't think that I know about—I—I—I know that an affidavit was submitted. I have never seen it, to my knowledge, and wasn't consulted about it or anything, but I think—I think I have heard that that's true.

Green: Dr. Flinn, it's Dr. Raskin that you talked about in the psychiatry department. He concurred with your diagnosis of mental illness based upon what you told Dr. Raskin and what you showed Dr. Raskin, is that right?

Flinn: Yes. He led me to believe that he thought that there was a psychiatric problem and that the patient should be examined by a psychiatrist . . . .

Green: Dr. Raskin had never met or seen or probably even heard of Dr. Connolly when you went to see him; is that right?

Flinn: To my knowledge, he did not know him.

Green: So the basis of his, quote, diagnosis, close quote, was what you told him and what you chose to show him; is that right?

Flinn: Yes.

A short time later, Jim finished his examination of Flinn.

It was now midmorning and the next witness, about to be called, was the Court-appointed expert—Dr. Jonas R. Rappeport.

14

The Court-Appointed Expert

> [Truth] alone will empower us to find a solution to the difficult situation in which we live, so that we may at last have justice and peace. We know very well that peace is the fruit of justice, and that reconciliation can only be born of truth and justice.
>
> Adolfo Perez Esquivel

"I call," Judge Poppiti announced to the crowded courtroom, "Jonas R. Rappeport to the stand."

From the spectator benches the forensic psychiatrist—Chief Medical Officer of the Circuit Court for Baltimore, diplomate of the American Board of Forensic Psychiatry, faculty appointments at Johns Hopkins University and the University of Maryland—arose and came forward. As the psychiatrist walked towards the witness stand, he pulled a two-wheeled cart loaded with a large box of files and a briefcase.

Placing his hand on the Bible, with the American flag behind him, the black-robed jurist on his left, Dr. Rappeport duly swore to tell the truth, the whole truth, and nothing but the truth, and then took his seat.

John Parkins—Carpenter's pale, bespectacled associate, about 40 years old—was now at the podium, and the examination began. After reviewing for the jury Dr. Rappeport's credentials, including his numerous court appearances as an expert medical witness in both state and federal courts, Parkins focused the testimony on me.

The forensic psychiatrist, in a slow, instructive manner, explained to the jury that he had examined me, reviewed written material submitted by both the plaintiffs and defendants, and reviewed the conclusions of his employee, the psychologist, Dr. James Olsson.

Parkins: Did you form an opinion as to whether Dr. Connolly currently suffers from a diagnosable mental disorder?

Rappeport: Yes, I did.

Parkins: And would you please tell the jury what your opinion is?

Rappeport: My opinion is that Dr. Connolly did suffer from a mental disorder, namely, a paranoid personality disorder, as well as a compulsive personality disorder. These are two types of disorders that are listed in DSM-III.

Parkins: Doctor, did you form an opinion as to whether Dr. Connolly suffered from these disorders in the period 1979 through 1984?

Rappeport: Yes, I did.

Parkins: Please tell the jury what your conclusion was.

Rappeport: I believed there was very clear evidence that Dr. Connolly was suffering from these disorders in 1979, and that this had carried all the way through in 1984 and up until the present time when I saw him in 1987.

Parkins: Now, Doctor, the Court also asked you to determine for it or advise it whether Dr. Connolly was or is now in need of treatment?

Rappeport: That's correct.

Parkins: Did you form an opinion as to whether Dr. Connolly currently is in need of treatment?

Rappeport: Yes, I did.

Parkins: Would you please tell us what that conclusion is.

Rappeport: It was my feeling that he was in need of treatment and might possibly benefit from it.

Parkins: Do you believe he has been in need of treatment since 1979?

Rappeport: Yes, I do.

Shortly afterwards, Judge Poppiti announced the luncheon recess.

As the afternoon session began, the *News-Journal's* Tom Greer sat among the crowded spectators. Again pulling his two-wheeled cart behind him, piled high with files and a briefcase, the court-appointed forensic expert took the witness stand. Then, hour after hour, Rappeport explained to the attentive men and women of the jury that my complaints reflected a paranoid and compulsive mental disorder.

The next morning the scene repeated itself—Rappeport, pulling his cart of knowledge behind him, taking the witness stand, and hour after hour slowly explaining to the jury his diagnoses. He explained to the jury the criteria he had used in diagnosing both a paranoid and a compulsive personality disorder. And then he explained to the jury why he had determined that I fulfilled these criteria: because of my actions in confronting my opponents!

The Richards, Layton and Finger lawyer and the court-appointed expert continued. Rappeport was asked if my complaints to the President of the Medical Center, James Harding; to the Vice-President, Allston Morris; to Robert Flinn; to the Credentials Committee; to the Board of Medical Practice; and to the attorneys' Board of Professional Responsibility were indicative of a psychiatric disorder and consistent with his diagnosis. The psychiatrist explained that they were.

As Rappeport continued, on and on, to expound to the jury, the Holy Bible at his side and the American flag behind him, the black-robed Superior Court judge passively watched his court-appointed expert. I thought of the thousands of Americans whose blood had been poured out in Vietnam. I looked back at Rappeport testifying and I felt sick: I was witnessing an unparalleled perversion.

Finally, with it almost time for the luncheon recess on the second day of Rappeport's direct-exam, the examination was about to conclude. Parkins, leaving the podium, walked over to the jury, and turned to the witness.

"Assume, sir, that Dr. Labowitz said plaintiff Connolly suffered from mental illness and should be subjected to a psychiatric examination. In your professional view, do you believe that that statement would be true?"

Rappeport:	Yes, indeed.
Parkins:	Do you have any doubt whatsoever that such a statement, if made, would have been true?
Rappeport:	It depends on when it was made, but within the time period of '79 to '84, I—I would believe that it was true, yes.
Parkins:	Is there any doubt in your mind?
Rappeport:	None whatsoever.
Parkins:	Thank you very much. No further questions, your Honor.

After the luncheon recess, Rappeport, with his two-wheeled cart of knowledge and still under oath, again took the witness stand to provide Court's evidence. Jim, revolted by Rappeport, strode to the podium.

After preliminary questions the forensic psychiatrist was asked if he was paid a fee for his evaluation and Court testimony.

Rappeport:	Like all professionals. Like all professionals, we are paid for our time, yes.
Green:	And have you been or are you being paid in this case?
Rappeport:	I am being paid for my time as any professional would be, yes.
Green:	And can you tell us what your hourly rate is? . . . .
Rappeport:	Two hundred dollars an hour is my hourly fee for all time utilized in forensic evaluation, and $2,000 a day is the top—as far as it goes. [The Court-appointed psychiatrist was being paid by the Court.]

[A moment later:]

Green:	Doctor, have you ever been involved in litigation, before this lawsuit, where one physician was suing another physician?
Rappeport:	I could not recall one, no.
Green:	Do you have any personal feelings or beliefs about one physician suing another physician, bias?
Rappeport:	Gee, I think just because you're a physician, if you have a reason to sue somebody else, that is perfectly good. Nothing wrong with that physician. . . .
Green:	Do you have a personal aversion to doctors being sued in general?
Rappeport:	By other people?
Green:	By anyone, yes, sir.
Rappeport:	Not—not if there is good cause. I mean, yes, I—I—I think if you want my personal opinion about the malpractice crisis, I think things are getting overdone. I'm tired of paying a lot of malpractice insurance and being concerned, but I don't know that I have a bias. This is the system that we have in America, and I like America.

[Jim now began his attack on Rappeport's criteria which he had used to support his diagnosis that I was paranoid.]

Green:	Under unwarranted suspiciousness, every piece of evidence which you listed in your report refers to issues of fact or law which are at issue before the ladies and gentlemen of this jury in this lawsuit.
Rappeport:	Yes.

Jim then proceeded carefully, step-by-step, interrogating the psychiatrist on the other criteria which he had used to make his diagnoses: hypersensitivity, tendency to be easily slighted, exaggeration of difficulties by "making mountains out of molehills," and readiness to counterattack. And in each instance, the psychiatrist admitted that he found no evidence to support his criteria and diagnoses other than issues or matters which were in controversy in this lawsuit and which the jury would decide, with the exception of his and Olsson's observation during the interviews of my "restricted affectivity."

In his report, Rappeport had said:

> During my interviews with Dr. Connolly, he represented the epitome of total coldness, humorlessness and lack of any apparent feeling. . . . Of the thousands of patients that I have examined, I believe that he represents one of the most controlled, expressionless persons that I have seen. He practically did not move throughout the interviews. He refused anything to drink, and if my recollection is correct did not even use the bathroom, despite the fact that I found it necessary to take a couple of breaks during our interviews.

My attorney angrily confronted the psychiatrist.

Green:	Those were your observations of Dr. Connolly sitting in front of you [during] a Court-ordered examination, and he didn't tell jokes and he didn't go to the bathroom as often as you did?
Rappeport:	Yes.
Green:	And that was one of the reasons you listed in your report that in three hours he didn't have a Coke and he didn't go to the bathroom?
Rappeport:	Right.
Green:	And when you said, "We psychiatrists use all of our bodies to make our diagnoses," I guess the bladder is part of that.
Rappeport:	Yes, indeed.
Green:	Similarly, with respect to your diagnosis of compulsive personality disorder, you

list four of the required criterion, restricted ability to express warm and tender emotions, and the best evidence you could come up with was "Doctor Connolly's behavior during my interview and that of Doctor Olsson," Is that right?

Rappeport: Yes.

Green: Did you ask him about his five children?

Rappeport: Yes, I did.

Green: Did he express any warm or tender emotions towards them?

Rappeport: As I recall, not particularly.

[And:]

Green: You thought the best way to gauge Dr. Connolly's . . . ability to express warm and tender emotions was you . . . grilling him, pounding on him, cross-examining him, testing him?"

Rappeport: That wasn't the best way. That was one of the ways I conduct my interview. . . . That was part of the whole evidence of my evaluation. That was not singled out as a single thing. (#35)

[A minute later:]

Green: So is it fair to say, Doctor, that except for those observations . . . of Dr. Connolly's behavior, humor, bathroom habits, every criteria which you say supports your diagnosis of personality disorder is a matter which is from the issues in this lawsuit?

Rappeport: Seems to be, yes.

[A few minutes later:]

Green: Doctor, as I understand your testimony of yesterday afternoon and this morning on direct examination by Mr. Parkins, you spent a good deal of time analyzing documents and issues in the lawsuit and questioning Doctor Connolly about the lawsuit. Would I be correct, in the thirty-eight-page—well, the thirty-five pages of your report, you say nothing derogatory or bad or in any way which casts any doubt in your mind as to the veracity or believability of Doctor Labowitz?

Rappeport: No. I mean, yes, you're correct.

Green: That was totally unimportant to you in determining how you saw the psychiatric issues in the case?

Rappeport: I was—I wasn't evaluating Doctor Labowitz.

Green: Did you assume that Doctor Labowitz was blameless in the things that Doctor Connolly charged him with?

Rappeport: I attempted and believe I did not assume one way or the other . . . .

Jim then told the psychiatrist that, in reviewing the thirty-five-page report, "I could not find that you said one nice thing about Dr. Connolly, not one thing. Do you want to look through there and tell the jury that there was one nice thing that you found about Dr. Connolly?"

Rappeport: It depends on what you call nice. I said he was oriented in all spheres. He gave excellent answers. In fact, I recall saying he did very well in part of the mental status—on the sensorial part of the mental status.

Green: In other words, he knew where he was, who he was and—

Rappeport: He did very well on one other part of it. I think it was the similarities and other things. I wasn't aware otherwise, no, that I did say anything good or bad about him. I wasn't aware I was saying anything bad about Doctor Connolly.

Green:	You even criticized him for his description of his service in Vietnam, didn't you?
Rappeport:	You call that criticism?
Green:	Well, why don't you tell the jury what you wrote?

The witness, my attorney, and Judge Poppiti searched their respective copies of the psychiatric report for the proper page number. Identifying it as page 33, Jim read from Rappeport's report: ". . . When telling me about . . . [his Vietnam service], Dr. Connolly is somewhat deceptive. He speaks to me, and has spoken to others, his testimony before the Senate Judiciary Committee, of having volunteered for the service and volunteered to go to Vietnam. With further discussion, it is apparent that it was to his benefit to sign up for the Berry Plan and that his decision to go to Vietnam was also to his benefit, in that he could take care of his military obligation at that time and select the Navy and an essentially non-dangerous situation. . . ."

After reading the excerpt my attorney asked, "And you find that deceptive?"

Rappeport replied that it was his understanding that it was to my advantage to enter the Berry Plan and to volunteer for the Navy in order "to keep from going into a more dangerous thing. By volunteering he could select the branch of service he wanted."

Jim, incensed, asked the psychiatrist if I had not told him that I volunteered for the Navy in order to be assigned as a doctor with the Marines in Vietnam.

"He told me—," Rappeport stammered, "I believe he said he volunteered so that he would not have to go into the Army or the Marines, but could go into the Navy."

Green:	In any event, you thought the Navy was a non-dangerous situation and Vietnam was a non-dangerous situation?
Rappeport:	It was certainly less dangerous than the Army, as I understood it, yes.
Green:	Do you know how many Navy men were killed in Vietnam?

Rappeport: No, I don't.

A few minutes later the testimony concluded and Poppiti recessed the Court. As Rappeport docilely retreated from the witness stand, I stood up and joined my brother, Tom, by the spectator section. With a big smile on his face, nodding towards Rappeport, Tom quipped, "The charlatan crawls away."

It was now late Friday afternoon and the Labor Day weekend was beginning. Rappeport's testimony would resume on Tuesday morning, September 8.

Rappeport had testified for two days. After the first day, the *News-Journal's* Tom Greer reported the trial action under the banner headline: PSYCHIATRIST SAYS CONNOLLY SUFFERS TWO MENTAL DISORDERS.

After the second day of testimony, the *News-Journal's* bold headline read: PSYCHIATRIST: DOCTOR'S LETTERS GIVE EVIDENCE OF MENTAL ILLS. The article continued, stating that Dr. Jonas R. Rappeport "said that Connolly's letters, complaining about Labowitz and others to medical and government agencies, bore out Rappeport's conclusions that Connolly suffered from paranoid personality disorder and compulsive personality disorder."

In spite of their extensive coverage, much of it relating to the attack on my mental health, the *News-Journal* still had not informed the people of Delaware that their Board of Medical Practice had refused to respond to complaints of unethical conduct! The newspaper had refused to do its public duty.

That weekend a dozen red roses arrived at my home. The enclosed card, unsigned, said, "Like gold in a furnace, the dross is consumed by fire, but the pure gold will issue forth."

With the Labor Day weekend over, on Tuesday morning Schnucki, Maria, Christina, Ronny and Anna were back in school, and Rappeport was called back to the witness stand. As the psychiatrist made his way to the witness stand, for the first time he was not pulling his two-wheeled cart.

That morning, Jim's cross-examination was short.

Green:	Is it your testimony, Dr. Rappeport, that no matter how unfair, illegal, or improper Dr. Labowitz's actions may have been toward Dr. Connolly, it makes no difference in your opinion as to Dr. Connolly?
Rappeport:	Makes no difference as to my diagnosis?
Green:	Yes, sir.
Rappeport:	I guess I would have to say that based on what I made my diagnosis on and that is Dr. Connolly's behavior, reactions, et cetera, and lack of any supporting evidence to that, to what you stated, yes, that it made no difference. (#36)
Green:	I have no further questions. Thank you.
The Court:	Mr. Parkins, you may question the witness, please.

John Parkins began his re-direct exam. Soon he asked Rappeport, "Did you have, during your evaluation process of Dr. Connolly, occasion to review statements by other physicians concerning Dr. Connolly's psychiatric status?"

Rappeport:	Yes, throughout the materials various people, Dr. Levinson, others, had expressed a feeling that there was something wrong with Dr. Connolly emotionally.
Parkins:	Did you also review the affidavits of Dr. David Raskin, a Wilmington psychiatrist; Dr. Lawrence Weiss, a Philadelphia psychiatrist; and also Dr. Robert Sadoff, another Philadelphia psychiatrist?
Rappeport:	Yes, I did.
Parkins:	And could you please summarize for the jury what those three affidavits said?
Rappeport:	They indicated that they had reviewed certain materials and it wasn't—and my recollection is not exactly what materials,

but I had assumed that this included some of the complaints that Dr. Connolly had filed, his writings, et cetera, and I believe they spelled it out to some extent, and that they were of the opinion, based on this material, and what they, I take it, were told, that there was—I think they used the word "probability" that Dr. Connolly was suffering from a mental illness.

Parkins: Did you understand that those three psychiatrists, Dr. Raskin and the two Philadelphia psychiatrists, had not had an opportunity to examine or interview Dr. Connolly?

Rappeport: Yes.

[A few minutes later:]

Parkins: During some of my direct of you I asked you whether, in your professional opinion, Dr. Connolly suffered from a diagnosable mental disorder from the years 1979 through 1984. The reason I asked you that is because that was the question which the Court asked you.

Rappeport: That's correct.

Parkins: I am going to ask you whether you believe he's suffered from such a disorder from 1979 through the present.

Rappeport: Yes, I do.

Parkins: And do you believe that he has been in need of treatment from 1979 through the present?

Rappeport: Yes, I do.

[And:]

Parkins: Doctor, one last question. I asked you at the close of your direct examination to assume that Dr. Labowitz had said that Dr. Connolly has a psychiatric problem. After having given your cross-examination, I am going to ask you again,

	is there any doubt in your mind that if Dr. Labowitz had made such a statement, it would have been true?
Rappeport:	I have no doubt whatsoever.
Parkins:	And let us assume that Dr. Labowitz made a statement, as it is alleged, that Dr. Connolly was in need of psychiatric treatment. Assume that Dr. Labowitz said that. After your cross, is there any doubt in your mind that that statement would have been true if he had said that?
Rappeport:	No, indeed.
Parkins:	Okay. One moment, your Honor.
The Court:	Yes.

Parkins turned to Carpenter, they conversed for a moment, then Parkins announced: "Nothing further, Your Honor."

The Court:	Thank you, Mr. Parkins. Mr. Green.
Green:	May I have just a few brief minutes, Your Honor?
The Court:	Yes.
Green:	I guess we have heard that "brief" before.

Jim then re-cross-examined the court-appointed expert.

Green:	You indicated that you reviewed an affidavit by Dr. Raskin and an affidavit by Dr. Weiss and an affidavit by Dr. Sadoff; is that right?
Rappeport:	Correct.
Green:	First of all, Dr. Sadoff is a very good friend of yours, is he not?
Rappeport:	Yes.
Green:	Are you aware that Dr. Raskin, Dr. Weiss, and Dr. Sadoff are all hired by Dr. Labowitz to render opinions or give affidavits in this?

Rappeport: That was my assumption, that they were asked to render an opinion either by him or some of the other related people, yes, uh-hum.

Green: And that they were all paid by the defendants?

Rappeport: Yes.

Green: And that none of them had ever met or evaluated or even talked with Dr. Connolly?

Rappeport: Oh, yes. Yes, I was aware of that. . . .

Green: . . . . And is it your understanding, Doctor, that those physicians, such as Dr. Flinn and Dr. Reese, who made some kind of statement or comment that Dr. Connolly had a mental problem or psychiatric problem, were affiliated with the Medical Center?

Rappeport: Oh, yes. That's how they became involved.

Green: I have nothing further. Thank you, Doctor.

After a brief recess, Jim called Dr. James Groves, our psychiatric expert from Boston, to the witness stand. Groves was prepared to rebut Rappeport's testimony. He had examined me in Boston only a few months earlier and had been emphatic in stating that I was in good health. (He had summarized his report: "I found no psychiatric disease or illness in this man. . . .There is, however, an unusually perfectionistic value system, rooted in an extraordinarily fortunate childhood and unusually stable temperament, so that to the novice or naive observer it might distantly resemble some elements of some personality disorders. But there is nothing here even close to a diagnosable personality disorder.")

Unfortunately, however, Dr. Groves would not be presenting his diagnosis to the jury. The Court had urged both parties during the pretrial preparations not to bring in additional psychiatrists. Judge Poppiti had said that if we brought in Dr.

Groves to testify on an examination of me, then he would "entertain any appropriate application in behalf of the defendants to expand their witness list." Thus, although my attorneys had counted on the Boston psychiatrist giving his opinion of my mental state, under these conditions, they decided against it. They did not want the Court to permit our opponents to hire yet another psychiatrist, demand another examination, and add further to their parade of doctors. And more importantly, the basis for my opponents' psychiatric attack was abundantly clear.

My attorneys, however, were concerned. Would their decision not to have Dr. Groves offer his opinion on my mental state lead the jury to infer that Groves felt that there was a mental illness? To avoid misleading the jury, one week before trial, August 17, Jim had requested of Judge Poppiti a ruling barring the defendants from commenting on the fact that Dr. Groves would not offer an ultimate opinion on my mental state. On August 18, Judge Poppiti denied our request: The defendants could comment on the fact that plaintiffs would not offer an expert opinion by Dr. Groves on my mental state.

The dark-haired staff psychiatrist at Harvard Medical School and Massachusetts General Hospital now took the witness stand. As Jim interrogated him, Dr. Groves clearly and concisely refuted Rappeport's report and testimony: The diagnosis of a paranoid personality disorder was invalid; the diagnosis of a compulsive personality disorder was invalid; there were serious errors in both the way he had conducted the examination and in the way he had reported it; the report was flawed, and the diagnoses that it purported to make were worthless. Dr. Groves, however, stopped short, as had been agreed upon previously, of telling the jury that his examination had revealed my mental health to be excellent.

Groves had now finished his emphatic yet controlled criticism of Rappeport. Parkins would soon begin his cross-examination and would capitalize on the Court's pretrial decision.

First, Parkins and Carpenter clarified with the Court—the jury was not present, they had not yet been brought back into the courtroom—that Dr. Groves would not be presenting *his* diagnosis. He would not be testifying that I was in good mental health. Parkins also clarified that asking Dr. Groves whether he was being presented to offer his diagnosis of Dr. Connolly would *not* open up the door to questions from plaintiff about what his diagnosis was. The issue, having already been addressed at pretrial, was reconfirmed by Labowitz's lawyers, Judge Poppiti, and my lawyers. Judge Poppiti then turned to the witness (the jury still had not returned), and asked: "Do you understand the dialogue that I have been having with counsel thus far?"

Groves:	I think I do.
The Court:	Do you understand that you have been called as an expert witness in this case to offer an opinion—this is my understanding—with regard to the process of Dr. Rappeport and how he formulated the diagnosis?
Groves:	Right.
The Court:	And you understand that you are not being called as a witness to offer your own diagnosis, if you had any?
Groves:	Right.
The Court:	Does that clear it up, counsel? I think the witness understands the parameters.
Parkins:	If I can remember the Court's wording, that's exactly what I intended to ask.
The Court:	Any other matters out of the presence of the jury, please?

There being no response, the black-robed judge then called for the jury, and Parkins cross-examined the Boston psychiatrist for the next hour. As he was concluding, Parkins solemnly asked, "As I understand, you have told the jury that you have been working with the plaintiffs' team for two years?"

Groves:	That's correct, more than two years. . . .
Parkins:	And I also understand that you are not being offered today to present your own diagnosis of Dr. Connolly; is that correct?
Groves:	That's correct.
Parkins:	Is that correct?

Groves: That's correct.
Parkins: Thank you very much, Doctor. (#37)

Then, turning to Judge Poppiti, Parkins announced, "Your Honor, I have no further questions of this witness."

The courtroom was silent. My mind exploded at the travesty! The implication to the jury was clear: If Dr. Groves had worked with my lawyers and me for more than two years and yet was not presenting his own diagnosis, then he must think that I am psychiatrically ill. Groves's testimony had been perverted and the jury deceived. This was more than just courtroom trickery. The judge had participated in the jury's deception.

During the recess, still angered, I asked Jim why Poppiti had permitted Groves to be set-up by Parkins. My attorney replied that he had argued precisely the same point to the judge, but Poppiti had decided that the Rules of Evidence did permit a witness to be asked what they are not testifying on. For me, however, it remained an orchestrated travesty!

The fight continued—day after day, week after week. New witnesses meant more direct-and cross-examinations, more exhibits for Vince at the prothonotary's table, more arguments out of the presence of the jury on the admissibility of various issues, and more testimony. And the friendly court-watcher continued to take notes and supply cellophane-wrapped peppermint candy.

Dr. James Olsson—the chief psychologist for the Circuit Court of Baltimore, faculty appointment at the University of Maryland School of Medicine, and past president of the Maryland Psychological Association—was now on the witness stand. The fifty-year-old court-appointed psychologist had found no evidence of a paranoid personality disorder in his psychological tests, but he had diagnosed a compulsive personality disorder. For two hours the psychologist elaborated to the jury on his conclusions. He declared that if Dr. Labowitz had said I suffered from a mental disorder and that I was in need of psychiatric evaluation or treatment, then Dr. Labowitz would have been right.

After the re-direct and re-cross, Judge Poppiti asked the attorneys if there were any other questions of the witness. Quickly, I scribbled a note to Jim asking him to address one final question to the psychologist.

"Since we were planning to stay until 6:00, your Honor," Jim said, "I hate to disappoint anybody." Then, turning towards Dr. Olsson, he said: "Doctor, can you tell us what is the best example of Dr. Connolly's—the best example, evidence of Dr. Connolly's compulsive behavior?"

Olsson: That's a very general statement. Do you mean in the test or do you mean in any—in any respect?

Green: Any respect.

Olsson: Well, I think probably what type of behavior would be the most inflexible and the most maladaptive would be his way of having to do things in his own certain kind of way. That is rigid and that—it would not take into consideration what impact he is having on other people, and that he would feel that he is correct and the other person is basically incorrect in this matter. And he's very strong and rigid in sticking by this.

Green: Is there a—something that is the best example of that?

Olsson: Well, I think, again, I don't have—other than the interview material I have itself, which shows that he, again, is going through, again, this situation with this behavior with his lawsuit, again, many people of the compulsive or paranoid nature do get involved in lengthy litig—litigious kind of interactions with people, so that they can't give up. They want to stick in there and prove that they're the ones who are right, and this, I guess, would be the best example of that that we could come up with here. (#38)

The trial now shifted its focus to the 1979 abortion issue. Before proceeding with the abortion, Levinson had wanted me to tell him if there was "any contraindication to intrauterine saline for abortion?" The gynecologist was now on the witness stand.

Green: The question is that your consult says, "Any contraindication to intrauterine saline for abortion?" Isn't that asking Dr. Connolly to approve or disapprove a method of terminating the pregnancy?
Levinson: No.
Green: It's not?
Levinson: It is not. I am merely asking him is there danger to the kidneys, what is the extent of her medical disorders, would my saline bother that or not. (39)

[And, a short time later:]

Green: . . . Dr. Labowitz came into the hospital and he did give medical clearance for the abortion; is that correct?
Levinson: Yes, he did.
Green: Did he approve the method of the abortion, that is, intrauterine saline injection?
Levinson: Yes, he did. (40)

[And later:]

Green: Your letter [of complaint to the county medical society] does say that the abortion had nothing to do with your consult to Dr. Connolly, does it not?
Levinson: That's correct.
Green: And that is your testimony today?
Levinson: That's correct. (41)

As I came back from the luncheon recess and entered the hallway outside courtroom 204, I saw the old court-watcher standing alone by a window overlooking Rodney Square. "How's the trial coming?" I asked.

"You're ahead," he said, smiling. "You can tell who's a liar and who's telling the truth."

"I hope the jury agrees with you."

We talked for a few minutes, then I excused myself, saying, "I think you'll like our next witness. He's a professor from the University of Delaware." The court-watcher reached into the pocket of his tattered jacket and offered me some hard candy. Taking a few, I thanked him and walked into the courtroom.

For weeks we had told the jury, while our opponents had denied it, that Labowitz had defamed and libeled me, wrongfully interfered with my professional and business relations and practice, engaged in unfair competition and had conspired with others to irreparably damage my practice and prevent legitimate competition in the practice of rheumatology in Delaware. As the sole judge of these issues, the jury's understanding was going to be greatly clarified by our next witness. Dr. John Stapleford, an economist, was about to testify—without considering whether Dr. Labowitz was guilty or not—on the basis of his review of the income and gross receipt records of the three full-time rheumatologists (Drs. Labowitz, Newman and Connolly) in the Wilmington area.

If the jury's verdict was for us, then the economist's testimony would enable them to translate the damages into dollars.

Dr. Stapleford—tall, personable, appearing to be in his late thirties—took the witness stand. The director of the Bureau of Economic and Business Research at the University of Delaware was relaxed, as if he was instructing a group of students. Carefully, he presented his findings to the jury.

He had reviewed my corporate income tax returns and Dr. Labowitz's. In fiscal year 1978 Dr. Labowitz was the only full-time rheumatologist in the Wilmington area. I opened my practice on January 2, 1979, thus becoming the second full-time rheumatologist. On July 1, 1980, Dr. Newman was hired by Dr. Labowitz and became the third full-time rheumatologist in the Wilmington area. This situation then continued through fiscal years 1981, 1982, and 1983. Then, on May 15, 1984, a month and a half before the end of fiscal year 1984, Dr. Newman left Labowitz's corporation and set up his own practice.

The economist walked to the middle of the courtroom floor and, working from an oversized chart, explained to the men and women of the jury the total rheumatologic income from the full-time practice of rheumatology in the Wilmington metropolitan area from fiscal year 1978 through fiscal year 1984. (Since Dr. Newman's tax returns were unavailable, the rheumatologic income pie for the area was not calculated after fiscal year 1984.)

Fiscal Year 30 Jun	Dr Lab. Gross Re-ceipts	Dr Lab. Com-pen-sation	Mrs Lab. Com-pen-sation	Dr New. Com-pen-sation	Pension Profit Share	Dr Con. Gross Re-ceipts
Thousands of Dollars						
1978	268	97	9	---	33	---
1979	360	136	12	--	44	12
1980	344	125	12	--	43	93
1981	390	117	12	38	40	103
1982	483	143	13	52	48	115
1983	654	255	15	80	56	116
1984	586	163	15	78	39	68

Dr. Stapleford explained to the jury that by June 30, 1980 (the end of fiscal year 1980), after eighteen months in practice, I had a 21.4% share of the market (my percentage of gross receipts relative to the total gross receipts, both mine and Dr. Labowitz's). Dr. Labowitz's gross receipts actually declined about 5% between 1979 and 1980.

By a simple calculation, totalling the gross receipts from Dr. Labowitz's and my office between the years 1978 and 1984, Dr.

Stapleford arrived at the total gross income for each year from the full-time practice of rheumatology. He then explained that he had made conservative assumptions on this marketplace and, given my 21.4% of the market by the end of fiscal year 1980, he had calculated my lost income from the practice of rheumatology up through 1986 and my lost future income through fiscal year 2004, which was a few months short of my sixty-fifth birthday.

The expert witness carefully explained the conservative assumptions he had made relative to supply and demand in this regional rheumatologic market. He explained to the jury, that *gross receipts* of a business are *not* the same as take-home (or net) income; business expenses—employee salaries, payroll costs, office and medical supplies, rent, utilities, and other operating expenses, had to be paid. The economist testified that in fiscal years 1981, 1982, and 1983, my net income respectively from my corporation was $51,500, then $50,400, and then $50,959. Since fiscal year 1983, I had had no net income—the net losses of the corporation had exceeded the salary.

In calculating my losses, given the nature of this market (an oligopoly) and assuming that all three rheumatologists were equal in terms of skills and respect of their fellow professionals and patients, the economic expert assumed since I had had 21.4% of the market share in fiscal year 1980 (after 18 months in practice), that gradually, over the next three years (by the end of fiscal year 1983), I would have had 33.3% of the market.

For more than an hour Jim had the economist carefully explain to the jury the basic economic principles involved and the specifics relative to this particular market—a burgeoning demand and an under-supply of full-time rheumatologists. Then, the groundwork having been laid, Jim leaned forward on the podium and asked the witness: "Based upon your review of the income and gross receipt records of the three full-time rheumatologists in the Greater Wilmington Metropolitan area, between 1978 and 1984, and the economic assumptions which [you] have just described, what is the amount of Dr. Connolly's lost income from the practice of rheumatology to and including 1986?"

Stapleford: Through 1986 it is the figure of $561,304.

Green: Based upon your review of the income and gross receipt records of the three full-time rheumatologists in the Greater Wilmington Metropolitan area between 1978 and 1984 [and] the economic assumptions which you just described, what is the present value of Dr. Connolly's lost future income from the practice of rheumatology?

Stapleford: It would be $2,449,526.

The expert explained that the calculated *past lost earnings* (through fiscal year 1986) was arrived at by taking my projected share of the market (33.3%), and subtracting both the expected operational costs and the income that I had actually received in the past. He then explained that the *future lost income* was similarly calculated by projecting my earnings using an 8.3% growth rate of gross receipts through the year 2004. (The actual growth of gross receipts in the Wilmington metropolitan area from fiscal year '78 through fiscal year '83 was 23.4%; the annual *national* growth of gross receipts for physician care over the past sixteen years had averaged 8.3%; thus, the economist had chosen the conservative 8.3% average and applied it to Wilmington.)

With his conservative assumptions, the economic expert had calculated that if I had 33.3% of the market, then my past and future lost income was over three million dollars. He then explained to the jury that if they determined that my share of the market would be more or less than 33.3%, by simple calculations they could interpolate the monetary damages. In fiscal year 1980 I had had 21.4% of the market; the jury, if they chose, could assume that my future market share would be 10%, 15, 20, 25, 30, 35, or 40%. At 10% market share, for example, the past earnings lost would be $25,390, plus the future lost income, which would be $615,021. Dr. Stapleford continued to give increments of 5%, up through 40% at which the figures would be $648,690, plus $2,972,144.

A few minutes later, Jim asked the expert one final question.

Green: Once again, in your professional opinion, do you believe that the assumptions upon which you based your calculation at one-third of the market are the best and most reliable assumptions from an economic point of view?

Stapleford: Yes.

Parkins now cross-examined for the defense. He challenged the general economic assumptions, and then he specifically attacked my ability to attract and retain patients.

Parkins smugly asked: "Doctor, let's assume that the evidence has shown that Dr. Connolly was involved in a dispute with a Dr. Levinson about a patient abandonment. And let's assume that the evidence has shown that Dr. Levinson was one of the best-known physicians in the Wilmington area. . . . Would that impact on your assumption that Dr. Connolly has an equal ability to attract referrals?"

After a brief clarification of the question, the economist responded, "To the extent that that physician felt that the situation between . . . Dr. Levinson . . . and Dr. Connolly was not confidential, and, in fact, spread around at his discretion."

Parkins: Suppose Dr. Flinn has come in and the jury finds and believes his testimony that he heard from fifty different sources about this and Dr. Flinn said that as a figure of speech, but that he heard that from any number of sources. Would that refer to his ability to get referrals?

Stapleford: Yes, particularly to the extent that the individuals hearing the story would feel that the source of the story was reliable.

[And:]

Parkins: Then I would just like to talk about—suppose for the moment there was publicity, perhaps in the newspapers or elsewhere, surrounding the filing of this lawsuit. Could that affect his ability to obtain referrals?

Stapleford: Yes, I would think so.

Parkins: Would you agree with me . . . that publicity, if it wasn't attributable to Dr. Labowitz . . . would not be [Dr. Labowitz's] fault, would it?

Stapleford: Yes.

Parkins: Yes, you would agree with me?

Stapleford: Yes.

Parkins: Let's assume that the evidence as shown or there were leading members of the medical community who heard a presentation by Dr. Connolly and after having heard that presentation drew a conclusion that he might have a psychiatric problem. Would such an event adversely affect his inability to get referrals?

Stapleford: Yes. You would think it would to the extent that those were physicians that might be in a position to do referrals or were associated with such physicians.

Parkins: That would be true, would it not, whether or not Dr. Connolly had in fact a psychiatric problem?

Stapleford: Yes.

Parkins: . . . . Let's assume there has been evidence to the effect that psychological and psychiatric tests and observations have indicated that at least on occasion Dr. Connolly could appear to be cold or aloof . . . . Would that have an impact, if the jury were to believe that, on Dr. Connolly's ability to retain patients?

Stapleford: . . . The average person might feel much more comfortable with somebody they felt they had a rapport with and was very personable.

An hour later Parkins had finished his cross-examination and Jim was into the re-direct exam.

Green:	If you were to assume that Dr. Labowitz's personality and reputation among his peers were such that Dr. Connolly had a better respect among fellow physicians, and a better rapport with the patients, and a more attractive personality as far as keeping patients, would the one-third share still be a valid assumption?
Stapleford:	No.
Green:	What would then happen?
Stapleford:	The share would be higher.

A short time later Dr. Stapleford's testimony was completed, and the jury was dismissed for the evening.

As my attorneys and I packed our briefcases, I was furious. Parkins had repeatedly hammered and disparaged my patient rapport, my personality, and my respect in the community, asking Dr. Stapleford if such testimony would render his calculations inaccurate or worthless. Yet, while Parkins had made personality, rapport, and respect central to his cross-examination, Poppiti's earlier decision had denied us the opportunity to present to the jury the fact that Labowitz had sued many of his own patients, including the disabled arthritic patient, LaRaye Thomas, for $272.50, and that two of his ex-secretaries had signed affidavits stating that Labowitz had billed the federal and state governments (Medicaid) for services not rendered.

(While LaRaye Thomas was trying to pay off her debt to Labowitz in 1983, his gross receipts were $654,000 and his compensation was over one quarter of a million dollars!)

This was the same physician that the medical profession had declared blameless. Not one doctor—in more than fifty-six months—had been willing to acknowledge a single instance of wrongdoing by Labowitz!

Leaving the courtroom, Jim, C.J., and I walked down the circular marble stairs and out to the street. "Why doesn't

Poppiti," I angrily asked, "permit us to bring in Labowitz suing forty-eight of his own patients?"

C.J. was resigned. "We've asked him again, Ron. Poppiti doesn't want it in."

Labowitz's ex-partner and co-author of the letter to the *Delaware Medical Journal*—the studious, bearded, bespectacled Dr. James Newman—was duly sworn and now began his testimony.

As Jim interrogated him, the witness acknowledged that *prior* to publication of my article describing my use of the medications in treating fibrositis, he and Labowitz were both familiar with the medications' side effects, and both of them had attended the Arthritis Foundation meeting that had considered the funding of my fibrositic research in which I described these medications. Also, Labowitz had reviewed my article for the *Delaware Medical Journal* prior to its publication, and he had shown it to Newman who had "glanced over it." Yet they never had expressed concern to me about the use of this medication. Then, after publication of my article, they had written their critical Letter to the Editor.

Parkins cross-examined the witness about being named a co-conspirator.

Parkins: Sir, was there any motivation by you to damage Dr. Connolly's reputation or practice?

Newman: No, sir.

Parkins: Did—was there any financial incentive which motivated you to in any way attempt to harm Dr. Connolly?

Newman: No, sir.

[And:]

Parkins: Dr. Newman, have you at any time participated in any plot or plan or agreement to injure Dr. Connolly?

Newman: No, sir.

Parkins:	Are you aware of any agreement that exists between anyone else to injure Dr. Connolly?
Newman:	No, sir.
Parkins:	Are you aware of any plot by other people to injure Dr. Connolly?
Newman:	No.
Parkins:	Are you aware of any such plan to injure Dr. Connolly?
Newman:	No, sir.
Parkins:	I am going to ask you as a layman to conjure up conspiracy as you understand it and ask you whether you have, in any way, participated in a conspiracy to injure Dr. Connolly?
Newman:	Absolutely not.
Parkins:	Are you aware of the existence of any conspiracy to injure Dr. Connolly?
Newman:	No, sir.

Russell J. Labowitz, the defendant, now followed Newman on the witness stand. As Jim interrogated him, each of the various issues in turn was focused, and contradictions associated with his professional performance were highlighted, including his sworn testimony as an expert witness in another case that he was board-certified in rheumatology—when in fact he had twice flunked his boards.

After two days of grilling, Jim finished his examination. The defendant was then examined by his attorney. Earnestly the dark-suited, prestigious lawyer, Edmund N. Carpenter, interrogated his client. Earnestly, the dark-suited, prestigious physician, Russell J. Labowitz, responded. The crowded courtroom listened attentively.

Finally, the direct-, cross-, re-direct-, and re-cross- examinations were completed. Throughout, Labowitz swore under oath that he was blameless.

The defendants called to the witness stand the editor of the *Delaware Medical Journal*, Dr. Bernadine Paulshock. She testified that, as my manuscript was in the process of publication, she had solicited the Letter to the Editor from Labowitz, who had then asked and received permission to have Newman sign the letter with him.

After Paulshock, the defendants called the chairman of the Department of Psychiatry at the Medical Center of Delaware, Dr. David Raskin. It was to him that Flinn had gone shortly after I had presented my complaints; Roth had talked to Raskin as she was preparing her psychiatric motion for the Court; Raskin had filed affidavits to support Labowitz. The middle-aged psychiatrist was now being examined by Parkins concerning his June, 1985 affidavit.

Parkins: Would you please summarize for the jury what conclusions you reached in that affidavit?

Raskin: I felt on the basis of the data I had seen, that data was consistent with a person who was suffering from a delusional system, and that a psychiatric evaluation was necessary and desirable to determine whether that was the case. That's basically my conclusion.

Parkins: When you say consistent with a delusional system, what is a delusional system?

Raskin: A delusion is—consists really of two things. One, an idea which is either untrue or is not held by the majority of one's peers or family or community. And the second prong of the delusion, which is what we usually evaluate as psychiatrists, is that it is fixed. That is, you can't get a person, as you can with most reasonable people, to consider other alternatives. You can't get them to reflect on other ways of looking at the issue, of looking at their own involvement in causing a problem, of looking at alternative explanations. People with delusions have a fixed

> idea that is unshakable. So those are the two prongs of the delusion.

The case was going to the jury in one week. Both sides now presented brief testimony from a few final witnesses. Among the witnesses, my attorneys presented Madeline Boone: Dr. Labowitz *had* told her, before referring her to me, that she had lupus. The defendants presented available doctors from the Medical Center's Medical Credentials Committee (who had "resigned" me from the hospital staff for not submitting to their demand of "a psychiatric evaluation by a mutually agreeable psychiatrist"). They denied conspiring against me.

One of the Credentials Committee members, Dr. Alan J. Fink, was also questioned by Carpenter on the psychiatric issue. Fink testified that he had concurred with the rest of the committee in questioning my judgement in the filing of the complaint against Labowitz, in my manner of doing so, and he also concurred that a psychiatric evaluation was in order. On cross-examination, Jim elicited that Fink was a medical partner of Dr. Charles Reese (the Credentials Committee's chairman who had filed the initial affidavit in support of the defendants' psychiatric motion). Fink also testified that the Credentials Committee had not interviewed Madeline Boone and could not recall reviewing the patient's medical records.

Finally, on October 5, the last witness left the stand. For more than a month, members of both the plaintiff's party and the defendant's party, bound by solemn principles—based upon God, flag, judicial justice, and democracy—had solemnly addressed the issues. Then, under oath, the jury had been presented with diametrically opposed testimony.

The polarized testimony was over. The jury's task was to ferret out who was lying and who was telling the truth.

Our position, and the position of our opponents, had clearly been presented. The various issues, controversies, and tactics of the past nine years had been reflected throughout the six-week trial.

As Jim, C.J., and I walked back to the office we felt that the past six weeks of trial had gone well: Our witnesses had been consistent and substantive; and they had held up well under cross-examination.

Tomorrow the jury, representing the people, would hear the closing arguments.

15
The Decision

Isn't it perfectly clear that the Medical Center and that Dr. Flinn were trying to help Dr. Connolly in suggesting he get a psychiatric examination? . . . They were trying to protect you and me and other future patients from being exposed to a doctor who was having problems. And these efforts in this courtroom are twisted and distorted and tortured into something entirely different, and you are asked to believe the twisted, distorted, different version. That's what becomes of their good-faith efforts.

Edmund N. Carpenter, II, Esq.
Richards, Layton & Finger

As I finished a breakfast of buttered toast, jam, a small glass of milk, and a glass of orange juice, Sieglinde and I talked about the final arguments, which would be starting in a little more than an hour. We had taken the children out of school for the day so that they could attend with Sieglinde. We wanted them to be present for Jim and Carpenter's summation of the trial: their lives would be affected by the outcome.

Getting ready to leave, I gave Sieglinde a hug and kissed her. "I'll see you all down at the courtroom," I said.

Throughout the trial Jim and C.J. had practically lived between the courthouse and their office; sometimes at 5:30 in the morning they were still at work.

Sitting at the counsel's table next to Jim, I watched the courtroom, wired with excitement, prepare for the closing arguments. The attorneys were arranging their papers and discussing last-minute strategy; Vince was setting out exhibits on the prothonotary's table; the court reporter loaded his stenograph with fresh paper; and behind me a stream of talkative spectators were filling up the benches. In the front bench on the left sat our friend the courtwatcher.

"Jim," I said, leaning over, "you've done a super job."

"I'm *really* nervous," Jim replied quietly, looking at his hands. "I hope I don't bomb it. I've never been nervous like this before. I couldn't sleep; I was up most of the night."

I looked at Jim as he spoke; he was pale and hunched over. "Jim," I said, "you've already done your job. The jury already has all the evidence and all the facts. Don't worry. You've done your job; it was super!" And it had been.

Five minutes later, the courtroom settled down. Turning, I saw Sieglinde and the children among the crowd of spectators. At the front of the courtroom, the bailiff announced Judge Poppiti's arrival. All the people in the courtroom stood. The black-robed judge strode in, took his seat, called for the jury, and the session began.

"Good morning, ladies and gentlemen," Judge Poppiti said as he greeted the jury. Then, after a brief comment to them, he turned to Jim, "Mr. Green, you may address the jury, please."

Jim, wearing a dark suit and standing tall, calmly walked to the podium, arranged his notes, squared his shoulders, and in a steady, strong, personable voice, addressed the Court.

"Thank you, Your Honor. May it please the Court. Good morning, ladies and gentlemen. Here we are. No witnesses today. As I indicated at the outset of the trial, Mr. Carpenter and I would have an opportunity to address you again at the close of the evidence. . . .

"Ladies and gentlemen . . . we started six weeks ago, August 24th, a little over six weeks. On that summer day, I had the privilege of addressing you in my opening remarks. It's now fall, and although the weather has been somewhat colder outside, it's gotten warmer in here, not only from hot air from the lawyers, I trust. With the judge's limitations on our closing arguments, hopefully you will all be out of here before winter.

"I do want to thank you sincerely, not only on behalf of Dr. Connolly, but on behalf, I'm sure of the Judge and Mr. Carpenter and Dr. Labowitz and, of course, Mr. Seitz and Mr. Parkins . . . for your attention. It's been, I know, a tremendous sacrifice for all of you. It's been a tremendous amount of dedication that you have shown. And as Judge Poppiti indicated . . . it's a duty which, if not taken seriously by people like you, our system couldn't work, the system which guarantees that every citizen, rich or poor, black or white, man or woman will be treated with equal justice under the laws and will have a decision on cases, in the courts . . . [before] an impartial jury, a jury of his or her peers. . . .

"Why do we have juries that . . . are drawn from all walks of life, such as yourself, and not have juries made up, in a case like this, all of doctors? . . .

"It's because a jury drawn from all walks of life represents the collective wisdom and the collective conscience and the collective common sense of the community. They know when something makes sense. And they know when it just doesn't add up. They know when somebody is being truthful from their own experience in life—dealing with other people, growing up, being educated, and living. And they know when . . . somebody is less than truthful. And perhaps most importantly, they come into a case without any preconceptions, without any prejudices, and without any knowledge about the facts or the people involved.

"And that's only right. What I'm going to ask you to do is to exercise that common sense, and exercise that collective conscience, and exercise that collective ability of people from all walks of life, to find out what is the truth and what is not the truth, and what is the result of those facts. I'm going to ask you, as I asked you at the outset of this case, to find in favor of my client, Dr. Connolly, and to enter a judgment in his favor.

"One thing which, as I just mentioned, is crucial to determinations of common sense and issues of fact in any case, and I submit most especially in this case, is credibility. You, ladies and gentlemen, are the sole judges of each witness's credibility, whether that witness has spoken on the witness stand or through previous documents, previous sworn testimony or exhibits in the case. You are the sole and exclusive judges of credibility of each and every witness, and the believability of each and every document that has been . . . submitted.

"You can consider the witness's demeanor on the stand, how they acted on the stand, how they reacted on the stand, the consistency of the witness's testimony, whether the testimony of the witness on the stand or in a document was impeached by our witnesses, or was impeached by other documents; whether the witness testified consistently before or differently before.

"You can consider a witness's partiality with respect to the issues in the case; friendships, acquaintanceships, all effect or may effect a witness's partiality. But most importantly in determining credibility, I would ask you to consider whether the testimony made sense, whether it adds up, or whether it just is unlikely that that is the way things happened or the way things probably happened, and the way that people reacted to certain facts.

"If it does not add up, if you do not believe the witness, if you do not believe the facts which flow from a document, then you can disregard it entirely. And if you disregard or disbelieve a witness, you can disbelieve anything else that that witness said. That's your prerogative, your common sense.

"Ladies and gentlemen, there have been a lot of witnesses, and I'm not going to go through each one. I'm going to make a few remarks about Dr. Labowitz. And I am going to ask you to question, in certain very serious and very important respects, his credibility.

"There is an exhibit in evidence which is a . . . deposition transcript. You have heard a lot about depositions. It's Exhibit 6 E. It's just a couple of pages from a deposition. A deposition, as you heard many times during the course of the case, is a sworn testimony, not here before the Court, but before an officer of the Court, a notary public, a court reporter.

"And in Plaintiff's Exhibit 6 E, Dr. Labowitz was giving a deposition as an expert on lupus, an expert rheumatologist. And he was asked, 'Are you a diplomate of the American Board of Rheumatology?' And he answered, 'Yes.' And this was in 1979. This was just after Dr. Connolly came to town. He was asked. 'When did you first become a diplomate of the American Board of Rheumatology?' And he said, '1972.' The answers to both of those questions by Dr. Labowitz were patently untrue. They were false under oath. He gave as a reason that he didn't understand the question. It was late in the day.

"Ladies and gentlemen, a member of the medical profession who specializes in rheumatology, who is . . . board-certified in internal medicine but not in rheumatology, had to understand those questions. A first-grader could understand those questions. I submit, ladies and gentlemen, that the only reason that Dr. Labowitz testified that way, never thinking that we would learn about it, was to enhance his reputation in the medical community as a rheumatologist, to unfairly compete in that practice of medicine. . . ."

The jury, raptly attentive, focused on Jim. His superb and moving presentation was spoken to each of them.

We had felt throughout the litigation that Labowitz had lied under oath. Now Jim focused for the jury the multiple contradictions, and then, continuing, he highlighted another area.

"In my opening statement, many weeks ago, I asked you to consider several propositions which may . . . have been novel to you. First, that medicine is a business. And we have brought in witnesses . . . [to] corroborate what I asked you to accept at the beginning, most especially Dr. Stapleford, who said it is not only a business, but it is a multi-billion-dollar business, and the principles of economics which apply to any other business apply equally to the practice of medicine.

"I asked you to consider a proposition which you may have never considered before, that in the practice of medicine, as in all walks of life, there may be people who do not practice by the most ethical standards. There may be people for whom a financial reward is more important than the common good or the public welfare, or, in this case, patient care.

"And I asked you to consider that in the administration of medicine in Delaware, and essentially as we have seen it in the Medical Center, there are certain unwritten rules which appear to have more force and more effect in the practice of medicine and the control of doctor's lives than the numerous and multitudinous written rules which they circulate among their members.

"If you may recall, I took a stab at drafting what those unwritten rules were. They were, 'Pay your dues' and 'Don't make waves.' I suggested to you, ladies and gentlemen, and I suggest again today, that the decline and fall of Dr. Connolly's medical practice, which was begun by Dr. Labowitz's desire to unfairly compete and control the practice of rheumatology . . .

was accomplished and completed because Dr. Connolly broke those two rules.

". . . We have had a lot of testimony about medicine and doctors and diagnoses and lab reports, etc., how a diagnosis is made, how a differential diagnosis is made. To my right is a document, as you may recall, which was prepared during the course of Dr. Stapleford's testimony. Dr. Stapleford was an economist, is an economist, from the University of Delaware. He testified in numerous respects about the practice of rheumatology and the practice of rheumatology in the Greater Wilmington area in particular.

"Plaintiff's Exhibit 18, if you will recall, was a listing by Dr. Stapleford in the course of his testimony, which showed the gross receipts of the full time rheumatologists practicing in New Castle County, Greater Wilmington area, between 1978 and 1984. If you will recall, he started in 1978, which was a year when Dr. Labowitz was the only full-time rheumatologist in Delaware, and ended in 1984, because at that time, Dr. Newman left Dr. Labowitz's practice, went out on his own. And he did not have the income records available from Dr. Newman to show his gross receipts.

"In a nutshell, what Dr. Stapleford's diagram shows is that Dr. Connolly began in January of 1979. In the first six months of '79, which would be the end of the fiscal year, he had received about $13,000 worth of gross receipts. One year later, he had almost $94,000 of gross receipts, a significant rise, and a percentage share of the rheumatological market in Wilmington, Greater Wilmington area, of over 21 percent.

"That was the peak in terms of percentage of the market. Although the gross receipts went up a little bit over the next couple of years, in comparison to the total market, the percentage went down significantly after peaking in 1980.

"There is a rapid growth, a significant growth, a tailing off, and a reduction in terms of percentage of the market, to a situation in 1984 where Dr. Connolly's practice was operating at a net loss. That continued, and the tax returns are in evidence. In '85, there was a net loss. In '86, there was net a loss."

Jim continued, carefully explaining the essential issues and evidence in the lawsuit. He then began his conclusion.

"Ladies and gentlemen, since 1957, when Dr. Connolly entered . . . college, to prepare for medical school, thirty years [ago], there's never been a question of his character or his competence to practice medicine or his integrity in the practice of medicine. There's never been a question about his ability to care for patients or his desire to care for patients. His mental ability and his competence in the practice of medicine had never been questioned for thirty years.

"Ladies and gentlemen, I suggest that if he had not had the temerity to file a complaint against a section chief, [a] complaint which he felt had to be investigated, and a complaint which Dr. Reese . . . said the Code of Ethics required Dr. Connolly to file, his mental condition, his mental health would never have been made an issue. It is not an issue. It's a rubber crutch devised by Dr. Flinn and adopted by Dr. Labowitz and his attorneys to undermine and completely destroy Dr. Connolly's practice. And who could possibly gain from it? Dr. Labowitz in the practice of medicine, and Dr. Flinn from having no complaints about any member of his staff.

"These attacks against Dr. Connolly had nothing to do with that phrase that we have heard so often throughout the trial, 'patient care.' That's what we're all concerned with. Is it? Ladies and gentlemen, is that what the evidence shows, that these people, Dr. Labowitz and Dr. Flinn and Dr. Lazarus are concerned with patient care, or are they concerned with their own greedy self-interests? They have literally destroyed his career. And Dr. Labowitz stands at the bottom of that pyramid holding it all together.

"Ladies and gentlemen, ask yourselves if you want physicians to practice medicine in that manner, if you want them to undermine their fellow physicians for the sole purpose that they can have more patients and consequently more income for themselves? Do you want to have that kind of activity, so that the waiting list to see a doctor . . . [is] even longer, so the doctors have more and more income? Ask yourselves whether the way Dr. Flinn investigated the complaint against Dr. Labowitz is the way that you want the medical profession to investigate complaints of misconduct. And send a message, ladies and gentlemen, to Dr. Labowitz and to Dr. Flinn and to Dr. Lazarus, a message that the entire medical profession will understand, that Dr. Connolly deserves better treatment by the medical profession, deserved a fair chance to make his living in medicine, and that the people of Delaware demand better treatment.

"Thank you."

The courtroom remained silent as Jim picked up his notes from the podium and slowly walked to his chair. His performance had been superb, a masterful and moving presentation. The Court called for a fifteen-minute recess, after which Edmund Carpenter would present his closing arguments.

In American courtrooms throughout the country the quintessential drama of our society is played out daily. Courtroom 204, Superior Court, Wilmington, Delaware—like every courtroom—embodied the heart and soul of America.

In front of the courtroom stood the American flag: "Oh, say, does that star spangled banner yet wave, O'er the land of the free, and the home of the brave."

Resting on the witness stand was the Holy Bible: The heart of the incredibly rich Judeo-Christian tradition, revered over the millennia. God intervening in human history. Hope of eternal life.

The black-robed judge: The hope of society for a better tomorrow. The alternative: anarchy—fighting in the streets.

The jury: The men and women who represent the people of our democracy.

Depending on what occurs in these courtrooms, our nation is either nourished or poisoned.

Mr. Carpenter—a past president of the American Judicature Society, and a past president of the Delaware State Bar Association—was now ready for his closing address. The Court had reconvened, and Judge Poppiti turned to the counsel for the defendant. "Mr. Carpenter, you may address the jury, please."

Edmund Carpenter—wearing a dark suit, a white handkerchief in his breast pocket, his silver hair smoothed neatly back—moved to the podium, paused, and then began.

"With deference to Your Honor, ladies and gentlemen of the jury, the case of Connolly versus Labowitz is drawing to a close.

And in a little while, perhaps a little longer than all of us would hope for—but in a little while, after counsel have concluded their closing arguments to you, and after His Honor, Judge Poppiti, has instructed you on the applicable principles of law, you will retire to begin your deliberations.

"This has been a long case. And in many ways an unpleasant case. I, of course, join with Mr. Green's comments of thanks to you for the time, attention, energy you have put into this case. We have noticed how you have followed the testimony attentively, taken notes, listened carefully, despite the fact that the case has been very long by Superior Court standards, certainly, and at times, I'm sure, boring.

"We recognize the importance of what you are doing for your fellow citizens, both Dr. Connolly and Dr. Labowitz. It's been a long case, as I say, and an unpleasant case in some ways, but also a sad case, sad because there has been brought before you testimony, very importantly by witnesses appointed by the Court, which was sad to hear, testimony which I'm sure you wish had not been presented, and I am sure you wish you had not had to listen to it.

"But it was necessary to present to you all the facts in this case, so that you could make a reasoned decision on what has been the controversy presented to you. . . .

"When I came before you back in August, August 24, I told you what I expected the testimony would be in this case. I regarded my remarks to you at that time as a commitment to you to see that evidence was offered and, to the extent possible, introduced in support of every single thing I told you. I submit that I have fulfilled that commitment now. And I am going to review, in connection with the reference to the things I talked about on August 24th, the testimony which you have heard in this case.

"I told you, you may remember, that all of us, I guess from time to time, have a temptation to blame our mistakes, our failures, on others, but that this case would be the sad case about someone who blames all of his mistakes and all of his failures on other people, not only Dr. Labowitz, but Dr. Flinn, Dr. Levinson, Dr. Lazarus and a host of others.

"And furthermore, I told you this was going to be a case about someone who feels other people are out to get him. They are conspiring against him. . . .

"Mr. Green continues this theme of blaming others in his closing remarks to you. [Carpenter's eyes flooded with tears as he spoke to the jury.] And remember how he condemned Dr. Lazarus, who is not a defendant in this case, and criticized Dr. Flinn, who is not a defendant in this case, and criticized the entire medical community, those doctors who care for you and me [Carpenter pulled the handkerchief from his breast pocket and wiped his eyes, his lips quivering; then, again maintaining eye contact with the jury, continued], and say they are all out doing something that is despicable and that you ought to punish them, those doctors that take care of us and our families. . . .

"Remember I told you, too, back in August that not all doctors, contrary to popular belief, are successes. Some doctors find that success eludes them for various reasons. Some doctors simply do not desire to fulfill their minimum obligations to their patients, to come in and see them on a Sunday.

"Some doctors simply do not fulfill their minimum obligations to their hospitals and try to get out of those obligations, try to seek a courtesy staff or consultant staff appointment, where they don't have to do anything. . . .

"Some doctors simply don't have the kind of personality it takes to be a successful doctor, a personality which may be particularly important in the subspecialty of rheumatology, where you are dealing with people, frequently older people, who are enduring constant pain. That takes a special kind of personality . . . .

"And so it was we come back full circle, to a case of a doctor who is not succeeding, whose practice appears to be failing, but who seeks to blame all of those shortcomings on others.

"You will recall that Dr. Connolly had wonderful opportunities. He had a fine education. He came from a prominent family. . . . And it is a sad case, because it deals with a failure, despite lots of opportunities. . . .

"And remember I told you, too, that Dr. Connolly had brought various complaints against Mrs. Roth, the former attorney for Dr. Labowitz, who had to withdraw when she was appointed a United States judge. And I suspect some of you were quite doubtful when I told you that the evidence would show that Dr. Connolly complained to the Board on Professional Responsibility, the lawyer's discipline organization, and when that board dismissed his complaint, that he filed a petition in the Delaware Supreme Court, naming . . . the Board on Professional Responsibility and the Assistant Disciplinary Council and the General Disciplinary Council and Mrs. Roth, naming them all.

"And you will recall Dr. Connolly identified his petition . . . . This is the petition against the Board on Professional Responsibility. This is the kind of thing that Dr. Connolly was doing. Now, of course, the Board on Professional Responsibility is not a defendant here today, but here are some of the other complaints to which I then referred and which you may have found fantastic and suspected they could not be proved.

"And remember, too, that I mentioned that Dr. Connolly named a lot of people as conspirators. I suspect some of you found it incredible and questioned whether or not there would be evidence that Dr. Connolly really did name a lot of prominent physicians in this community as conspirators against him. Remember my words. He was finding conspirators under every bush.

"Well, now you have heard. Dr. Connolly . . . has identified the . . . Medical Center . . . . He has named Dr. James Newman, Dr. David Raskin, Dr. Lazarus, Dr. Flinn, Dr. Levinson....All of these have been named by him. You should weigh—I urge you to weigh in your deliberations what this means, that he has named all of these respectable physicians [Carpenter's eyes again welled up with tears, yet he continued his oration, uninterrupted], leaders in this community, as wanting to conspire against him, as out to get him.

"You have now actually seen many of those people that he has named. Did they look like sleazy, strike-in-the-dark conspirators? I think instead you may have concluded they looked like what they are, leaders in this community, caring doctors . . . .

"Isn't it perfectly clear that the Medical Center and that Dr. Flinn were trying to help Dr. Connolly in suggesting he get a psychiatric examination? They were trying to assist him in overcoming a problem. They were trying to protect you and me and other future patients from being exposed to a doctor who was having problems.

"And these efforts in this courtroom are twisted and distorted and tortured into something entirely different, and you are asked to believe the twisted, distorted, different version. That's what becomes of their good-faith efforts. (#42)

"Dr. Connolly has seized on the various steps by others to protect him, to protect future patients, and each one of them, he selected and he has isolated and said, 'This is part of a conspiracy against me.' And he has distorted that and twisted it and presented it to you as part of a crazy, fantastic plot. . . .

"The evaluation procedures at the hospital, which you and I as future patients rely on to protect us against the doctor who should not be practicing there; the evaluation procedures, the credentialling process, all is once again distorted, twisted into some kind of a plot.

"The efforts of the Credentials Committee, composed . . . of leading doctors, after Dr. Connolly put on a bizarre performance before them—their efforts to suggest —suggest that he have a psychiatric examination led Dr. Connolly to condemn every single member of that committee as a conspirator. Those are the doctors, all that were able, that came here to testify yesterday.

"All of the steps taken to protect you and me and everyone in this courtroom as future patients are here derided, ridiculed, criticized, and described with hatred and venom. In the end, I submit, as I suggested in my opening, what you see is that Dr. Connolly has made Dr. Labowitz the scapegoat . . . upon whom he blames everything.

"Now, let me turn to the specific charges and discuss them as briefly as I can. I'm not going to dwell at length on the testimony with respect to damages, because we contend there are no damages recoverable in this case, and we contend—and all those lines that you'll see on the questionnaire that His Honor, Judge Poppiti, is going to describe to you, where it refers to damages, the answer is zero. Your verdict should be simply for Dr. Labowitz. Vindicate these victims, Dr. Labowitz and his organization, vindicating those victims of Dr. Connolly. . . . "

"Dr. Connolly, in early 1983, decided to publicly blame somebody other than himself for his own failings. He started looking for that scapegoat. He started his complaints first to Mr. Harding, then Dr. Morris, then to Dr. Flinn, then to the Credentials Committee, then to the New Castle County Medical Society, then to the State Board of Medicine, then to the American College of Physicians, to the Board on Professional Responsibility, to the Delaware Supreme Court, and now to you. I have left some out. I didn't even mention the Senate Judiciary Committee, and so on. And he has selected his principal scapegoat, Dr. Labowitz . . . ."

The defendants' counsel now discussed the Credentials Committee's investigation of the defendant's referral of Madeline Boone.

"[The Credentials Committee] deliberated on it. They know the practice with respect to medical research, referrals, evaluations. They were doctors who knew the meaning of lupus and fibromyositis. And they found the claim so baseless, and presented in such a strange and bizarre way, that they, first of all, said the claim is without merit. And they secondly suggested a psychiatric evaluation. There is no need for you, I submit, to second-guess those distinguished doctors who understood that situation. . . .

"Now, Mr. Green has apparently made a point that nobody thought Dr. Connolly had a problem until he complained to the Credentials Committee. But the truth of the matter is, no one had had an opportunity—or none of this group had had an opportunity to scrutinize Dr. Connolly until that complaint was made, and then they saw that he was picking out these isolated little threads and attempting, in his mind, to weave them together in a pattern which Dr. Rappeport described to us as characteristic, typical of a paranoid personality disorder.

"Now, what about Dr. Rappeport and Dr. Olsson, the psychiatrist and the psychologist who were appointed by the Court, not hired, like Dr. Groves, by the plaintiffs, who were appointed by the Court, with no bias to determine what the situation was here? It's important to keep in mind that only those two doctors, Dr. Rappeport and Dr. Olsson, submitted any diagnosis for your consideration. Dr. Groves did not submit a diagnosis. Indeed, he went out of his way to say that he was not submitting any diagnosis. And . . . you may have wondered why that was. At page 214 of Volume 18, he was asked: 'And I also understand that you were not being offered today to present your own diagnosis of Dr. Connolly: is that correct?

"'Answer: That's correct.

"'Question: Is that correct?

"'Answer: That's correct.'

"The plaintiffs presented no diagnosis. The only diagnoses in this case are to the effect that Dr. Connolly is suffering from a mental disorder and has been suffering from a mental disorder since at least 1979 and that all statements made by Dr. Labowitz and the others to the effect that Dr. Connolly needed a psychiatric evaluation or that Dr. Connolly needed psychiatric treatment are true. Dr. Olsson testified to that. And Dr. Rappeport testified to that.

"On the other hand, Dr. Groves, who told you that over the course of the last couple of years, he spent some seventy-two hours working on this case in the employ of Dr. Connolly— Dr. Groves did not furnish any diagnosis. He contented himself with sniping at Dr. Rappeport and Dr. Olsson.

"In your deliberations, you may want to consider why it is, if Dr. Connolly does not have any problem in this area, the plaintiffs presented no witness to say that.

"His Honor, Judge Poppiti, is going to tell you that the law presumes that the parties will bring forward favorable evidence if they have favorable evidence . . . .

"Now, there has been some contention about damage arising from Dr. Labowitz's submissions to the Credentials Committee. And you will recall there has been introduced into evidence a blank form, an evaluation form which was the form filled in by Dr. Labowitz in his position as head of the section of rheumatology, evaluating Dr. Connolly. This is a procedure designed to protect, once again, you and me and everyone in this courtroom, potential patients, by evaluating all of the doctors in the hospital every two years.

"The problem with the plaintiffs' contention here is that none of us have seen the evaluation which was actually submitted... in this case. It is privileged, pursuant to a statute of this state, and, therefore, like many personnel records of this kind, could not be disclosed. And the reason for that is perfectly apparent, it's to enable the hospital to obtain candid, accurate evaluations . . . ."

And Mr. Carpenter began his concluding remarks to the jury.

"You will recall when I first came before you in August, I referred to the fact that there were a number of vague, unspecified complaints, and I guess they are still here. But now you have seen the doctors who are charged with being conspirators. Now you have heard what actually happened, and you have learned that the purpose of the doctors on the Credentials Committee was to stretch out a helping hand to Dr. Connolly, to offer him a psychiatric evaluation. And you have learned how Dr. Flinn wanted to help with that problem. And you know how the Medical Center had an obligation to make sure an impaired physician didn't continue to practice there.

"It is going to be argued that with all this smoke there must be fire. We submit there is a fire. And it's in Dr. Connolly's mind. That's the only fire, twisting, turning, distorting every little event into some kind of a fantastic plot. Not a single doctor came here from Wilmington to support Dr. Connolly's charges. Only his hired expert, Dr. Groves, attempted to snipe at the doctors who did testify, Doctors Rappeport and Olsson, appointed by the Court.

"Yes, this has been a long case. It has been an unpleasant case. And it has been a sad case. I'm sure it's long and unpleasant for Dr. Connolly and for you, but most of all, it's long and unpleasant and sad for the victim, the real victim in this case, Dr. Labowitz. I urge you to return a verdict vindicating him, finding in his favor. He is the one who has suffered in this case. Thank you." (#43)

"Thank you, Mr. Carpenter," Judge Poppiti responded. "We'll take a fifteen-minute recess at this point, please."

After the recess, Jim, as attorney for the plaintiff, would be permitted a brief rebuttal.

The Court reconvened. "Mr. Green," Judge Poppiti announced, "you may make your final remarks to the jury, please."

"Thank you, Your Honor. If it please the Court. Good afternoon for the last time, ladies and gentlemen. You may wonder why the plaintiff's attorney gets two tries and the defense counsel only one. I'm sure Mr. Carpenter would suggest that I need twice as many attempts as he does.

"It's because the plaintiff has the burden of proof in a case, which means that we have to show you in most instances by a preponderance of the evidence. That is that the evidence shows more likely than not that the fact which we want you to find in our favor is so. Not by 'beyond a reasonable doubt' or any other heavier burden, but just more likely than not, by a preponderance of the evidence.

"Mr. Carpenter said a great deal that I would like to respond to. . . . I'll ask you to please consider everything he said in the light of the evidence that was presented and the witnesses that presented that evidence and the documents which you will have with you in short order. . . .

"Mr. Carpenter said something about sleazy, strike-in-the-dark conspirators. Well, you don't have to be sleazy to be a conspirator. You can be a doctor, and you can wear a necktie, and you can be as bright and educated as Dr. Flinn; if you go about an unlawful purpose with someone else or if you try to achieve a lawful purpose unlawfully, I submit, ladies and gentlemen, that's what each of them did for various reasons, known only to them. . . .

"Why in the world would Dr. Lazarus—no explanation has been offered—who has been described as a stranger to Dr. Connolly, why would he go to the lengths he did to withdraw that application, an application probably as good or better than any he had ever seen? Dr. Labowitz and Dr. Newman both said they were members of this society since medical school. Here's Dr. Connolly, board-certified, letters of recommendation, and he gets his application yanked? Because Lazarus—Dr. Lazarus talked to Dr. Labowitz. What must have been said to cause him to do something that he had never done before, never done since? How bad was it? How much was he poisoned by what Dr. Labowitz had said before that?

"Mr. Carpenter said, 'Well, these doctors were just trying to help Dr. Connolly. They were good-faith efforts to help him. They were Dr. Flinn's efforts to protect future patients. The credentialing process, if a doctor who should not be practicing, what they were doing is trying to protect you and me and everyone in this courtroom.' And I wrote that down. Were the reports and evaluations which Dr. Labowitz submitted to the Credentials Committee about Dr. Connolly, and were his discussions with Dr. Lazarus, to help you and me? Did Dr. Labowitz refer Madeline Boone to Dr. Connolly to help you and me? Was Dr. Lazarus influenced by Dr. Labowitz to withdraw his application to the American College of Physicians to help you and me and all the people in the courtroom? Was Dr. Connolly kicked off the staff of the Medical Center to serve you and me and the other people in the courtroom? Was Dr. Labowitz motivated to help you and me by never addressing any criticisms to Dr. Connolly?

"Mr. Carpenter said there's no need to second-guess these doctors, referring to the Credentials Committee. Remember that each one of these doctors on the Credentials Committee had already had before him at some point all of the reports that Dr. Labowitz was submitting over a period of time, criticizing Dr. Connolly. They had all been poisoned long before that Credentials Committee, just as Dr. Lazarus had. For some reason Dr. Lazarus at least had the good taste not to sit on the Credentials Committee that day.

"Ladies and gentlemen, there is a need to second-guess those doctors, because they did not even make an educated guess. They abdicated their responsibility to you and to me and to Dr. Connolly. They were not motivated to help you and me and all the people in the courtroom. They were motivated by greed and self-protection and the desire to do what their head—department head, Dr. Flinn, had already decided should be done. . . ."

And Jim made his final plea to the jury.

"Ladies and gentlemen . . . Dr. Labowitz' attorney has been talking about . . . patient care. And it does make a difference. And you can help it make a difference by looking at the facts in this case with a critical eye in determining where the truth lies.

And I'm confident, ladies and gentlemen, that when you do that, you'll find for Dr. Connolly, and you'll give him an award that sends a message to the Medical Center and to the profession that says this is the kind of doctor we want, and this is the kind of profession we want in Delaware.

"Thank you."

"Thank you, Mr. Green," Judge Poppiti replied. Then, turning to the jury, the Superior Court Judge said that, in light of the hour, he would give them jury instructions commencing at 9:00 the next morning.

After the jury filed out, Judge Poppiti spoke a few minutes with the attorneys, and then recessed the Court.

"Jim, your presentation was excellent!" I said.

"Thanks, Ron. We'll see what the jury thinks."

Jim, C.J., and I reviewed the trial as we headed back to the office. Throughout the seven weeks, within the restrictions decided by the judge, we had presented our case to the jury precisely as we had planned. At the same time, our opponents' position, tactics, and demeanor throughout the trial had accurately represented their conduct throughout the litigation. The jury, for seven weeks, had witnessed the two polarized positions. We were on target; we were pleased; we had accomplished our objective.

Central to our opponents' position was the testimony of a parade of distinguished-appearing doctors who had rendered their opinions that Dr. Labowitz was blameless, and, therefore, I was mentally ill—to be more specific, paranoid and compulsive. Central to our position was our conviction that there were overwhelming facts which documented disgraceful medical behavior and that there had been a systematic refusal by top medical administrators to address complaints of unethical conduct. Also, there were stark contradictions between our opponents' public posture and their professional conduct.

At dinner that evening, as Sieglinde, the children, and I discussed the closing arguments, Ronny, now in sixth grade, commented, "Mr. Green sure sank their battleship."

Tomorrow Judge Poppiti would instruct the jury on applying the law to the facts.

Shortly after 9 the next morning, with the court-watcher and a few others scattered among the spectator benches, the Court reconvened, the jury filed in, and Judge Poppiti began his instructions to the jury.

"Ladies and gentlemen, now that you have heard all of the evidence and the arguments of the attorneys in this case, it becomes my duty to give the instructions concerning the law applicable to this case. It is your duty as jurors to follow the law as I shall state it to you, and apply that law to the facts as you find them from the evidence in the case. . . .

"Ladies and gentlemen . . . you are the sole and exclusive judges of the facts of the case, of the credibility, that is the believability of the witnesses, and of the weight and the value to be given to their testimony. It is your sworn duty to determine the facts, and to determine them only from the evidence that has been presented to you during the course of this trial without regard to what the attorneys or the Court may have said about the facts. You are to apply the law as I state it to you . . . to the facts and in that way decide this case. . . .

"You, of course, have heard the arguments, the statements of counsel, both at the beginning and at the end of this case. You have also heard that these statements are not evidence. Rather, they are designed to assist you in your review of the evidence presented in this case. If your recollection of the evidence is different from the statements of counsel, you should rely upon your recollection. . . .

"As I have stated, it is your duty to determine the facts, and in so doing you must consider only the admitted evidence in this case. The term 'evidence' includes the sworn testimony of the witnesses and the exhibits admitted into the record.

"So, while you should consider only the evidence in the case, you are permitted to draw such reasonable inferences from the testimony and exhibits as you feel are justified in light of common experience. In other words, you may make deductions and reach conclusions which reason and common sense lead you to draw from the facts which have been established by the testimony and the evidence in the case."

For the next hour and three quarters, Judge Poppiti continued, instructing the jury on topics ranging from direct and circumstantial evidence to expert testimony, from assertion of privilege to preponderance of the evidence, from civil conspiracy to liability for acts of co-conspirators, from statutory immunities governing medical peer review to the representation of the Medical Center of Delaware and Dr. Labowitz by the same law firm, from defamation to libel to slander to *slander per se*, from interference with business and professional relations to unfair competition, from compensatory and punitive damages to the need for a unanimous verdict.

As the judge was concluding, he read the interrogatories—the questions—which the jury would answer in rendering their verdict. The first question was: "Do you find by a preponderance of the evidence that the referral of Madeline Boone wrongfully interfered with Dr. Connolly's existing or prospective business relations? Yes or no."

The next question was: "Do you find by a preponderance of the evidence that the referral of Madeline Boone was intended to allow Dr. Labowitz to unfairly compete with Dr. Connolly? Yes or no."

In all, there were forty-five questions that the jury was to answer—questions relating to Labowitz's activities as Chief of the Section of Rheumatology, his interference with my American College of Physicians membership, his statements concerning my mental health, my loss of hospital privileges, and the Credentials Committee hearings, as well as compensatory and punitive damages.

When the Superior Court Judge had finished, the jury had listened to fifty-nine pages of jury instructions and ten pages of jury interrogatories. At 11:19 a.m., on Tuesday, October 7, 1987, Judge Poppiti dismissed the jury from the courtroom in order for them to begin their deliberations.

A short time later, the Court was recessed. As Jim and C.J. conversed, I walked over to greet one of the spectators, a friend who worked down the street, in the Federal Court. "Ron, I'll tell you, if the jury gives you a 'yes' on Madeline Boone, you're in; they like your case. If they don't, watch out!"

I turned to the old court-watcher. "What do you think?"

The old man smiled as he pointed to his tattered note pad. "Doc, I thought you had 'em; I thought you were ahead. But after hearing those jury instructions . . . you're not gonna win a nickel."

"Why do you say that?" I asked.

"They were too long and too complicated. The jury fell asleep. They're not lawyers."

"These people lied throughout the trial," I said, pointing to my opponents. "Don't you think the jury picked that up?"

"I thought you were gonna win, Doc," he replied. "But now the jury's confused." As we left the courtroom, Jim, C.J., and I considered our chances. It had been a long case, but we had a good chance. The issues were not complicated.

On the way home I stopped by a drug store and bought two boxes of Russell Stover Chocolates, one for the court-watcher and one for Vince, who had handled the trial exhibits. It had been nice to meet them. I would give them the candy after the verdict.

Gannett's *News-Journal* had extensively publicized my opponents' psychiatric charges in both its pre-trial and trial coverage. Incredibly, however, the newspaper still had not informed the public that its State Board of Medical Practice had refused to fulfill a solemn public duty: to investigate complaints of unethical medical conduct!

It had been more than two years since I had personally handed the editors of the newspaper a copy of the Board's letter to me stating that my complaint against Drs. Labowitz and Lazarus "does not come under the jurisdiction of the Board." And during my trial testimony I had told the Court that it was only after the state Board had refused to do their public duty that I filed the lawsuit.

Sieglinde and I, as well as our supporters, were pleased with the trial. Was Lazarus's Christmas Eve denial of ACP membership legitimate? Did anyone think Labowitz's only referral to me over the years, Madeline Boone, was legitimate? Had Labowitz written his Letter to the Editor in order to enhance medical knowledge? Must a physician violate his or her religious convictions by participating in an abortion?

Can written evaluations in the workplace be concealed from the one being criticized? Was it acceptable to the public that the Medical Center and the State Board of Medical Practice had refused to investigate complaints of unethical conduct?

Were my privileges at the Medical Center revoked because doctors were concerned about patient care? Or were they revoked because my opponents had thus far been unsuccessful with their psychiatric motion in Court?

Had the doctors supported Labowitz because they themselves had refused to investigate medical misconduct, and if Labowitz lost they would be publicly accountable? Was the medical profession's psychiatric attack an orchestrated scam? Was it a travesty of the legal system?

What did the jury—the people—want? Wasn't it clear?

We felt that our witnesses had provided substance and had held up well under cross-examination. I also felt sure that some of the jurors would be strong supporters for us; they would support a doctor's right not to participate in an abortion. They not let us down.

Sieglinde and I were optimistic. Our ordeal was over; I had had my day in Court, and I had a chance to win. And whether we won or lost, we could now move on with our life. In gratitude we sent flowers to Jim and his family, and to C.J. and his family.

I was sitting in my office the next afternoon at 2:40 when the telephone rang. "Dad," Schnucki, our sixteen-year-old, said, "any word from the jury yet?"

"No," I replied. "I'll call you as soon as I hear." Schnucki had been home by herself; the other children had not returned from school, and Sieglinde was at the home of a friend with terminal cancer. As soon as I hung up the phone, it rang again. This time it was Jim. "The jury's back!" he exclaimed. "Can you get down to the courtroom in ten minutes?"

I was able to get an extra five minutes from him. My mind was racing. I called Dad at home in Alapocas. "That's great news!" he said. "I think it would be best if I didn't make an appearance in the courtroom, but call me immediately afterwards. Good luck, Ron!"

I called Mary, and then Tommy. After asking Florence to drive Schnucki to the courthouse, I dashed to my car, hoping to arrive in the courtroom before they started.

Hurrying down Lovering Avenue, I passed the Delaware Academy of Medicine, where Levinson had accused me of patient abandonment eight years earlier. Exhilarated, I sped along the Brandywine Park Drive and followed along the river to the foot of King Street. The moment was finally here.

Entering the courthouse, I hurried up the circular marble stairs, oblivious to the crowd milling around the courtroom, swung open the waist-high wooden gate, and joined my attorneys at our table. Jim looked over to C.J. and me, "Where did all these people come from?" he said, nodding to the crowd behind us. "They beat us over here."

Seeing Tommy at the wooden partition behind me, I went over to talk. "Good luck, Ron!" he said. We shook hands, and as I sat down Judge Poppiti called the court to order. It was 3:14.

"Counsel, Dr. Connolly and Dr. Labowitz, and ladies and gentlemen, we are about to take a verdict in this case. It has been a long and straining trial for everyone involved. And I would expect the process of returning the verdict, which may take some time in going through the answers to interrogatories, will require your full patience, attention, and silence. I would expect everyone will conduct themselves as professionally as we have over the past seven to eight weeks. Jury, please."

As the jury filed in, I searched their faces. Their expressions were unchanged from what they had been throughout the trial.

"Mr. Foreman," Judge Poppiti said, "has the jury reached a verdict, sir?"

"We have," replied the foreman.

"May I have a copy of your verdict sheet?" After receiving the copy, the judge, expressionless, handed it to Vince, the prothonotary clerk. The clerk would read the jury questions, and the foreman would reply.

Standing, the prothonotary clerk faced the jury foreman. "Mr. Foreman, please rise," the clerk said. "Do you find by a preponderance of the evidence that the referral of Madeline

Boone wrongfully interfered with Dr. Connolly's existing or prospective business relations?"

The jury foreman, who was standing in front of his seat, with his copy of the interrogatories in his hand replied without expression: "No."

The clerk continued. "Do you find by a preponderance of the evidence that the referral of Madeline Boone was intended to allow Dr. Labowitz to unfairly compete with Dr. Connolly?

The foreman replied: "No."

"Therefore, you do not answer whether you find by a preponderance of the evidence that the referral proximately caused Dr. Connolly damages?"

"That's correct."

The prothonotary clerk continued.

"Do you find by a preponderance of the evidence that Dr. Labowitz abused his position as Chief of [the] Section of Rheumatology to interfere with Dr. Connolly's business and professional relations?"

"No."

"Do you find by a preponderance of the evidence that Dr. Labowitz unfairly competed with Dr. Connolly through abuse of Dr. Labowitz's position as Chief of Section of Rheumatology?"

"No."

"Therefore, you do not answer whether you find by a preponderance of the evidence that the interference or unfair competition proximately caused Dr. Connolly damages."

"That's correct."

"Do you find by a preponderance of the evidence that Dr. Labowitz defamed Dr. Connolly through critical reports to the Medical Center of Delaware?"

"No."

"Do you find by a preponderance of evidence that Dr. Labowitz has proven that the reports are true or substantially true?"

"Yes."

As I followed on my copy of the jury interrogatories, I had one thought in my mind: I'm getting wiped out—unless the jury quickly reverses itself.

The clerk continued. "Therefore, you do not find that Dr. Connolly has proven by a preponderance of the evidence that Dr. Labowitz abused the common interest privilege, nor that Dr. Labowitz's reports proximately caused Dr. Connolly damages?"

The foreman, still remaining expressionless, replied: "That's correct. We did not."

"Do you find by a preponderance of the evidence that Dr. Labowitz interfered with Dr. Connolly's membership to the ACP?"

"No."

"Do you find by a preponderance of the evidence that Dr. Labowitz unfairly competed with Dr. Connolly in connection with ACP membership?"

"No."

"Do you find by a preponderance of the evidence that Dr. Lazarus conspired with Dr. Labowitz to interfere with or unfairly compete with Dr. Connolly in connection with ACP membership?"

"Yes." (Finally, I said to myself, the jury had given us our first interrogatory. The psychiatric interrogatories were coming; we still had a chance for victory.)

Vince continued. "Do you find by a preponderance of the evidence that the conspiracy proximately caused Dr. Connolly damages?"

"No," intoned the jury foreman.

"Do you find by a preponderance of the evidence that Dr. Labowitz interfered with the 1983 Credentials Committee hearing on Dr. Connolly's misconduct complaint against Dr. Labowitz?"

"No."

"Do you find by a preponderance of the evidence that Dr. Flinn or Dr. Raskin conspired with Dr. Labowitz to interfere with the 1983 Credentials Committee hearing?"

"No."

"Do you find that the Medical Center of Delaware, through the actions of Dr. Flinn or Dr. Raskin, conspired with Dr. Labowitz to interfere with the 1983 Credentials Committee hearing?"

"No."

"Therefore, you did not answer whether you find by a preponderance of the evidence that any of such actions proximately caused Dr. Connolly damages?"

"That's correct."

"Do you find by a preponderance of the evidence that Dr. Labowitz defamed Dr. Connolly by making statements that he suffered from mental illness or should be subjected to a psychiatric evaluation?"

"No."

"Do you find by a preponderance of the evidence that Dr. Flinn or Dr. Raskin conspired with Dr. Labowitz to defame Dr. Connolly by making statements that he suffered from mental illness or should be subjected to a psychiatric evaluation?"

"No."

"Do you find by a preponderance of the evidence that the Medical Center of Delaware, through the actions of either Dr. Flinn or Dr. Raskin, conspired with Dr. Labowitz to defame Dr. Connolly by making statements that he suffered from mental illness or should be subjected to a psychiatric evaluation?"

"No."

"Therefore, you did not answer whether you find by a preponderance of the evidence that any such statements proximately caused Dr. Connolly damages?"

"That's correct."

"Do you find by a preponderance of the evidence that Dr. Labowitz interfered with Dr. Connolly's practice by making statements that he suffered from mental illness or should be subjected to a psychiatric examination?"

"No."

"Do you find by a preponderance of the evidence that Dr. Labowitz unfairly competed with Dr. Connolly by making statements that he suffered from mental illness or should be subjected to a psychiatric examination?"

"No."

"Do you find by a preponderance of the evidence that Dr. Flinn or Dr. Raskin conspired with Dr. Labowitz to interfere or unfairly compete with Dr. Connolly by making statements that he suffered from mental illness or should be subjected to a psychiatric examination?"

"No."

As I checked off on my copy of the interrogatories the clerk and jury foreman's dialogue, I realized that I *was* going to be wiped out.

"Do you find by a preponderance of the evidence that the Medical Center of Delaware, through the actions of Dr. Flinn or Dr. Raskin, conspired with Dr. Labowitz to interfere or unfairly compete with Dr. Connolly by making statements that he suffered from mental illness or should be subjected to a psychiatric examination?"

"No."

"Therefore, you did not answer whether you find by a preponderance of the evidence that the foregoing actions proximately caused Dr. Connolly damages?"

"That's correct."

"Do you find by a preponderance of the evidence that Dr. Labowitz, acting through his attorneys, wrongfully interfered with Dr. Connolly's existing and prospective relations with the Medical Center of Delaware in connection with the termination of his staff privileges?"

"No."

"Do you find by a preponderance of the evidence that Dr. Flinn or the Medical Center of Delaware conspired with Dr. Labowitz to interfere with Dr. Connolly's existing and prospective relations with the Medical Center of Delaware in connection with the termination of his staff privileges?"

"No."

"Therefore, you did not answer whether you find by a preponderance of the evidence that such conduct proximately caused Dr. Connolly damages?"

"That's correct."

"Do you find by clear and convincing evidence that Dr. Labowitz's or any co-conspirator's conduct warrants an award of punitive damages for defamation?"

"No."

"Therefore, you did not state the amount of punitive damages for defamation?"

"That's correct."

"Do you find by a preponderance of the evidence that Dr. Labowitz's or any co-conspirator's conduct warrants an award of punitive damages for wrongful interference or unfair competition?"

"No."

"Therefore, you did not state the amount of punitive damages?"

"That's correct."

"What is the amount of total damages, both compensatory and punitive, if any, that you award?"

"Zero."

"Thank you, sir," the clerk said.

Judge Poppiti took the verdict sheet from the clerk, had a short discussion with the attorneys at a sidebar conference, and then addressed the jury: "I think you know how the attorneys and the parties appreciate the time and attention that you have given to your fellow citizens over the past six and a half weeks. You have served them well, and you have served the system well." The Superior Court judge then discharged the jury.

Turning to the attorneys, he said: "Are there any other matters before the Court, please?" Then, after a pause, he announced: "We are in recess."

The courtroom erupted with commotion. I turned to Jim; there were tears in his eyes. "Thanks for a super job," I said. "I feel good; we did our job. The jury's verdict is their responsibility."

I walked back to greet Mary, Wilson, Tom, Schnucki, a friend of Schnucki's, and Florence. I was greeted with shock, anger, and some tears. The verdict had been unanimous—for Dr. Labowitz; not one juror had held out for us!

Labowitz's supporters were jubilant. His lawyers were receiving congratulations. I looked around for the court-watcher. Not seeing him, I walked over to Vince, reached into my briefcase, and handed him the two boxes of Russell Stover Chocolates. "Thanks for your help during the trial," I said. "Please give the second box to our friend."

"I will," Vince replied. "Thanks, Dr. Connolly."

As I rejoined my family, the *News-Journal's* Tom Greer was interviewing Labowitz. Leaving the courtroom, as we walked down the circular marble stairs, I turned towards Tom exclaiming loudly, "Carpenter is the poorest of the poor!"

Grabbing my arm, Tom hushed me, saying, "That's all right, Ron! It's all right."

We talked for a few minutes outside the courthouse. Across the street, in Rodney Square, the American flag looked as it had for as long as I can remember. Tears glistened on Mary's cheeks. "What will you do now, Ron?"

"We'll be fine," I responded. "Sieglinde and I will make out fine. These people are pathetic!"

Our little group disbanded a few minutes later. A lawyer from my father's office, Mike Eaton, walked with Schnucki, her friend, and me, as we headed back towards the parking lot. As we were halfway down the next block I heard someone call from behind: "Dr. Connolly! Dr. Connolly!" Turning around, I saw Vince, the young prothonotary clerk, running after me. As he approached, he handed me the box of candy that I had given him fifteen minutes earlier. Earnestly he said, "I'm sorry, but my supervisor says I can't accept this."

16

The Victory

> Yet, as Dostoyevsky knew, and the whole history of mankind has proven, without God, or a higher moral authority, the things most precious to us humans are often denied to us.
>
> Philip Dimitrov, Prime Minister of Bulgaria, addressing the Woodrow Wilson Center in Washington, DC —March 1992

The quintessential American drama for this Delaware Superior Court case was over; the Court had rendered its decision; the jury—the people—had spoken, and society had been either nourished or poisoned.

I drove Schnucki to her friend's house, and then I drove home. As I parked in the driveway, Ronny, now in the sixth grade, was walking down the front walk. "Ronny, we lost," I said as I put my arm around him.

"Can't I finish this year at St. Edmond's?" Ronny said.

"Sure," I replied. "You can finish the school year; then we'll decide what to do."

As we entered the house, Maria, a sophomore in high school, walked into the front hallway. I gave her a hug as I explained the outcome of the lawsuit. Like Ronny, she was disappointed but not surprised. "Mom got back a half-hour ago," Maria explained. "Then she went with Christina and Anna down to the courthouse."

A short time later Sieglinde returned with Christina, now in seventh grade, and Anna, who was in first grade. The courtroom had been locked when they arrived. There were no tears from Sieglinde or the children. They had all become accustomed to disappointments over the past five years. "It's too bad," Sieglinde said. "But that's what they want, so that's what they'll get."

I had done my best; there was nothing more that I could do.

A few hours later Sieglinde and I drove to Alapocas. We thanked Dad for all his help. Sitting at the dining room table, we reviewed the verdict. Dad—eighty-one years old, with gray-white hair and blue eyes—was pale and depressed. He had worked a lifetime for his family; he was respected in the community. Eight years ago a doctor's wife had said she wanted me "run out" of the community, and now, as a result of the actions of numerous community leaders, we would have to leave Delaware.

The next morning I read Tom Greer's front-page article in the *News-Journal*:

> A Superior Court jury on Thursday ruled against Dr. Ronald G. Connolly, who accused fellow Wilmington rheumatologist Dr. Russell J. Labowitz of ruining his medical practice and sued him for damages.
>
> The verdict . . . was delivered Thursday afternoon in answers to 26 written questions based on the case. The jury answered 25 questions in Labowitz's favor, ending with a response that awarded zero damages to Connolly. . . .
>
> Connolly showed no emotion at the verdict. He smiled as he shook hands with friends and supporters as he left the courtroom. . . .
>
> Labowitz, quietly jubilant, shook hands with his lawyers, Edmund N. Carpenter, II and John A. Parkins, Jr. He was embraced by his tearful wife, Susan.
>
> Labowitz told a reporter that when the case began he was "saddened by the situation" and didn't think anyone would benefit. He said he was sorry the case had come about, but was happy at the outcome.
>
> "My professional ethics, which were questioned, have been shown to be the highest, as I have tried to achieve and will continue to," Labowitz said.

That evening, we had a family dinner at Mary and Wilson's. The next afternoon, Sieglinde and I sat at the kitchen table with Schnucki, Maria, Christina, Ronny, and Anna. I told them how proud we were of each of them; for years they had shown spirit and courage in the face of vicious attacks by powerful people and institutions.

The jury's decision had been a great disappointment, but, beyond that, it seemed to me inherently contradictory: The jury had found that a) Labowitz had not interfered with my membership to the ACP, and b) had not unfairly competed in connection with ACP membership, but that c) Lazarus *had* conspired with Labowitz to interfere with or unfairly compete with me in connection with ACP membership! And yet d) that conspiracy proximately caused me *no* damages—not a penny.

Further, the jury's decision that Lazarus conspired with Labowitz to interfere with or unfairly compete with me seemed to contradict their earlier finding that Labowitz had not abused his position as Chief of the Section of Rheumatology to interfere with my business and professional relations, and had not defamed me through critical reports to the Medical Center.

In addition, the jury had found that Labowitz had proven that the critical reports were true or substantially true; yet the jury had *never* seen these reports! They had been shielded from Court discovery by the immunity privilege granted medical peer review.

Connolly, Bove, Lodge and Hutz's expenses for the litigation were $596,607.45. I could not ask them to appeal the Court's decision to the Delaware Supreme Court.

The lawsuit had not exposed my opponents: I had been made the scapegoat. Each time I had presented complaints—whether against Labowitz or Roth, against the medical administrators or the lawyers' Board on Professional Responsibility, whether to the Senate Judiciary Committee or the Delaware Supreme Court—my opponents had been portrayed as blameless, and my complaints had been portrayed as without merit, and therefore inappropriate.

I had decided years ago, when I opened Lazarus's letter on Christmas Eve 1982, to confront those who had been attacking me. During the first twelve months of the litigation I had begun a journal for the purpose of writing my story when the trial was over. Now was the time.

I continued my medical practice—but also I had plenty of time to work on my book. Meanwhile, Sieglinde and I mulled over how to reconstruct our lives. We decided that now was not the time to make any major decisions. The children liked their schools, and they should at least finish the present year.

The patients remaining in my practice were supportive, but I was frustrated. I had only enough patients to keep busy one day a week. I received scarcely any referrals. It was clear that working at my office would not rebuild my practice, nor restore my reputation. I was not generating an income, and I was unable to support my family.

Every time Sieglinde and I talked of moving and starting anew (I was now forty-seven years old), it reinforced my sense of loss. Much of my work of the past thirty years had been wiped out. I was depressed as I considered the labyrinth of rules and regulations—dotting each "i" and crossing each "t"—that I would be required to follow when we moved to another state, as I applied for medical licensure, hospital privileges, and employment with another doctor or medical institution.

Greater than the loss of my medical practice was the loss of my reputation—the foundation upon which my future depended. My expectations were mired in what I believed was the slander and false witness of numerous people, many of whom I had never met.

In contrast to these bleak considerations, although my professional life was in shambles, my self-image and self-confidence had never been better. I felt that my adversaries were cowards and that they had hidden their professional misconduct behind the professional monopoly of medical and legal peer review. Their defense had been that their professional peers had found them blameless. I was proud; my defense was me, my performance, my record.

Before the litigation could be officially concluded, a few matters remained to be decided. Judge Vincent Poppiti ordered that the verdict was for the defendant. Since Labowitz was the prevailing party, certain fees were awarded as costs in favor of the defendant, whereby I was ordered to pay $5,716.37, of which $5,231.99 was to pay the court-appointed expert, Dr. Jonas R. Rappeport, for his expenses while testifying at trial against me. (Connolly, Bove, Lodge and Hutz paid these expenses.)

Also, in December, 1984 the Court, in the process of deciding our Omnibus Motion, had found that there were not good grounds for the defendants' Affirmative Defense that "Plaintiffs lack capacity to sue due to incompetency, caused by mental illness." The Court had imposed sanctions against the defendant by awarding us attorneys' fees for our work in opposing this Affirmative Defense. In January, 1985, my attorneys had filed affidavits with the Court submitting their fees, which had totaled $19,455; in February, 1988, more than three years later, the Court finally ordered the defendants to pay. The award granted was $4,278.

The litigation was over. I wished that it had been declared a mistrial.

Had witnesses perjured themselves while testifying for Labowitz? Had the court-appointed expert, Jonas Rappeport—whose thirty-five-page report and trial testimony were documented in the public record—perjured himself?

It was my opinion that I had been fighting against a medical-profession monopoly. After Labowitz and Lazarus had conspired to interfere with my American College of Physicians membership, I had confronted them. The medical establishment had then systematically provided a shield for them by refusing to investigate my complaints and by orchestrating the psychiatric attack. Thus, shielding not only Labowitz and Lazarus, but also the medical profession's betrayal of their public duty to investigate complaints of unethical conduct.

It seems ironic to me that in our highly technological and scientific world of today, rarely is the scientific method more frequently ignored or perverted than in the administration of medicine. Certainly, the sound construction of a medical-care system that is efficient and responsive to our society should be an attainable goal. It is in other countries.

Yet trained spokesmen for the profession continue to convince the public that the medical profession's licensed monopoly is still in the best interest of the public. In today's sophisticated world, this is an anachronism, similar to the application of blood sucking leeches to treat a dying patient.

On November 23, 1987, I sent a four-and-a-half page letter to more than 350 of my patients, summarizing facts in the lawsuit. They had been reading the *News-Journal's* version; it was time that they heard from me. In the letter I told of Dr. Labowitz's being the only full-time rheumatologist in Delaware when I had started my practice in 1979 and his disappointment that I had not accepted his offer of employment. I related Dr. Labowitz's disparaging evaluations of me to my peers—evaluations which I still had never seen. And I explained Dr. Levinson's charge of patient abandonment, the referral of Madeline Boone, the Letter to the Editor, and the denied membership in the American College of Physicians. I also related the unwillingness of the medical profession to respond to my complaints, Dr. Flinn's statement that the Code of Ethics was "meaningless," and the May 1983 refusal of the Delaware Board of Medical Practice to acknowledge that complaints of patient care were within their jurisdiction. I concluded the letter to my patients by citing national statistics on the rate of disciplinary actions per state, as compiled by the Federation of State Medical Boards: Delaware was tied for last in 1982 and was dead last in 1984. I also cited the sworn testimony of Dr. Labowitz's billing of Medicaid no-shows and his lawsuits against forty-seven of his own patients.

Two weeks later I sent virtually the same letter to more than 250 doctors with whom I had worked since opening my practice. At least there was a possibility that such a letter of explanation would help my practice. But only one doctor replied:

> I received your lengthy letter. I read it with increasing disappointment. I regret you wrote it.
>
> You had your day in Court. At the conclusion of the trial when your case had been thoroughly presented, the jury did not support your case.
>
> The American legal system with trial by jury may not be perfect, nonetheless, I believe in it. What I extract from your letter is a failure to accept a verdict. If you are unwilling to accept a verdict, I wonder if you are unwil-

ling to accept the system that rendered the verdict. That is worrisome. So I am disappointed you wrote the letter.

Regretfully,

Because the Delaware Board of Medical Practice's refusal to respond to my complaints of unethical conduct had triggered my lawsuit, and because the Board is instituted and supervised by state legislators, and because the above statistics from the Federation of State Medical Boards supported the fact that the medical profession's supervision of itself was a serious problem, I sent a copy of my letter to leaders in the state General Assembly.

Unfortunately, I did not receive a single reply.

I also sent a copy of my letter to Governor Michael N. Castle, saying, "It certainly would be in the public interest if the people of Delaware comprehensively evaluated the Board of Medical Practice and resolved these problems."

On December 10, 1987, Governor Castle responded by letter, noting that some changes had already been made since the Board's letter to me in 1983. The governor then said: "Further, the Board underwent review by the Joint Legislative Sunset Committee this past legislative session and that Committee reviewed the Board's operations and concluded that it did discharge its duties in a responsible manner."

I had finished the course. I had presented what I felt was documented evidence of fraud by the state Board of Medical Practice to the judicial, legislative, and executive branches of our state government, as well as to Gannett's *News-Journal*. My evidence, I felt, had been ignored; no one was willing to act.

Thirteen months later, in January, 1989, another trial began in Delaware Superior Court. Four female patients accused a prominent Wilmington neurosurgeon of sexually assaulting them during the course of physical examinations in 1984 and 1985. The civil lawsuit had been triggered when the state Board of Medical Practice had been negligent in investigating the women's complaints!

The women had also gone to the Attorney General's office, which, unfortunately for them, had informed the state Board that there was not enough evidence to proceed and to "cease and desist" their investigation.

During the four women's pretrial litigation, sixteen more women came forward saying that they also had been sexually abused by the neurosurgeon. They did not join the suit as plaintiffs but only as potential witnesses. The Court did not allow them to testify. After a fourteen-day trial, the jury was split, and a mistrial was declared; ten jurors favored the women, two jurors favored the neurosurgeon.

In a hospital parking lot, a Wilmington doctor briefly spoke to me about my devastated practice. "They think you're anti-Semitic," he blurted out.

"Anti-Semitic!" I said. "Look at the sworn testimony. This is what they said." I told him that the jury had found that Dr. Lazarus and Dr. Labowitz *had* conspired against me. I explained that for more than three years I had been attacked and had peacefully tolerated the attacks. I further explained that in my first year of practice, when I had been accused of patient-abandonment for not participating in the abortion, there had been talk of "running me out of town."

Look at the record.

The truth is that much of what happened was anti-Christian.

A few additional observations:

On February 18, 1988, Pierre duPont, the ex-governor of Delaware and now a partner at Richards, Layton and Finger, withdrew from the Republican Presidential Campaign after consulting with his top campaign advisors, including his finance advisors, Edmund N. Carpenter and his wife.

Dr. Robert B. Flinn, the Chairman of the Department of Medicine at the Medical Center of Delaware, wrote a letter on September 30, 1988, to the husband of one of his ex-patients. This man, a friend of mine, was upset by the actions of the hospital during the litigation, and had previously written to Dr. Flinn. Dr. Flinn replied:

> . . . I share your concern and worry about Dr. Connolly. Unfortunately, I know a great deal about the

entire case, and the more one knows about it the more painful the whole situation becomes. . . .

It is the considered opinion of the physicians, and this is a wide group of physicians, with in-town psychiatric opinions that Dr. Connolly had at that time a psychiatric illness. At no time was the question of Dr. Connolly's medical competence ever raised or judged. The only decisions that were made by both the legal profession in several different settings, and the courts, was that the suit that Dr. Connolly brought against Dr. Labowitz was unfounded; that Dr. Labowitz did not do anything wrong; and the medical profession recommended that he seek psychiatric help. In addition, I had long conferences and conversations with Dr. Connolly and I also recommended that he seek psychiatric counselling. . . .

Who then is right—Dr. Connolly, or all of the physicians and all of the lawyers, the jury, and virtually the entire medical profession? I am afraid you will have to reach your own conclusion.

On a lighter note, I am delighted to hear from an old friend.

Sincerely yours,
Robert B. Flinn, M.D.

Chairman
Department of Medicine

Clinical Professor of Medicine
Jefferson Medical College of
Thomas Jefferson University

In June of 1989, Susan Faw, the attorney who had worked at Richards, Layton and Finger before becoming the Disciplinary Counsel of the Delaware Supreme Court's Board on Professional Responsibility, still occupied the position of Disciplinary Counsel. And Richard Poole, the attorney who, as an Assistant Disciplinary Counsel, had investigated for the Board my complaints against Ms. Roth, was now a member of the Board on Professional Responsibility.

On July 2, 1991, The Honorable Jane Roth advanced from the United States District Court in Delaware to the Court of Appeals for the Third Circuit.

Currently, Dr. Labowitz is still Chief of Rheumatology at the Delaware Medical Center. His ex-partner, Dr. Newman, also has a thriving practice; new patients can wait more than a month for an appointment.

Was I ever permitted to see my performance evaluations, written by Dr. Labowitz and used by the Credentials Committee at the Medical Center in order, we were told, to improve medical care?

No.

Two of Dr. Labowitz's ex-secretaries had signed sworn affidavits stating that he had often billed Medicaid for an office visit if a Medicaid patient failed to keep an appointment. And Dr. Labowitz himself had testified that there was a period of time when it was his office policy "that if a patient did not show, whether they're Medicaid, private or whatever, they were billed for it." Did I ever learn how the Delaware Attorney General's office exonerated Dr. Labowitz of fraudulently billing Medicaid and "found no instance where he billed the state when he didn't see the patient"?

No.

Dr. Lazarus had testified that, in his role as Governor for Delaware of the American College of Physicians, when he was concerned about his own actions and was concerned that a lawsuit would be filed against him, he was told by an official of the College: "You have a way out. Turn it over to the Credentials Committee, and that absolves you." Is such abuse of the immunity privilege still possible?

Unfortunately, yes.

For five years I had presented what I believed were glaring deficiencies in medicine, deficiencies that had had a major effect on me in particular and on the practice of medicine in general. There was no one left to petition. I had been to countless prestigious professionals and public officials with an array of distinguished titles: Doctor. Lawyer. Honorable. Governor. Public Editor. Ombudsman. Congressman. Justice. Attorney General. Executive Vice-President for Medical Affairs. Chairman of the Credentials Committee. President of the state Board of Medical Practice. Editor-in-Chief. Your Honor. Senator. Chairman of the Department of Medicine. Managing Editor. Disciplinary Counsel. Professor of Medicine. Chief Justice. Chairman of the Professional Conduct Committee. Esquire. President of the State Medical Society. Columnist. Reporter. Hospital President. Chairman of the Board on Professional Responsibility.

Now, I have told my story. The experience of countless others has yet to be told. Judging from the responses I elicited when I confronted my opponents, it is clear to me that I had been sitting on a nerve center and a great effort had been made to suppress my story.

I had been appalled by medical peer review. One of the primary reasons I had filed the lawsuit on August 1, 1983, was to publicly document under oath what was happening. In retrospect, I was successful.

My greatest disappointment was *not* the actions of individual doctors, nor was it the fact that the "system" did not work, but rather that the people in charge of the system—those who readily seek prestige, financial rewards, power, and public recognition—seemed, with few exceptions, not to be trying to make the system work. It seemed to me that they had actively and systematically thwarted the process. Their *acceptability* of fraud is a far greater problem than the original misconduct.

Meanwhile, the average citizen struggles in hopes of a better tomorrow.

Prestigious leaders may propagate new committees and commissions, budget more funds, and legislate new laws—but all of this will be to no avail if existing standards are not enforced. In my judgment, elite individuals were excused from being accountable for their conduct as they ignored standards demanded of the average citizen.

The lawsuit is over—for the lawyers, the doctors, the judges and the *News-Journal*, but not for my family and me. In 1988 my expenses exceeded my revenues by $23,081, and I had no salary. In July, 1989, I closed my office and put it, as well as our home, up for sale. As we prepared to leave Delaware, I wondered if I could obtain a medical license in another state and privileges at another hospital.

"I don't want anyone else living in my house or sleeping in my room!" Schnucki, eighteen years old, said after a prospective buyer walked through our home. For Maria, seventeen years old, who was beginning to blossom as a young artist, the upcoming move would be equally disruptive. And, early one morning before leaving for work, I looked at Christina—fourteen years old, her black hair falling over her shoulders, asleep with her teddy; she also would miss her home, as would Ronny, thirteen years old, and Anna, nine. The task before us now was to make a new home.

I sent a letter to my patients, telling them that I would be closing my office. Tears rolled down the cheeks of a fifty-four-year-old black woman as she sat in my office, and so also with the eighty-one-year-old Jewish widow, and the fifty-one-year-old housewife who had immigrated from Ireland. They said that I was a doctor who had time for them, listened to them, and cared for them.

Our good friend and co-worker over the years, Florence Pullella, was looking for another job.

Sieglinde's overriding instinct in response to our experience has always been compassion; my instinct has been to tell our story, and hopefully to restore some order.

My family and I have been violently uprooted, and in the process my reputation and career have been destroyed. But at least I had a chance against my opponents; not a fair chance, but a chance, which is something that many people never have. I have a good education, my father had financed my home expenses and his law firm had financed my legal expenses. I was one of the lucky ones.

At the beginning of our journey, I said that my experience represents but a single biopsy of American medicine. Does it accurately reflect a serious national problem, or was it an isolated aberration? You decide.

In 1988, Joseph Califano, Jr., Secretary of Health, Education, and Welfare from 1977 to 1979, said: "Just as history teaches that war is too important to be left to generals, so recent American experience teaches that medicine is too important to be left to doctors and politicians."

As the more than $800 billion medical pie for 1993 is sliced up, should the public continue to grant the medical profession a licensed monopoly? Or, to make an understatement, is it like the fox guarding the hen house?

Obviously, doctors are as vulnerable to conflicts of interest as are other people. As the United States undertakes health care reform, I propose that the various State Boards of Medical Practice be turned over to representatives of the public—the consumer, the taxpayer, industry, government—to those who are paying the bills. The medical profession should be subjected to the same checks and balances that characterize the rest of our democracy; they should not have autonomy to license, supervise, and discipline their peers!

Also, our country, like most industrialized countries should provide universal health care coverage; the poor as well as the rich should have access to care.

Should the public continue to grant autonomy to the lawyers? Yes, what about the legal profession?

Now, a final question: In retrospect, would I file the lawsuit again? Yes, only sooner. It is the only civil recourse. I feel my opponents mistook tolerance, for weakness.

Sieglinde, our children, and I had run the gauntlet.

And we had won!!

I had done my duty. I was free and my family was free!

The cost had been great, but it would have been much greater if I had capitulated. As it was, I had preserved myself and my family.

For me, the deepest consequence of my experience is that the values transmitted by my parents, my schools and my Judeo-Christian tradition were true. THEY WORK! My faith in

God was sufficient. During these years, although often I was blinded to the future, I never felt lost. My religion and Sieglinde are my fulfillment.

I believe that we evolve in our understanding of the laws of science and the laws of the spirit. Truths of our material world and truths of our spiritual world look at One Truth from different perspectives. The two complement each other and fulfill each other; neither one possesses the autonomy to dictate to the other; both are essential.

Introibo ad altare Dei, ad Deum qui laetificat juventutem meum.

I have the deepest gratitude and appreciation for the love and values of Sieglinde, Mom and Dad, family, friends, and the priests, brothers, and sisters, from the contemplative sisters at the Visitation to the chaplains in Vietnam, from those at Ursuline, St. Edmond's and Archmere to those at Georgetown University, and from those at Presentation Parish in Sacramento to those at St. Joseph's-on-the-Brandywine Parish in Wilmington. Their lives are exemplified in the humanity, vision and joy of an old nun, a friend, kneeling with head bowed and bony hands clasped in prayer. Her life is a profound inspiration to me.

What an incredible gift, to be part of creation! Today. Yes; what the heart loves, it keeps, and all is well.

I think back twenty-some years, to the day when Father Bernard Bush had dinner with Sieglinde, me and three friends in my San Francisco apartment. When asked how much he was willing to bet that God existed, he had quietly responded, "I'll bet my life on it."

The California hills, black oak trees and poppies are basking in the warm sunshine. Today. Now. For Sieglinde and me and our children it's a special day. We are lucky; we are blessed.

*APPENDIX**

* Various portions of these exhibits are underlined and marked. This was done during the course of the litigation and while writing this book.

New Castle County Medical Society, Inc.

Executive Director
EUGENE C. SYROVATKA, J.D.

(EXHIBIT #1)
-from page 17

DELAWARE ACADEMY OF MEDICINE
LOVERING AVENUE & UNION STREET
WILMINGTON, DELAWARE 19806
PHONE (302) 658-3168

December 26, 1979

Ronald G. Connolly, M.D.
2300 Pennsylvania Avenue
Wilmington, DE 19806

Dear Doctor Connolly:

Thank you for meeting with the Professional Conduct Committee. We hope that you regarded your appearance as a learning process and not a disciplinary one.

The Committee, at no time, attempted to infringe on your rights. The abortion was not an issue at any time. At issue was the fact that another physician had requested a medical clearance from you on a seriously ill patient, under your care, who was to undergo a surgical procedure.

It is the opinion of the Committee that you should have complied with the request either by clearing this patient yourself or made arrangements with another physician to do so. The Committee feels that you did not act prudently and in the best interests of your patient.

It is hoped that, in the future, should a similar situation occur, you will either personally comply with the request for a consultation or make other satisfactory arrangements.

Sincerely yours,

Eugene C. Syrovatka, J.D.
Executive Director

ECS/ih

American College of Physicians
4200 Pine Street
Philadelphia, PA 19104
(215) 243-1200
(800) 523-1546
TWX 710 670 0586

Robert H. Moser, MD, FACP
Executive Vice President

(EXHIBIT #2)
-from page 29

Alfred Lazarus, MD; FACP
ACP Governor for Delaware
Professional Building, Suite 38
1701 Augustine Cut-Off
Wilmington, DE 19803
(302) 655-8009

December 21, 1982

Ronald G. Connolly, M.D.
6 Quail Run
Greenville, Delaware 19807

Dear Dr. Connolly:

The credentials subcommittee has deferred your application for membership in the College of Physicians. The reason for this is your lack of adequate participation in the teaching program and meeting the responsibilities of your section according to the reports of the credentials committee of the Department of Medicine of the Wilmington Medical Center. In view of that, the committee and the local committee and I did not feel that your application at this time was sufficient to warrant membership in the college. If this improves next year I would be most happy to endorse your application.

Best personal regards.

Sincerely yours,

Alfred Lazarus, M.D.

AL:mh

(EXHIBIT #3)
-from page 49

Subchapter I. License Requirements

§ 1701. Statement of purpose.

Recognizing that the practice of medicine is a privilege and not a natural right of individuals, it is hereby deemed necessary as a matter of policy in the interests of public health, safety and welfare to provide laws and provisions covering the granting of that privilege and its subsequent use and control, and to provide regulations to the end that the public health shall be promoted and that the public shall be properly protected against unprofessional, improper, unauthorized and unqualified practice of medicine and from unprofessional conduct by persons licensed to practice medicine. (60 Del. Laws, c. 462, § 1.)

§ 1702. Requirements for practice of medicine.

No person shall practice medicine in this State without having first obtained from the Board of Medical Practice a certificate to practice medicine and a current active registration therefor as provided in this chapter. (60 Del. Laws, c. 462, § 1; 62 Del. Laws, c. 417, § 1.)

Effect of amendment. — 62 Del. Laws, c. 417, effective July 11, 1980, inserted "first" and substituted "to practice medicine and a current active registration" for "of authorization therefore and a license."

§ 1703. Definition of practice of medicine; application of chapter.

(a) As used in this chapter, "medicine" means the science of restoring or preserving health and includes medicine, surgery, osteopathic medicine and surgery, forensic medicine and all the respective branches of the foregoing.

(b) As used in this chapter, "practice of medicine" means to:

(1) Establish an office in furtherance of the activities stated in paragraphs (2), (3) and (4) of this subsection;

(2) Investigate or diagnose or offer to investigate or diagnose any physical or mental ailment, condition or disease of any person, living or dead;

(3) Sell or give to, suggest, recommend, prescribe or direct for the use of any person, any drug, surgery, medicine, appliance or other agent, for the prevention, cure or relief of any ailment or disease of the mind or body or any symptom thereof, or for the cure or relief of any wound, fracture, bodily injury or deformity; or

(4) Hold oneself out in any manner as engaged in the practice of medicine or to use in connection with his name, the words or letters "Dr.", "Doctor", "M.D.", "D.O.", "Healer" or any other title, word, letter or designation which may imply or designate one engaged in the practice of medicine.

(c) As used in this chapter, the "unauthorized practice of medicine" shall refer to the practice of medicine as defined in subsection (b) of this section by persons not permitted to perform any of the acts set forth in said subsection.

(EXHIBIT #4)
-from page 50

(14) Willful failure to report to the Board as required by § 1728(b) of this title;

(15) Willful failure to report to the Board as required by § 1728(c) of this title;

(16) Willful failure to divulge information relevant to authorization or competence to practice medicine to the Board or any committee thereof upon its request;

(17) The violation of this chapter, or the violation of an order or regulation of the Board directly related to medical procedures, the performance of which would harm or injure the public or any individual.

(c) The certificate to practice medicine and surgery issued to any person shall be subject to restriction, revocation or suspension, either permanently or temporarily in case of inability of the person to practice medicine and surgery with reasonable skill or safety to patients by reason of 1 or more of the following:

(1) Mental illness or mental incompetence;

(2) Physical illness, including, but not limited to, deterioration through the aging process or loss of motor skill;

(3) Excessive use or abuse of drugs, including alcohol.

(d) The Board may establish by class and not by individual requirements for continuing education and/or reexamination as a condition for recertification to practice medicine.

(e) No person who files a complaint with the Board, provides information to the Board or its investigative committee, or who testifies as a witness at a Board hearing concerning unprofessional conduct, as that term is defined in subsection (b) of this section, by a person licensed to practice medicine and surgery in this State, or concerning the inability of such licensee to practice medicine for the reasons set forth in subsection (c) of this section, shall be held liable in any cause of action arising out of the filing of such complaint, the providing of such information or the giving of such testimony, provided that such person does so in good faith and without malice. (60 Del. Laws, c. 462, § 1; 62 Del. Laws, c. 90, s. 3.)

Effect of amendment. — 62 Del. Laws, c. 90, effective July 3, 1979, added subsection (e).

§ 1732. Complaints; investigative committees.

(a) It shall be the duty of the Board to investigate, either upon complaint or, whenever it shall think proper, upon its own motion, cases of unprofessional conduct or inability to practice medicine as defined by subsections (a), (b) and (c) of § 1731 of this title, unauthorized practice of medicine and medical malpractice claims, to formulate charges against any person to whom a certificate to practice medicine in this State has been issued if the circumstances warrant, to proceed, upon due notice to respondent of such charges and of the time and place of hearing, to hear such charges upon sworn testimony and other evidence, to determine whether or not disciplinary action is warranted, and, in the event it shall find disciplinary action to be warranted, to make findings of fact

(EXHIBIT #5)
-from page 50

STATE OF DELAWARE
DEPARTMENT OF ADMINISTRATIVE SERVICES
BOARD OF MEDICAL PRACTICE
MARGARET O'NEILL BUILDING
P. O. BOX 1401
DOVER, DELAWARE 19901

TELEPHONE: (302) 736 - 4753

May 4, 1983

Ronald G. Connolly, M.D.
Professional Association
2401 Pennsylvania Avenue
Wilmington, Delaware 19806

Dear Dr. Connolly:

The Delaware Board of Medical Practice wishes to inform you that after considerable review of your complaint dated March 15, 1983 against Doctor Russell Labowitz and Dr. Alfred Lazarus that your complaint does not come under the jurisdiction of the Board.

Sincerely,

Vincent G. Lobo, Jr., D.O.

Vincent G. Lobo, Jr., D.O.
President
Delaware Board of Medical Practice

VGL/rss

(EXHIBIT #6)
-from page 55

IN THE COURT OF COMMON PLEAS OF THE STATE OF DELAWARE

IN AND FOR NEW CASTLE COUNTY

RUSSELL J. LABOWITZ, M.D.,	:	
Plaintiff,	:	
v.	:	Civil Action No.
LARAYE THOMAS,	:	
Defendant(s).	:	

COMPLAINT

1. As a result of medical services rendered by the plaintiff to the defendant on or about June 26, 1980 the defendant is indebted to the plaintiff in the amount of $ 272.50.

WHEREFORE, plaintiff demands judgment against the defendant in the amount of $ 272.50 plus costs and interest.

PAUL H. SPILLER
Kimmel & Spiller, P.A.
401 Market Tower Building
Wilmington, DE 19801
Attorney for Plaintiff

(EXHIBIT #7)
-from page 59

IN THE SUPERIOR COURT OF THE STATE OF DELAWARE

IN AND FOR NEW CASTLE COUNTY

RONALD G. CONNOLLY, M.D., P.A., and RONALD G. CONNOLLY, M.D., Plaintiffs,	)	
v.	)	C. A. No. 83C-AU-1
RUSSELL J. LABOWITZ, M.D., P.A., RUSSELL J. LABOWITZ, M.D., and JOHN DOES 1, Defendants.	)	

MOTION FOR PSYCHIATRIC EXAMINATION
AND FOR A PROTECTIVE ORDER

Defendant Labowitz hereby moves the Court for an Order that plaintiff submit to a psychiatric examination to determine his competency to maintain this action. Good cause for the psychiatric examination is set forth in the Affidavit of Charles L. Reese, III, M.D., attached hereto.

An appointment has been made for the examination to be done by David E. Raskin, M.D., on October 7, 1983, at 10:00 a.m., Department of Psychiatry, Delaware Division, Wilmington Medical Center, Wilmington, Delaware.

Defendant Labowitz further moves the Court for a protective order, staying all discovery and proceedings in this matter, pending the completion of the psychiatric evaluation.

Dated: September 16, 1983

Jane R. Roth
Richards, Layton & Finger
One Rodney Square
P. O. Box 551
Wilmington, DE 19899
Attorney for Defendant Labowitz

(EXHIBIT #8)
-from page 61

IN THE SUPERIOR COURT OF THE STATE OF DELAWARE

IN AND FOR NEW CASTLE COUNTY

RONALD G. CONNOLLY, M.D., P.A. and RONALD G. CONNOLLY, M.D.,

Plaintiffs,

v. C. A. No. 83C-AU-1

RUSSELL J. LABOWITZ, M.D., P.A., RUSSELL J. LABOWITZ, M.D., and JOHN DOES 1,

Defendants.

<u>DEFENDANTS' AMENDMENT TO THE ANSWER TO THE COMPLAINT</u>

Defendants hereby amend their Answer to the Complaint pursuant to Superior Court Civil Rule 15(a) to add a Third Affirmative Defense as follows:

<u>THIRD AFFIRMATIVE DEFENSE</u>

<u>Plaintiffs lack capacity to sue due to incompetency, caused by mental illness.</u>

[signature]
Jane R. Roth
Richards, Layton & Finger
One Rodney Square
P. O. Box 551
Wilmington, DE 19899
Attorney for Defendants
Labowitz, M.D., P.A. and
Labowitz, M.D.

Morton R. Kimmel by JRR
Morton R. Kimmel
Kimmel & Spiller
401 Market Tower
Wilmington, DE 19801
Attorney for Defendants
Labowitz, M.D., P.A. and
Labowitz, M.D.

Dated: September 23, 1983

(EXHIBIT #9 a-b)
-from page 61

IN THE SUPERIOR COURT OF THE STATE OF DELAWARE

IN AND FOR NEW CASTLE COUNTY

RONALD G. CONNOLLY, M.D., P.A. and RONALD G. CONNOLLY, M.D.,	)	
Plaintiffs,	)	
v.	)	C. A. No. 83C-AU-1
RUSSELL J. LABOWITZ, M.D., P.A., RUSSELL J. LABOWITZ, M.D., and JOHN DOES 1,	)	
Defendants.	)	

DEFENDANTS' AMENDMENT TO MOTION FOR PHYSICAL EXAMINATION AND FOR A PROTECTIVE ORDER

Defendants hereby amend their Motion, filed on September 16, 1983 by adding to the first paragraph thereof the following sentence:

> Good cause for a psychiatric examination exists further in the allegation of plaintiffs that they have suffered monetary loss to their professional practice due to the actions alleged in the Complaint. It is the contention that any failure of plaintiffs' professional practice has been caused by plaintiff Ronald G. Connolly, M.D.'s mental illness, and not by any action or conspiracy on the part of defendants.

Defendants hereby further amend the Motion by changing the second paragraph to read as follows:

> An appointment has been made for the examination to be done by Lester Bronheim, M.D., on October 11, 1983, at 1:15 p.m., in Dr. Bronheim's office, Suite 21, 1701 Augustine Cut-Off, Wilmington, Delaware.

(EXHIBIT #9b)

Jane R. Roth
Richards, Layton & Finger
One Rodney Square
P. O. Box 551
Wilmington, DE 19899
Attorney for Defendants
Labowitz, M.D., P.A., and
Labowitz, M.D.

Morton R. Kimmel
Kimmel & Spiller
401 Market Tower
Wilmington, DE 19801
Attorney for Defendants
Labowitz, M.D., P.A. and
Labowitz, M.D.

Dated: September 23, 1983

(EXHIBIT #10)
-from page 62

New Castle County Medical Society, Inc.

Executive Director
Isobel S. Haring

Delaware Academy of Medicine
Lovering Avenue & Union Street
Wilmington, Delaware 19806
Phone (302) 658-3168

August 26, 1983

Ronald G. Connolly, M.D.
2401 Pennsylvania Avenue
Wilmington, DE 19806

Dear Dr. Connolly:

This will confirm my telephone call to your office on Friday, inviting you to attend the New Castle County Medical Society - Peer Review Committee Meeting, Wednesday, September 7th, at 12:15, Delaware Academy of Medicine - Lover Level Conference Room 3.

If you have any questions, please contact Dr. Gustave Berger. Return the enclosed card indicating your attendance.

Sincerely yours,

Mary Anne Leski

Mary Anne Leski

NEW CASTLE COUNTY MEDICAL SOCIETY

PEER REVIEW MEETING

( ) Yes, I will attend the Peer Review Meeting, Wednesday, September 7th, 12:15, Delaware Academy of Medicine.

( ) No, I will not attend this meeting.

____

(EXHIBIT #11)
-from page 67

American College of Physicians
4200 Pine Street
Philadelphia, PA 19104
(215) 243-1200
(800) 523-1546
TWX 710 670 0586

Robert H. Moser, MD, FACP
Executive Vice President

Alfred Lazarus, MD, FACP
ACP Governor for Delaware
Professional Building, Suite 38
1701 Augustine Cut-Off
Wilmington, DE 19803
(302) 655-8009

September 1, 1982

Credentials Committee
American College of Physicians
4200 Pine Street
Philadelphia, Pa. 19104

Dear Sirs:

On May 28th I endorsed a proposal for membership on Dr. Ronald G. Connolly.

I have subsequently learned that he has failed to meet his obligations for teaching at the Medical Center and his Chief of Section has found him deficient in this area. Although, he does do some teaching down state in Delaware, I feel that he should meet the obligations of his primary hospital.

I have discussed this with my committee on membership and they are in unanimous agreement.

I would like to withdraw my recommendation for membership on Dr. Ronald G. Connolly.

Sincerely yours,

Alfred Lazarus, M.D.

AL:mh

(EXHIBIT #12)
-from page 68

§ 1768. Immunity of persons reviewing medical records, medical care and physicians' work.

(a) The Board of Medical Practice, the Medical Society of Delaware, their members, or the members of any committees appointed thereby, and members of hospital and osteopathic medical society committees, or of a professional standards review organization established under federal law (or other peer review committee or organization), whose function is the review of medical records, medical care and physicians' work, with a view to the quality of care and utilization of hospital or nursing home facilities, home visits and office visits, shall not be subject to, and shall be immune from, claim, suit, liability, damages or any other recourse, civil or criminal, arising from any act or proceeding, decision or determination undertaken or performed or recommendation made so long as such member acted in good faith and without malice in carrying out the responsibilities, authority, duties, powers and privileges of the offices conferred by law upon them under this chapter (excluding only subchapter VI of this chapter) or any other provisions of the Delaware law, federal law or regulations, or duly adopted rules and regulations of the aforementioned committees, organizations and hospitals, good faith being presumed until proven otherwise, with malice required to be shown by the complainant.

(b) The records and proceedings of any such committees or organizations as described in subsection (a) of this section shall be confidential and shall be used by such committees or organizations and the members thereof only in the exercise of the proper functions of the committee or organization and shall not be public records and shall not be available for court subpoena or subject to discovery; and no person in attendance at a meeting of any such committee or organization shall be required to testify as to what transpired thereat. No physician, hospital, organization or institution furnishing information, data, reports or records to any such committee or organization with respect to any patient examined or treated by such physician or confined in such hospital or institution shall, by reason of furnishing such information, be liable in damages to any person or subject to any other recourse, civil or criminal. (24 Del. C. 1953, § 1768; 57 Del. Laws, c. 492; 58 Del. Laws, c. 50; 58 Del. Laws, c. 226; 60 Del. Laws, c. 462, § 3; 62 Del. Laws, c. 90, § 2.)

Effect of amendment. — 62 Del. Laws, c. 90, effective July 3, 1979, substituted "The Board of Medical Practice, the Medical Society of Delaware, their members, or the members of any committees appointed thereby, and members of hospital and osteopathic" for "The members of the Board of Medical Practice or of any committee appointed thereby, and members of hospital and medical society and osteopathic" at the beginning of subsection (a).

This section provides confidential protection for records and proceedings of committees charged with professional standards, review and enforcement as well as civil and criminal protection for those performing those functions. Danklef v. Wilmington Medical Center, Del. Super., 429 A.2d 509 (1981).

When section applicable in foreign forum. — This section applies to bar production of the privileged records of a committee where the underlying transaction occurred in Delaware even though suit is brought in another forum. Danklef v. Wilmington Medical Center, Del. Super., 429 A.2d 509 (1981).

(EXHIBIT #13a-b)
-from page 69

1 MR. SERRITELLA: You mean, formally address?

2 BY MR. NEUBERGER:

3 Q Did you respond in any sort of way?

4 MR. SERRITELLA: Do you understand the question?

5 THE WITNESS: Yes.

6 MR. SERRITELLA: "Yes," you understand the question?

7 THE WITNESS: Yes, I understand the question.

8 MR. SERRITELLA: The answer is --

9 THE WITNESS: All right. There is a letter that I

10 wrote to the Credentials Committee allowing them to pass on his

11 application.

12 BY MR. NEUBERGER:

13 Q Okay. Were there any other communications with you

14 besides that from the Philadelphia people?

15 A From them to me?

16 Q Right.

17 A No.

18 Q Okay. Were there any phone conversations or written

19 letters between the two of you?

20 A No other written communications, but several phone

21 conversations.

22 Q Who communicated with you?

23 A I communicated with Dr. Gorsuch, Dr. George Gorsuch,

(EXHIBIT #13b)

1 who is the Executive Assistant -- I forget for what. He's in
2 charge of admissions; administrator-physician.
3 With regard to the application, I was concerned -- I
4 don't know how I was concerned or why -- but as a result of my
5 action, there might be a suit against me, and I asked the College,
6 "If there were a suit, would they support it?" They said,
7 "Yes." I asked them -- they said, "You have a way out. Turn it
8 over to the Credentials Committee and that absolves you." That
9 is the mean by which they acted.
10 Q Okay. Were you aware at that time that Dr. Connolly
11 sought to bring you before the Credentials Committee of the
12 Wilmington Medical Center?
13 A I think that's what prompted this. Yes, I was aware of it
14 I think Dr. Morris informed me there was some question of that.
15 Q Were you aware that sometime after that Dr. Connolly
16 tried to bring the dispute between you and he before the
17 Board of Malpractice in Dover?
18 A I think somebody told me about that, but I don't know
19 who.
20 Q You are aware that that type of thing occurred?
21 A That probably is what led to my conversation with
22 Dr. Gorsuch.
23 Q Do you recall anything else Dr. Gorsuch said to you?

(EXHIBIT #14)
-from page 69

1 A Well, pretty much, that at least for membership,
2 they were getting very relaxed, and if somebody hadn't raped
3 somebody, they would accept them for membership, not Fellowship.
4 Q Had Dr. Labowitz applied for membership in the
5 American College of Physicians?
6 A Not during my tenure.
7 Q If he had up to now, you would be aware of it,
8 wouldn't you?
9 A I would be aware of it as of my tenure.
10 Q You are still a Governor?
11 A I'm still the Governor for another six months.
12 Q Did you at any time ever advise Dr. Labowitz of the
13 results of Dr. Connolly's application for admission to the
14 American College of Physicians?
15 A I don't understand what you are getting at. What
16 results?
17 Q Did you ever tell Dr. Labowitz that Dr. Connolly had
18 been admitted to the American College of Physicians?
19 A I was not informed officially he was admitted. I
20 learned from the rumor mill.
21 Q After you learned from the rumor mill, did you ever
22 tell Dr. Labowitz that?
23 A Probably. May have. I don't know.

(EXHIBIT #15)
-from page 73

This section and 13 Del. C. § 708 as it stood prior to its 1974 amendment were in direct conflict. In re Diane, Del. Ch., 318 A.2d 629 (1974).

Section 708 of Title 13 as it stood prior to its 1974 amendment was held controlling over this section since the former was enacted latest in time. In re Diane, Del. Ch., 318 A.2d 629 (1974).

§ 1791. Refusal to perform or submit to medical procedures.

(a) No person shall be required to perform or participate in medical procedures which result in the termination of pregnancy; and the refusal of any person to perform or participate in these medical procedures shall not be a basis for civil liability to any person, nor a basis for any disciplinary or other recriminatory action against him.

(b) No hospital, hospital director or governing board shall be required to permit the termination of human pregnancies within its institution, and the refusal to permit such procedures shall not be grounds for civil liability to any person, nor a basis for any disciplinary or other recriminatory action against it by the State or any person.

(c) The refusal of any person to submit to an abortion or to give consent shall not be grounds for loss of any privileges or immunities to which such person would otherwise be entitled, nor shall submission to an abortion or the granting of consent be a condition precedent to the receipt of any public benefits. (24 Del. C. 1953, § 1791; 57 Del. Laws, c. 145, § 2.)

§ 1792. Assistance or participation in an unlawful termination of human pregnancy.

No person shall, unless the termination of a human pregnancy has been authorized pursuant to § 1790 of this title:

(1) Sell or give, or cause to be sold or given, any drug, medicine, preparation, instrument or device for the purpose of causing, inducing or obtaining a termination of such pregnancy; or

(2) Give advice, counsel or information for the purpose of causing, inducing or obtaining a termination of such pregnancy; or

(3) Knowingly assist or cause by any means whatsoever the obtaining or performing of a termination of such pregnancy. (24 Del. C. 1953, § 1792; 57 Del. Laws, c. 145, § 2.)

§ 1793. Residency requirements; exceptions.

(a) No person shall be authorized to perform a termination of a human pregnancy within the State upon a female who has not been a resident of this State for a period of at least 120 days next before the performance of an operative procedure for the termination of a human pregnancy.

(b) This section shall not apply to such female who is gainfully employed in this State at the time of conception, or whose spouse is gainfully employed in

1 MR. NEUBERGER: If there has been a
2 disciplinary action, it has been in violation of the
3 Medical Practices Act. In addition, this line of
4 questioning violates his First Amendment right to
5 religious freedom and it is designed to annoy,
6 embarrass and oppress him and I am directing him not
7 to answer it for those three reasons.
8 MRS. ROTH: I think I am perfectly
9 entitled to annoy, embarrass and oppress him! Am I
10 not?
11 MR. NEUBERGER: I think you are not, under
12 the rules. Of course not.
13 On the record. I don't want to be
14 unreasonable but I am taking this legal position and
15 I'm fully willing to brief the matter and allow you
16 to preserve any questions you want if you choose not
17 to put them into the record at this time.
18 MRS. ROTH: Well, we'll move on to other
19 things. But I fail to see in view of your present
20 claim how Section 1791 or the First Amendment has
21 anything to do with the line of questioning that I
22 was going to develop.
23 MR. NEUBERGER: I think it certainly is
24 something that is going to have to be litigated.

1 Q. Did you ever bill for services rendered to
2 Medicaid patients when those services were not
3 rendered?
4 A. To my knowledge there was a period of time, a
5 short period of time where office policy was that if
6 a patient did not show, whether they're Medicaid,
7 private or whatever, that they were billed for it.
8 Now, I'm not sure whether Medicaid was billed for
9 that. But I know that there was a time when my
10 practice was very busy and I resented the fact that
11 people did not have the courtesy to call me to
12 cancel their appointments and I had a large waiting
13 time for people who wanted to see me and I thought
14 it was very inconsiderate and adopted that policy
15 but changed it after realizing that it really wasn't
16 what I wanted to do in the long haul.
17 Now, during that period of time it's
18 possible that Medicaid patients were billed for not
19 showing. But it was done uniformally in the
20 practice, not just for Medicaid patients. →
21 Q. In other words, what you're saying is that
22 there was a cancellation charge or a no-show charge?
23 Is that what you're saying?
24 A. Yes, if there was no notification of

(EXHIBIT #18)
-from page 104

1 or something. And then she left and said, "What a
2 funny situation," because one of the two of them had
3 sued the other on a house thing within the past year,
4 and here they were working closely together -- to add
5 some humor to this unfortunate thing.
6 Q. Doctor, was the comment made or the
7 threat made by any member of the patient's family that
8 they would try to have Dr. Connolly run out of town as
9 a result of this incident?
10 A. I do not recall any statement of anybody
11 saying -- I think there were statements -- at the time,
12 there was a heated portion somewhere along the line.
13 Again, I don't remember all those kind of things. They
14 were very, very upset about this, that a professional
15 should treat a sick girl this way.
16 He was a member
17 of the regular medical fraternity,
18 They were just appalled that the daughter of
19 one of our Staff Chiefs should be treated this way.
20 And you might ask why I dealt with the
21 family more than this girl's husband. Her husband was
22 a person of limited capacity, and really would not have
23 been able to help near as much as one might hope. I

(EXHIBIT #19 a-b)
-from page 104

1 I think if you checked the nurse's notes,
2 you would find a similar notation, I would assume.
3 Q. Doctor, while asking him to advise you as
4 to whether there were any contraindications to the use
5 of intrauterine saline for an abortion, you are asking
6 him to assist you in the abortive process or the abor-
7 tion; were you not?
8 A. No, I don't think I was. That is your
9 opinion. Not mine. And I would emphasize again, you
10 are now asking me opinion, opinion and opinion. You
11 will be charged for my opinion, and your client should
12 understand this. This is not just factual. You are
13 getting into opinion right down the line.
14 Q. All right, doctor.
15 Your testimony is, then, that this was
16 not a request for his opinion as to the abortion?
17 A. I wanted to know if using saline would
18 have any damage to her kidneys. If it would, I would
19 have used another drug in the uterus rather than the
20 salt solution. I was not asking him to help me. I was
21 asking him the reverse. I was asking him, "Was there
22 any danger to the patient's kidneys."
23 I would not ask Dr. Connolly for one help

1 regarding an abortion. This would be an affrontary of
2 the same degree that he has afforded the patient and my-
3 self.
4 Q. Let me show you another consultation, and
5 I will ask that that be marked as the next Exhibit,
6 135.
7 (Wilmington Medical Center Con-
8 sultation dated 10/14/79 was marked for
9 identification as Plaintiffs' Exhibit
10 135 at Dr. Levinson's deposition.)
11 BY MR. GREEN:
12 Q. Are you familiar with that, doctor?
13 A. That same Sunday afternoon, I wrote this
14 formal request for Dr. Cor DeHart to see her. I had
15 alerted him the same day. Several days earlier I
16 alerted Dr. Connolly she was going in. He came into
17 the hospital. Reviewed the chart. Saw the patient
18 and wrote this. I must confess with the copy, I can't
19 read all of the details.
20 But his impression, I believe it reads
21 "Manic depressive," something. I can't read the next
22 line. He recommends "Would observe closely for manic
23 depressive episode."

(EXHIBIT #20)

-from page 107

ADDRESS REPLY TO:

P.O. Box 1668
Delaware Division

DELAWARE DIVISION
MEMORIAL DIVISION
WILMINGTON GENERAL DIVISION
EUGENE DUPONT MEMORIAL HOSPITAL

WILMINGTON MEDICAL CENTER
WILMINGTON, DELAWARE 19899

June 5, 1984

Ronald G. Connolly, M.D.
2401 Pennsylvania Avenue
Suite 112
Wilmington, Delaware 19806

Dear Doctor Connolly:

The Department of Medicine's Credentials Committee has reviewed your request to be made a consultant to the Wilmington Medical Center. They reviewed this in great care, but find that you do not meet the criteria for being a consultant.

Since the Credentials Committee of the Department of Medicine has now reviewed three different requests in trying to arrive at a proper appointment which would be acceptable to both you and the Medical Center, our Credentials Committee has reaffirmed their original recommendation that you be offered a position as an Assistant in the Section of Internal Medicine and a member of the Active Staff. I am therefore offering you that appointment which I hope you will accept understanding all the duties and obligations as well as privileges that go with the appointment. If this is acceptable to you, please let me know in writing within two weeks of the receipt of this letter. If I have not heard from you within two weeks, I will assume that you are not interested in an appointment at the Wilmington Medical Center, and you will be dropped from the staff.

Sincerely yours,

Robert B. Flinn

Robert B. Flinn, M.D.
Director, Department of Medicine

RBF/jva
cc: Allston J. Morris, M.D.
Vice President for Medical Affairs

A PRIVATE, NOT-FOR-PROFIT, NON-GOVERNMENT HOSPITAL, RECEIVING NO TAX SUPPORT FOR OPERATIONS

20203)

(EXHIBIT #21)
-from page 107

DIPLOMATE OF THE AMERICAN
BOARD OF INTERNAL MEDICINE

DIPLOMATE OF THE AMERICAN
BOARD OF RHEUMATOLOGY

RONALD G. CONNOLLY, M.D.
PROFESSIONAL ASSOCIATION
2401 PENNSYLVANIA AVENUE
WILMINGTON, DELAWARE 19806
(302) 655-6067

June 15, 1984

Robert B. Flinn, M.D.
Delaware Division
Wilmington Medical Center
501 West 14th Street
Wilmington, DE 19801

Dear Dr. Flinn:

I received your letter of June 5, 1984.

I accept the position in the Section of Internal Medicine. I could work during the months of September, October, November, February, March or April if two of these months would work into your schedule.

Sincerely,

Ronald G. Connolly, M.D.

RGC/fp

(EXHIBIT #22)

-from page 108

ADDRESS REPLY TO:

Robert B. Flinn, M.D.
Director
Department of Medicine

DELAWARE DIVISION
MEMORIAL DIVISION
WILMINGTON GENERAL DIVISION
EUGENE DUPONT MEMORIAL HOSPITAL

WILMINGTON MEDICAL CENTER
WILMINGTON, DELAWARE 19899

July 25, 1984

Ronald G. Connolly, M.D.
2401 Pennsylvania Avenue
Wilmington, Delaware 19806

Dear Doctor Connolly:

After receiving your letter that you would be willing to accept an appointment in the Section of Internal Medicine, thus transferring out of the Rheumatology Section, I forwarded this change in appointment back through normal channels. Appointment changes go through the Department's Credentials Committee and then over my desk; then on to the Central Credentials Committee and through Staff Council to the Board.

The Department of Medicine's Credentials Committee has agreed in principle with your change in status, but has reiterated to me its feeling that before giving its final approval that a psychiatric evaluation be made. As you recall, some months ago, I told you that we were concerned about you, and that the Credentials Committee of the Department of Medicine had recommended that you seek psychiatric attention. Therefore, in keeping with the Credentials Committee's request, if you are to have an appointment at the Wilmington Medical Center, it will be necessary for you to have a psychiatric evaluation by a mutually agreeable psychiatrist. If the psychiatric evaluation finds you in good mental health and recommends continued staff privileges, I will be happy to forward your application on to the Central Credentials Committee.

In an attempt to come to a conclusion on this matter, I would like to request that the evaluation be completed before the first of September. Should you choose not to go along with this request by the first of September, we will be forced to consider that you have resigned from our staff.

If there are any questions about this or if I can help you in any way, please feel free to contact me.

Sincerely yours,

Robert B. Flinn, M.D.
Director, Department of Medicine

RBF/jva

203)

(EXHIBIT #23 a-g)
-from page 111

NOTE: To avoid possible embarrassment of those people sued by Dr. Labowitz, their names and addresses have been deleted.

Civil Action No.	Amount	Remarks
219-03-1982	$170.00	Default Judgment
001-08-1980	Unknown	Served - Later Dismissed
224-03-1982	233.00	No Service Made
011-08-1980	149.00 (Complaint demands $239 - apparently an error in complaint)	Default
223-03-1982	94.00	No Service Made
030-07-1982	120.00	No Service Made

(EXHIBIT #23b)

Civil Action No.	Amount	Remarks
222-03-1982	$194.40	No Service Made
006-08-1980	Unknown	No Service Made - Dismissed Without Prejudice
005-08-1980	Unknown	No Service Made On Original Or Alias Summonses - Dismissed Without Prejudice
185-12-1982	738.00	Default - Attachment Made
039-07-1982	97.00	Default Judgment
250-08-1980	71.00	No Service - Dimissed For Failure to Prosecute
034-07-1982	75.00	Served - Later Dismissed
116-08-1980	102.00	Default Judgment

(EXHIBIT #23c)

	Civil Action No.	Amount	Remarks
	008-08-1980	$215.00	Default Judgment - Attachment Unsuccessful
	033-07-1982	75.00	Served
	077-01-1981	78.50	Incomplete Service - (Tried Three Times)
le	076-01-1981	Unknown	Answer Filed - Later Dismissed With Prejudice By Stipulation
	022-08-1980	141.00	Default Judgment - Attachment Made - Satisfied
	221-03-1982	72.56	Served
	016-06-1982	474.00	Default Judgment

(EXHIBIT #23d)

Civil Action No.	Amount	Remarks
038-07-1982	$128.54	No Service Made
165-05-1982	390.00	Default Judgment
037-07-1982	120.00	No Service Made
007-08-1980	Unknown	No Service Made - Dismissed Without Prejudice
010-08-1980	80.00	Default Judgment
074-01-1981	150.00	Default Judgment - Attachment Unsuccessful
012-08-1980	Unknown	Served - Later Dismissed Without Prejudice
073-01-1981	Unknown	Incomplete Service - Dismissed Without Prejudice

(EXHIBIT #23e)

Civil Action No.	Amount	Remarks
032-07-1982	$127.00	Default Judgment - Attachment Made - Satisfied
009-08-1980	98.00	Default Judgment - Attachment Attempted
036-07-1982	155.00	No Service Made
021-08-1980	120.00	Default Judgment
005-09-1980	Unknown	Served - Later Dismissed Without Prejudice
115-08-1980	64.00	No Service Made - Dismissed For Failure To Prosecute
003-08-1980	154.82	Default Judgment
220-03-1982	90.00	No Service Made

(EXHIBIT #23f)

Civil Action No.	Amount	Remarks
004-08-1980	$167.00	Default Judgment - Satisfied
102-02-1981	167.00	Default Judgment - Attachment Made - Satisfied
117-08-1980	89.00	No Service Made - Dismissed For Failure To Prosecute
017-06-1982	116.00	Default Judgment
031-07-1982	164.00 (Complaint demands $169.50 - Apparently an error in complaint)	Service Made On Fourth Summons - Default Judg- ment - Attachment Attempted
101-02-1981	95.00	Service Made - Later Dismissed For Failure To Prosecute
002-08-1980	127.50	Default Judgment - Attachment Made - Satisfied

(EXHIBIT #23g)

Civil Action No.	Amount	Remarks
027-04-1982	$ 82.00	Default Judgment
221-04-1982	272.50	Default Judgment
004-09-1980	308.00	Default Judgment - Attachment Attempted
035-07-1982	75.00	Default Judgment

(EXHIBIT #24 a-d)
-from page 116

1 Number one, the issue is the bringing of the motion in
2 this Court, and that was my determination. That was
3 my determination because of my concern.
4 THE COURT: I presume it was your determina-
5 tion based upon what the doctors told you.
6 MRS. ROTH: Well, it was based on more than
7 that.
8 THE COURT: Okay. But you use that. You used
9 it and pulled this out of the air in saying we are
10 going to offend Dr. Connolly and embarrass him by
11 filing this motion.
12 MRS. ROTH: I certainly did not.
13 THE COURT: I certainly wouldn't assume that,
14 either. So, the doctors had to tell you something.
15 MRS. ROTH: Well, I saw the recommendation of
16 the credentials committee that Dr. Connolly should have
17 a psychiatric evaluation. I was concerned myself from
18 the conversation that Mr. Green mentioned that I had
19 with Dr. Connolly about Dr. Connolly's mental p. 52
20 equilibrium. Therefore, on the basis of that alone,
21 I would have not done anything. But I saw the
22 recommendation, which Dr. Connolly has produced, of
23 the credentials committee saying they felt his complaint

(EXHIBIT #24b)

1 against Dr. Labowitz was unfounded, and recommending
2 that he have a psychiatric evaluation. I was concerned
3 that Dr. Connolly is bringing now in the courts of
4 this state a lawsuit against Dr. Labowitz based upon
5 the same unfounded contentions that he won't give up.
6 I called Dr. Reese, because I knew from
7 Dr. Connolly's letter that Dr. Reese would apparently
8 be of the opinion, since that was the recommendation of
9 the credentials committee, that Dr. Connolly needed a
10 psychiatric evaluation. I talked to Dr. Reese. I
11 said, based on, you know, the complaint that
12 Dr. Connolly made to the credentials committee, and
13 on your observations of Dr. Connolly, do you think,
14 you know -- does this bear out your opinion that he
15 needs a psychiatric evaluation? Dr. Reese said yes.
16 Dr. Reese is trained not to treat psychiatric condi-
17 tions, but as a neurologist. He is trained to recogniz
18 it. And with that medical training, he has -- he told
19 me, yes, I am of the opinion that he needs psychiatric
20 evaluation. And I said further, as he stated in his
21 affidavit, are you of the opinion that the bringing of
22 this suit is a manifestation of a psychiatric condition
23 That doesn't mean he can't go and treat a patient, but

(EXHIBIT #24c)

1 just in his ability to deal with his complaints about
2 Dr. Labowitz, is his mental status affecting his
3 ability to deal with these complaints rationally, or
4 is he using the courts of this state in an effort to
5 get a vindication which, in his mental condition, he
6 feels is necessary, but legally isn't so.
7 This lawsuit has caused great personal ✓
8 concern and damage and hurt to Dr. Labowitz, also.
9 There are papers filed by Dr. Connolly saying that
10 Dr. Labowitz was involved in Medicaid fraud. That was
11 printed in the newspaper. There was an Attorney
12 General's investigation of Dr. Labowitz because of the
13 allegations of Medicaid fraud. And the Attorney
14 General's Office, after fully investigating this
15 claim, said that it is entirely without basis. There
16 is no reason to say that there is any Medicaid fraud,
17 any claim, any improper activity of Dr. Labowitz in
18 this area at all. And they go on to say, moreover,
19 it appears that Dr. Labowitz is a caring and competent
20 physician. This is a letter from Alex J. Smalls,
21 Director of the Medicaid Fraud Control Unit, of
22 August 13, 1984. So that the complaints that
23 Dr. Connolly is making, my concern is that these are

(EXHIBIT #24d)

1 complaints which are directed at his apparent vendetta
2 against Dr. Labowitz, which is without justification,
3 has been found to be without justification by the
4 credentials committee, has found to be without
5 justification by the doctors who have reviewed the
6 letter to the Delaware Medical Journal, which is causing
7 Dr. Labowitz great personal pain, great personal
8 publicity, reaction to adverse publicity. And I am
9 concerned on the basis of Dr. Reese's opinion, on the
10 basis of my own observations, that this complaint, this
11 vendetta against Dr. Labowitz is a manifestation of
12 Dr. Connolly's mental condition. And I think it would
13 be valuable to have a psychiatric review of his mental
14 condition. I think this issue is in this case in
15 another aspect, also, and that aspect is, Dr. Connolly
16 says, my medical practice has failed. I haven't
17 succeeded. He is saying, it's got to be because of
18 this conspiracy of Dr. Labowitz.
19 I think if his medical practice has failed,
20 that there are other reasons that his medical practice
21 has failed, and one of them is, is he mentally
22 able to conduct a successful medical practice. And
23 I think for that reason --

(EXHIBIT #25)
-from page 129

STATE OF DELAWARE
DEPARTMENT OF ADMINISTRATIVE SERVICES
BOARD OF MEDICAL PRACTICE
MARGARET O'NEILL BUILDING
P. O. BOX 1401
DOVER, DELAWARE 19901

TELEPHONE: (302) 736 - 4753

January 21, 1985

Dr. Ronald G. Connolly
2401 Pennsylvania Avenue
Wilmington, Delaware 19806

Dear Dr. Connolly:

I wish to inform you the Board of Medical Practice has carefully considered all your complaints against Dr. Russell J. Labowitz.

None of the complaints that could be documented were of the magnitude that would warrant any action by the Board of Medical Practice against Dr. Labowitz.

The Board has spent considerable time on the merit of the complaints and it is the unanimous decision of the Board that it is not in the best interest to you, Dr. Labowitz, or the Medical Profession to pursue this matter any further.

The Board urges immediate resolution of this controversy.

Sincerely,

I. J. Tikellis, rsp

I. J. Tikellis, M.D.
President
Delaware Board of Medical Practice

IJT/rsp

1 relate to office personnel and the way we perceive
2 the office functioning are somewhat different.
3 I think that Dr. Labowitz's office was
4 part and parcel of his personality the way he
5 functioned as a person. And as I matured in my own
6 practice and as a person in private practice of
7 medicine, I became more and more convinced that it
8 was not really -- the office was not really going to
9 be representative of Dr. Newman and Dr. Labowitz,
10 but was going to continue to be representative of
11 Dr. Labowitz, and I felt I wasn't learning enough of
12 the business aspects of medicine. And we had other
13 business disagreements, that the sum total of which
14 led to the decision to go into practice on my own.
15 Q. Was there anything that you learned
16 about Dr. Labowitz as a result of this litigation
17 which affected your decision?
18 A. Absolutely not, and had nothing to do
19 with the litigation.
20 Q. Did Dr. Labowitz meet your standards of
21 being an ethical physician? Was that a
22 philosophical difference?
23 A. I felt Dr. Labowitz was an ethical
24 physician.

1 Q. Did he meet your standards?
2 A. Yes. I found his behavior to be
3 acceptable to me.
4 Q. Was the decision a mutually agreeable
5 decision to part ways or was it not agreeable to
6 both parties?
7 A. Well, I think that agreeable may not be
8 the best term to use in this situation. I think
9 that there was a growing division between us that I
10 perceived and that led to the decision to separate
11 from Dr. Labowitz, at least separate from a business
12 point of view.
13 And then when we tried to work out any
14 kind of ongoing practice within the same office in a
15 sharing type situation, substantive issues of
16 compensation and business arose that we couldn't
17 come to terms with. And because when two guys work
18 together and can't come to terms on very specific
19 issues, then you can't conceivably stay together.
20 Q. One last question, Doctor, for now and
21 then we will recess.
22 A. Is it going to be much longer? Because
23 if this can conceivably finish it today, I'd like to
24 do it.

(EXHIBIT #27 a-b)
-from page 141

1 question under advisement. Before we even proceed to
2 talk about what Mrs. Roth wants to discuss let me jump
3 back a moment to the earlier question because I think
4 I see what Mr. Parkins was questioning.
5 If in laying the foundation for questions
6 regarding the relationship between Dr. Flynn and any
7 involvement he may have with the Credentials Committee
8 insofar as it relates to the courtesy status of the
9 doctor, if it is, if there are no questions which are
10 answered by Dr. Flynn which would suggest that he had
11 any involvement whatsoever in Dr. Marro's application
12 which was granted for courtesy status, then I will not
13 permit Mr. Green to explore any business relationship
14 between Dr. Flynn and Dr. Marro.
15 If he had any involvement whatsoever in that
16 process then the answer is you can explore it.
17 MR. PARKINS: Now, I assume the Court's ruling
18 is irrespective of whether Dr. Flynn had any involvement
19 at all in Dr. Connolly's application?
20 THE COURT: That's correct.
21 MISS ROTH: Okay, Your Honor, at the commence-
22 ment of this litigation back in September of 1983 I
23 filed a motion for a psychiatric examination of Dr.

(EXHIBIT #27b)

Connolly supported by an affidavit of a physician, Dr. Charles Lee Reese, III, a neurologist certified by the Board of Psychiatry and Neurology who is trained to recognize psychiatric disorders although not to treat them, and who stated in his affidavit that he was familiar -- as he was familiar with the complaint made by Dr. Connolly to the Credentials Committee that he felt he was a manifest nut. It was a manifestation of a psychiatric disorder. This motion was presented to the Court.

THE COURT: I have a question. I even avoided reading the article in the paper that was in there recently because I realized this case was not especially assigned. Was there a definition given to or was there a label given to this assertion of a mental health problem?

MISS ROTH: As a specific category?

THE COURT: Yes.

MISS ROTH: No, there was not. There was a manifestation of a psychiatric disorder.

THE COURT: Okay.

MISS ROTH: The motion was presented to Judge Martin who on September 30th denied it but stated that

(EXHIBIT #28)
-from page 142

OFFICE OF DISCIPLINARY COUNSEL
BOARD ON PROFESSIONAL RESPONSIBILITY
SUPREME COURT OF THE STATE OF DELAWARE

L. SUSAN FAW
DISCIPLINARY COUNSEL

200 WEST NINTH STREET
P. O. BOX 1808
WILMINGTON, DE 19899
(302) 571-8703

June 4, 1985

CONFIDENTIAL

Ronald G. Connolly, M.D.
2401 Pennsylvania Avenue
Wilmington, DE 19806

RE: Informal Docket No. 47
Jane R. Roth, Esquire
(Complainant: Ronald G. Connolly, M.D.)

Dear Dr. Connolly:

As you are aware, Mr. Poole has investigated your complaint and has concluded that there is not a sufficient basis upon which to initiate formal disciplinary action against Mrs. Roth. I have reviewed his report to me of May 17, a copy of which you received, and I concur with Mr. Poole. Accordingly, I consider my file in this matter closed.

Thank you for cooperating with Mr. Poole in the course of his investigation of this matter.

Sincerely,

L. Susan Faw

LSF:era

cc: James S. Green, Esquire
Richard E. Poole, Esquire

1 agree with you on the patient having this
2 diagnosis." So it makes no sense to any of us.
3 Q. The last page of that document is a letter
4 from you to Dr. Connolly dated April 29, 1983. You
5 indicate that it was your opinion -- well, you state
6 "It is the committee's opinion and mine that
7 Dr. Labowitz has behaved in a very ethical fashion
8 and we simply do not agree with your
9 interpretation."
10 A. Yes.
11 Q. Several questions, Doctor. On what did you
12 base your opinion that Dr. Labowitz acted in a very
13 ethical fashion?
14 A. On all of the evidence that I could collect
15 and that the committee collected. You know, that's
16 basically what the committee's opinion was and I
17 also agreed with the committee, because I believe
18 all the evidence that the committee had I also had,
19 although I can't be sure because I wasn't in the
20 committee meetings.
21 Q. You say "We simply do not agree with your
22 interpretation." And isn't that the basis upon
23 which you say that Dr. Connolly needs psychiatric
24 help, because he has a different interpretation of

1 the facts than you?

2 A. If you look out a window and you see the sky

3 is blue and Dr. Connolly looks out the window and

4 says it's black, we do have a difference of

5 interpretation but the sky is blue.

6 The facts here and Dr. Connolly came

7 back to me saying people didn't understand, et

8 cetera, is that he has taken a series of facts and

9 managed or tried to get a link to put one fact

10 together, and very frequently the fact that he is

11 using as the link is false. All right? And in

12 addition -- So that if you get into a discussion

13 with Dr. Connolly, all these facts come up and he

14 feels that we don't understand him.

15 By saying that I disagreed with his

16 interpretation of the facts means in this specific

17 reference that further discussion with me about the

18 facts and that people didn't understand them is

19 really inappropriate. We looked at all the facts.

20 We looked at all his evidence and find that his

21 interpretation is flawed. And it's not only that I

22 disagree with his interpretation but everybody

23 else.

24 Q. I think you've answered my question.

(EXHIBIT #30 a-b)
-from page 153

RECEIVED
MAY 21 1985
J. R. R.

May 17, 1985

Jane Roth, Esquire
Richards, Layton & Finger
1 Rodney Square
P.O. Box 551
Wilmington, DE 19899

Re: Ronald G. Connolly Tape

Dear Ms. Roth:

I have listened to the tape of the meeting conducted with the committee of the Department of Medicine and Dr. Ronald G. Connolly.

It appears to me Dr. Connolly does have some strong unchangeable ideas about the motivations of Dr. Labowitz. It appears as if the data base for this is minimal, it appears as if Dr. Connolly is unwilling to consider any other explanations. A prudent person would consider the following kinds of possibilities:

1. The patient is distorting what Dr. Labowitz told her.

2. Dr. Labowitz is not interested in seeing this patient and would just as soon have someone else, Dr. Connolly or another person see her.

3. Dr. Labowitz may not agree with Dr. Connolly's treatment philosophy and may not want to refer patients to him but may not be actively sabotaging him. In order to develop these alternatives, Dr. Connolly would have to be talking with Dr. Labowitz about what had happened, why it had happened, etc., none of which is taking place. This is more the behavior of someone with a fixed delusional system and not the usual kind of behavior in the medical community where patients are frequently passed on to one doctor to another and there are frequent misunderstandings about the reasons for a referral or

WILMINGTON HOSPITAL
501 WEST 14TH STREET
P.O. BOX 1668
WILMINGTON, DELAWARE 19899

---

the patient distorts what the referring physician has said to him or her. I originally discussed some of the problems of Dr. Connolly's with Dr. Flinn about 2 years ago and after my examination of letters and the taping, I believe are consistent with the person who has a fixed delusional system about the motivations of Dr. Labowitz and perhaps other physicians.

Best wishes,

David E. Raskin, M.D.
Director of Psychiatry

DER:nls

1 conjunction with this litigation the nature of which
2 is" and there should be some index showing that.
3 "Do you need this material? Do you want it there to
4 conduct your evaluation or do you want it
5 afterwards?"
6 If he says "I want it there," then we
7 send it. If he says "I want it afterwards," we keep
8 it. If he says "I'm not interested in it," maybe
9 Mr. Carpenter can say, you know, his opinion is not
10 worth the paper it's written on.
11 MR. CARPENTER: There is a further
12 point, although I think your Honor has grasped the
13 significance of this. The necessity of his having
14 these materials readily available to him is enhanced
15 not only because we are talking about periods of
16 time that are somewhat remote now but also because
17 the nature of this illness as it has been explained
18 to us is that it is, I think the psychiatric term,
19 compensated. Which means that there are periods of
20 what perhaps you and I would call remission during
21 which time Dr. Connolly is not climbing the walls or
22 claiming that people are after him and he appears
23 even to a psychiatrist to be in reasonably good
24 shape. And the psychiatrist would need to know how

1 he acted on other occasions. And that's only
2 available to him through the documentation,
3 including the depositions in this case.
4 THE COURT: I think what I need to do
5 in this letter is articulate at least with some
6 degree of precision the claim that is made with
7 respect to his mental condition and suggest that
8 there are documents which a particular party
9 believes substantiates that claim. I don't think,
10 given this gentleman's reputation and with him
11 understanding -- and this is what he understands at
12 this point -- that he is the Court's expert, that
13 having him be aware of the claim is going to
14 influence him one way or the other.
15 MR. GREEN: Your Honor, I noted in one
16 of Dr. Rappeport's articles he said that when a
17 psychiatrist is called upon to estimate someone's
18 mental state at a past time, he becomes somewhat of
19 a psychohistorian I think is the word he uses. And
20 in that regard these documents which have been
21 generated are not the only thing but he talks about
22 interviews with family members.
23 THE COURT: He may want to do that.
24 MR. GREEN: I mean, I don't know where

(EXHIBIT #32 a-e)
-from pages 227-229

JONAS R. RAPPEPORT, M.D.
THE PROFESSIONAL ARTS BUILDING
101 W READ STREET
BALTIMORE, MARYLAND 21201
(301) 837-7888

PSYCHIATRIC CONSULTATION

Ronald G. Connolly, M.D., P.A., et al. v.
Russell J. Labowitz, M.D., P.A., et al.
C. A. No. 83C-AU-1

Ronald G. Connolly, M.D.

Dates of Interviews: May 22, 1987 3 hours
June 2, 1987 3 hours
June 12, 1987 2 hours

Referred by: The Hon. Vincent J.Poppiti
Superior Court of the State of Delaware
Court House
Wilmington, DE 19801

REASON FOR REFERRAL

Ronald G. Connolly, M.D. has been referred for psychiatric evaluation by The Hon. Vincent J. Poppiti per his letter of May 13, 1987. Judge Poppiti states ". . .Dr. Connolly has alleged that since approximately 1979, Dr. Labowitz has engaged in a course of conduct which has tortiously interfered with Dr. Connolly's practice and with his professional advancement at the Medical Center of Delaware. These allegations are denied by Dr. Labowitz.

"Dr. Connolly also alleges that Dr. Labowitz, and other physicians with whom Dr. Labowitz acted in concert or in a conspiracy, have made statements that Dr. Connolly suffered from a mental illness and should submit to a psychiatric

(EXHIBIT #32b)

PSYCHIATRIC OPINION

Diagnosis: Paranoid Personality Disorder and Compulsive Personality Disorder 301.00 and 301.40 DSM III.

It is my opinion, within reasonable medical certainty, that Dr. Ronald G. Connolly is suffering from personality disorders of a compulsive and paranoid type, based on my eight hours of personal interview and my review of most of the materials furnished to me by the plaintiff and the defendant.

It is my opinion, within reasonable medical certainty, that Ronald G. Connolly, M.D. presently has a diagnosable mental disorder, namely Paranoid Personality Disorder and Compulsive Personality Disorder. The particularity of the information obtained as a result of my examination and how it applies to his diagnosis is mentioned below. From a theoretical standpoint, Dr. Connolly is in need of psychiatric treatment of a psychotherapeutic nature, most probably a combination of dynamic and behavioral psychotherapy or other forms of "talking therapy." However, individuals with personality disorders, particularly the two of which Dr. Connolly suffers, do not do well in any type of treatment. They resist it and avoid it and it generally is not successful. This disorder is very fixed and since they do not "suffer" (anxiety, pain, etc.) their motivation for change is limited.

I believe further that from about 1979 through 1984 Dr. Connolly was suffering from the same mental disorders for the same reasons described in this report and that Dr. Connolly would have been in need of mental health treatment of the type described above.

I believe that Dr. Connolly suffers from a paranoid personality disorder based on his hypersensitivity to criticism from those around him. He takes a total situation and breaks it down into very minor points, looking at the minor points that fit his preconceived idea and paying no attention to those that refute his belief that he is being persecuted, criticized or maligned. In a similar fashion he is unable to look at any of his behavior as possibly contributing to the difficulties that he may or may not be having with others and that his very behavior causes others to react to him in what he perceives as an unfriendly or negative fashion.

I have added as Section 9 the full text of the sections of DSM III dealing with Personality Disorders and more specifically the Paranoid and the Compulsive Personality Disorders. Below I have only listed those features which are clearly found in my evaluation of Dr. Connolly.

(EXHIBIT #32c)

DSM III says, under Paranoid Personality Disorder (page 307), "When individuals with this disorder find themselves in a new situation, they intensely and narrowly search for confirmation of their expectations, with no appreciation of the total context. Their final conclusion is usually precisely what they expected in the first place. They are concerned with hidden motives and special meanings. . .

"Individuals with this disorder are usually argumentative and exaggerate difficulties by 'making mountains out of molehills.' They often find it difficult to relax, usually appear tense, and show a tendency to counterattack when they perceive any threat. Though they are critical of others, and often litigious, they have great difficulty accepting criticism themselves.

"These individuals' affectivity is restricted, and they may appear 'cold' to others. They have no true sense of humor and are usually serious. They may pride themselves on always being objective, rational and unemotional. They usually lack passive, soft, sentimental and tender feelings."

Under Associated Features (p. 308) "Individuals with this disorder are occasionally seen by others as keen observers who are energetic, ambitious and capable; but more often they are viewed as hostile, stubborn, and defensive. They tend to be rigid and unwilling to compromise. They often generate uneasiness and fear in others. Often there is an inordinate fear of losing independence or the power to shape events in accordance with their own wishes.

"They usually avoid intimacy except with those in whom they have absolute trust. They show an excessive need to be self-sufficient, to the point of egocentricity and exaggerated self-importance. They avoid participation in group activities unless they are in a dominant position.

". . . They are keenly aware of power and rank and of who is superior or inferior and are often envious and jealous of those in positions of power. . ."

Under Impairment, (p. 308) ". . . However, occupational difficulties are common, especially in relating to authority figures or co-workers. . ."

The diagnostic criteria for paranoid personality disorder (p.309).

"A. Pervasive, unwarranted suspiciousness and mistrust of people as indicated by at least three of the following: (Those that Dr. Connolly clearly shows are at least):

(EXHIBIT #32d)

(1) Expectation of trickery or harm. (Madeline Boone referred from Dr. Labowitz)

(4) Avoidance of accepting blame when warranted. (1979 abortion issue, no residents in private office, etc.) ✓

(6) Intense, narrowly focussed searching for confirmation of bias, with loss of appreciation of total context. (1979 abortion issue)

(7) Over concern with hidden motives and special meanings. (Madeline Boone referral, response from Dr. Lang re reduction in Dr. Connolly's duties)

B. Hypersensitivity as indicated by at least two of the following:

(1) Tendency to be easily slighted and quick to take offense. (Letter to editor) ✓

(2) Exaggeration of difficulties, e.g., 'making mountains out of molehills.' (Residents in office, Mrs. Roth's judicial appointment

(3) Readiness to counter attack when any threat is perceived. (Mrs. Roth, Dr. Lang's letter, etc.)

C. Restricted affectivity as indicated by at least two of the following:

(1) Appearance of being 'cold' and unemotional. (My evaluation and Dr. Olsson's, 1979 abortion issue)

(3) Lack of a true sense of humor. (my evaluation and Dr. Olsson's)

D. Not due to another mental disorder such as schizophrenia or a paranoid disorder." (No other mental disorder evidenced)

Under Compulsive Personality Disorder 301.40, DSM III says, "The essential feature is a Personality Disorder (p. 305) in which there generally are restricted ability to express warm and tender emotions; perfectionism that interferes with the ability to grasp "the big picture"; insistence that others submit to his or her way of doing things; excessive devotion to work and productivity to the exclusion of pleasure; and indecisiveness. . .

"Preoccupation with rules, efficiency, trivial details, procedures, or form interferes with the ability to take a broad view of things . . .

"Individuals with this disorder are always mindful of their relative status in dominance-submission relationships. Although they resist the authority of others, they stubbornly insist that people conform to their way of doing things.

(EXHIBIT #32e)

They are unaware of the feelings of resentment or hurt that this behavior evokes in others. . .

"Individuals with this disorder tend to be excessively conscientious, moralistic, scrupulous, and judgmental of self and others. . . When they are unable to conttol others, a situation, or their environment, they often ruminate about the situation and become angry, although the anger is usually not expressed directly. . . Frequently there is extreme sensitivity to social criticism, especially if it comes from someone with considerable status or authority."

The diagnostic criteria for compulsive personality disorder that apply to Dr. Connolly are: (p. 327, DSM III)

(1) restricted ability to express warm and tender emotions. (Dr. Connolly's behavior during my interview and that of Dr. Olsson)
(2) perfectionism that interferes with the ability to grasp "the big picture," e.g. preoccupation with trivial details, rules, order, organization, schedules, and lists (1979 abortion issue, Madeline Boone, interview and deposition behavior)
(3) insistence that others submit to his or her way of doing things, and lack of awareness of the feelings elicited by this behavior. (1979 abortion issue, no residents in the office, his testimony with reference to Mrs. Roth's appointment to the bench, etc.)
(5) indecisiveness. (Behavior with Dr. Olsson, although more evidence would be desireable.)

Clearly three of the five items listed in DSM III are met by Dr. Connolly based on the evidence that I have. However, reading between the lines and using clinical judgment as well as psychological test results, I believe that Dr. Connolly fits that definition. (As Chief Justice Potter Stewart once said with reference to the definition of pornography, "I shall not today attempt to further define the kind of materials I understand to be embraced within that shorthand definition and perhaps I could never succeed in doing so. . . but I know it when I see it.")

During my interviews with Dr. Connolly, he represented the epitomé of total coldness, humorlessness and lack of any apparent feeling except for the frequent flushing of his face and a minimal expression of some anger towards Dr. Labowitz. Of the thousands of patients that I have examined, I believe that he represents one of the most controlled, expressionless persons that I have seen. He practically did not move throughout the interviews. He refused anything to drink, and if my recollection is correct did not even use the bathroom, despite the fact that I found it necessary to take a couple

(EXHIBIT #33)
-from page 230

They are unaware of the feelings of resentment or hurt that this behavior evokes in others. . .

"Individuals with this disorder tend to be excessively conscientious, moralistic, scrupulous, and judgmental of self and others. . . When they are unable to control others, a situation, or their environment, they often ruminate about the situation and become angry, although the anger is usually not expressed directly. . . Frequently there is extreme sensitivity to social criticism, especially if it comes from someone with considerable status or authority."

The diagnostic criteria for compulsive personality disorder that apply to Dr. Connolly are: (p. 327, DSM III)

(1) restricted ability to express warm and tender emotions. (Dr. Connolly's behavior during my interview and that of Dr. Olsson)

(2) perfectionism that interferes with the ability to grasp "the big picture," e.g. preoccupation with trivial details, rules, order, organization, schedules, and lists (1979 abortion issue, Madeline Boone, interview and deposition behavior)

(3) insistence that others submit to his or her way of doing things, and lack of awareness of the feelings elicited by this behavior. (1979 abortion issue, no residents in the office, his testimony with reference to Mrs. Roth's appointment to the bench, etc.)

(5) indecisiveness. (Behavior with Dr. Olsson, although more evidence would be desireable.)

Clearly three of the five items listed in DSM III are met by Dr. Connolly based on the evidence that I have. However, reading between the lines and using clinical judgment as well as psychological test results, I believe that Dr. Connolly fits that definition. (As Chief Justice Potter Stewart once said with reference to the definition of pornography, "I shall not today attempt to further define the kind of materials I understand to be embraced within that shorthand definition and perhaps I could never succeed in doing so. . . but I know it when I see it.")

During my interviews with Dr. Connolly, he represented the epitome of total coldness, humorlessness and lack of any apparent feeling except for the frequent flushing of his face and a minimal expression of some anger towards Dr. Labowitz. Of the thousands of patients that I have examined, I believe that he represents one of the most controlled, expressionless persons that I have seen. He practically did not move throughout the interviews. He refused anything to drink, and if my recollection is correct did not even use the bathroom, despite the fact that I found it necessary to take a couple

(EXHIBIT #34 a-b)
-from page 230

They are unaware of the feelings of resentment or hurt that this behavior evokes in others. . .

"Individuals with this disorder tend to be excessively conscientious, moralistic, scrupulous, and judgmental of self and others. . . When they are unable to control others, a situation, or their environment, they often ruminate about the situation and become angry, although the anger is usually not expressed directly. . . Frequently there is extreme sensitivity to social criticism, especially if it comes from someone with considerable status or authority."

The diagnostic criteria for compulsive personality disorder that apply to Dr. Connolly are: (p. 327, DSM III)

(1) restricted ability to express warm and tender emotions. (Dr. Connolly's behavior during my interview and that of Dr. Olsson)

(2) perfectionism that interferes with the ability to grasp "the big picture," e.g. preoccupation with trivial details, rules, order, organization, schedules, and lists (1979 abortion issue, Madeline Boone, interview and deposition behavior)

(3) insistence that others submit to his or her way of doing things, and lack of awareness of the feelings elicited by this behavior. (1979 abortion issue, no residents in the office, his testimony with reference to Mrs. Roth's appointment to the bench, etc.)

(5) indecisiveness. (Behavior with Dr. Olsson, although more evidence would be desireable.)

Clearly three of the five items listed in DSM III are met by Dr. Connolly based on the evidence that I have. However, reading between the lines and using clinical judgment as well as psychological test results, I believe that Dr. Connolly fits that definition. (As Chief Justice Potter Stewart once said with reference to the definition of pornography, "I shall not today attempt to further define the kind of materials I understand to be embraced within that shorthand definition and perhaps I could never succeed in doing so. . . but I know it when I see it.")

During my interviews with Dr. Connolly, he represented the epitome of total coldness, humorlessness and lack of any apparent feeling except for the frequent flushing of his face and a minimal expression of some anger towards Dr. Labowitz. Of the thousands of patients that I have examined, I believe that he represents one of the most controlled, expressionless persons that I have seen. He practically did not move throughout the interviews. He refused anything to drink, and if my recollection is correct did not even use the bathroom, despite the fact that I found it necessary to take a couple

(EXHIBIT #34b)

of breaks during our interviews. A review of the various depositions reveals the same "restricted affectivity."

Beginning in the summer of 1978 when Dr. Connolly was visiting Wilmington, Delaware and spoke with Dr. Labowitz, Dr. Connolly was the person who did the rejecting. He did not seem to have the recognition that appropriate behavior for a junior physician entering the territory of an established practitioner is a personal visit. (Dominance - Submission) He apparently conducted his communications by telephone. He did not accept Dr. Labowitz's offer to join his practice but decided to go into practice himself. This is certainly his free choice. Later, in January 1979, when he opened his practice and joined the coverage group including Dr. Labowitz, he quickly felt put upon because the other doctors had larger practices and this necessitated Dr. Connolly's carrying a larger burden than his own practice generated for nights, weekends, and holidays. This condition is clearly expected and represents the natural course of events until a physician's practice builds up over a number of years, so that he might be equal to his other sign-out partners. It is expected and accepted in the medical profession that this represents "the paying of one's dues." Throughout the course of Dr. Connolly's career in Wilmington it would appear that he was not willing to "pay his dues." This is seen in repeated instances of his complaint. First with the coverage call, next with his participation in the outpatient clinic at the Wilmington Medical Center in which Dr. Connolly believes that he has participated to an excessive extent when as the "new boy on the block" he willingly takes two months' of Dr. Labowitz's service. However, within a year's time he takes umbrage at what he considers a lack of recognition and asks to be relieved of this responsibility. He clearly places undue importance on his contributions and does not appear to appreciate the fact that the youngest member of the hospital staff is called upon to give the most free work while he is building up his practice. (Dominance - Submission) Additionally Dr. Connolly, probably because of his compulsive nature decides that it is inconvenient or unacceptable after a brief trial to have the residents attend his private office hours but is only willing to see them at the hospital clinic. Dr. Connolly knows or should have known that internal medicine residents who are required to attend many sub-specialty clinics will frequently do anything they can to get away from the hospital and participate with their mentor in his private office. This is particularly true in a sub-specialty such as rheumatology which is essentially an outpatient practice. Nevertheless Dr. Connolly did not find this satisfactory for his patients. On the one hand he complains of not having enough patients and on the other hand he complains that he did not have the time to spend with the residents in his office. Additional-

(EXHIBIT #35)
-from page 295

1 Q. You thought the best way to gauge Doctor
2 Connolly's behavior during your interview -- excuse me --
3 to express Doctor Connolly's ability to express warm and
4 tender emotions was you, as you put it yesterday, grilling
5 him, pounding on him, cross-examining him, testing him?"
6 A. That wasn't the best way. That was one of the
7 ways I conduct my interview, but I don't think it is fair
8 to say I said that was the best way. That was part of the
9 whole evidence of my evaluation. That was not singled out
10 as a single thing.
11 Q. Second criteria which you say you found to exist
12 is perfectionism which interferes with the ability to grasp
13 the big picture. You list the abortion issue. This is at
14 page 12, sir.
15 A. Yes.
16 Q. The Madeline Boone, and then interview, and
17 deposition behavior. So except for your interview, the
18 other matters --
19 A. Well, we have also -- Oh, right. You're right.
20 Sorry.
21 Q. The other matters again involve issues of fact or
22 law before the jury in this case?
23 A. Yes.

1 Q Do you agree with the following statement,
2 Doctor: "It seemed that Dr. Connolly was very
3 conscientious, moral, straightforward and honest in
4 his attitudes"?
5 A That -- I don't know -- where are you reading
6 tjat from my report?
7 Q I am reading that from page 41 of Dr. Olsson's
8 deposition, that is a statement made by Dr. Olsson.
9 A Could you repeat that again, please?
10 Q "It seemed that Dr. Connolly was very
11 conscientious, moral, straightforward, honest in his
12 attitudes."
13 A Yes. Yes.
14 Q And at page 56, Dr. Olsson testified, "I
15 would say that he" -- referring to Dr. Connolly -- "is
16 a somewhat gregarious, socially capable man."
17 Would you agree with that?
18 A I'd have to question that. I saw no evidence
19 of that.
20 Q Is it your testimony, Dr. Rappeport, that
21 no matter how unfair, illegal, or improper Dr.
22 Labowitz' actions may have been toward Dr. Connolly,
23 it makes no difference in your opinion as to Dr. Connolly?

1 A Makes no difference as to my diagnosis?
2 Q Yes, sir.
3 A I guess I would have to say that based
4 on what I made my diagnosis on and that is
5 Dr. Connolly's behavior, reactions, et cetera, and
6 lack of any supporting evidence to that, to what you
7 stated, yes, that it made no difference.
8 MR. GREEN: I have no further questions.
9 Thank you.
10 THE COURT: Mr. Parkins, you may question
11 the witness, please.
12 REDIRECT EXAMINATION
13 BY MR. PARKINS:
14 Q Dr. Rappeport, near the end of your
15 examination Mr. Green read to you a portion of a
16 statement made by Senator Biden found on DX-52.
17 Let us first tell the jury that DX-52 is a transcript
18 of the hearing involving Mrs. Roth before the Senate
19 Judiciary Committee; is that correct?
20 A Yes, that's my understanding.
21 Q And Mr. Green read to you a statement by
22 Senator Biden, "And in my view Dr. Connolly is one
23 of the finest physicians in the State of Delaware and

(EXHIBIT #37 a-e)
-from page 304-305

time.

Any other comments, please?

MR. PARKINS: Your Honor, I'm mindful of the fact that only person is allowed to speak on each side, but I am a little concerned about the Court's last comment, perhaps because I misunderstand it.

But I am seeking a motion or ruling in limine that by asking Dr. Groves are you--do you understand that you are being presented to offer your own diagnosis of Dr. Connolly, that that will not open up the door to questions from plaintiff about what his diagnosis is.

THE COURT: Do you--

MR. PARKINS: Maybe I have not made myself very clear.

I intend to ask this witness whether he understands that his testimony today is being presented to offer his own diagnosis, if any, of Dr. Connolly.

THE COURT: And I expect that that will be a no response.

MR. PARKINS: Yes. And then the second--

(EXHIBIT #37b)

THE COURT: Is that accurate?

THE WITNESS: That's correct.

MR. PARKINS: I do not then--

THE COURT: Okay.

MR. PARKINS: I do not, then, expect that this opens up the door to plaintiff to inquire as to what the diagnosis, if any, is.

THE COURT: Mr. Green.

MR. GREEN: Your Honor, that's fine. I am not going to make that point. But I don't want Dr. Groves to be sitting up there fielding all kinds of questions from Mr. Parkins, not knowing when he can tell the truth and when he can't tell the truth.

THE COURT: Dr. Groves--

MR. GREEN: He's to always understand he is to tell the truth.

THE COURT: Do you understand the dialogue that I have been having with counsel thus far?

THE WITNESS: I think I do.

THE COURT: Do you understand that you have been called as an expert witness in this case to offer an opinion--this is my understanding--with

(EXHIBIT #37c)

regard to the process of Dr. Rappeport and how he formulated the diagnosis?

THE WITNESS: Right.

THE COURT: And you understand that you are not being called as a witness to offer your own diagnosis, if you had any?

THE WITNESS: Right.

THE COURT: Does that clear it up, counsel?

I think the witness understands the parameters.

MR. PARKINS: If I can remember the Court's wording, that's exactly what I intended to ask.

THE COURT: Any other matters out of the presence of the jury, please?

(There was no response.)

THE COURT: Jury, please.

(At 2:06 p.m. the jury entered the courtroom and took their seats in the box.)

THE COURT: Proceed, please, Mr. Parkins.

MR. PARKINS: Thank you, your Honor.

Dr. Olsson?

A Right.

Q But you are criticizing him based on these tests even though you don't know what some of the tests are?

A It depends on what I am criticizing him for.

Q You are criticizing him for making this diagnosis, aren't you?

A I am just not going to say that he makes that diagnosis.

Q Let's move on for just a moment.

As I understand, you have told the jury that you have been working with the plaintiffs' team for two years?

A That's correct, more than two years

Q And you have had frequent contact with the plaintiffs' team during the course of that time, haven't you?

A $7,300 worth.

Q $7,300 and running, as I recall. And I understand that you have been offered today as a witness to criticize Dr. Rappeport's and Dr. Olsson's

...thodology; is that correct?

A That's correct.

3 Q And I also understand that you are not
4 being offered today to present your own diagnosis of
5 Dr. Connolly; is that correct?

6 A That's correct.

7 Q Is that correct?

8 A That's correct.

9 MR. PARKINS: Thank you very much, Doctor.

10 Your Honor, I have no further questions of
11 this witness.

12 THE COURT: Mr. Green.

13 REDIRECT EXAMINATION

14 BY MR. GREEN:

15 Q Doctor, very briefly, has anything that
16 Mr. Parkins has shown you in DSM-III-R or anything that
17 he has asked you about in your cross-examination
18 changed or caused you to reconsider in any way the
19 opinions that you expressed this morning that
20 Dr. Olsson's opinion was invalid?

21 A No.

22 Q Or that Dr. Rappeport's opinion was invalid?

23 A No, it hasn't changed.

(EXHIBIT #38 a-c)
-from page 306-307

1 is not an issue.

2 Do you understand that now?

3 A. Yes.

4 Q With that clarification, do you--would

5 that cause you to change any of your responses?

6 A. No.

7 Q Okay. I certainly did not intend to

8 suggest Dr.--that Dr. Connolly's family is unimpor-

9 tant.

10 MR. PARKINS: Nothing further.

11 THE COURT: Any other questions of

12 this witness, please?

13 MR. GREEN: One further question,

14 your Honor.

15 THE COURT: Mr. Green.

16

17 REDIRECT EXAMINATION

18 BY MR. GREEN:

19 Q Since we were planning to stay until

20 6:00, your Honor, I hate to disappoint anybody.

21 Doctor, can you tell us what is the

22 best example of Dr. Connolly's--the best example,

evidence of Dr. Connolly's compulsive behavior?

A That's a very general statement.

Do you mean in the test or do you mean in any--in any respect?

Q Any respect.

A Well, I think probably what type of behavior would be the most inflexible and the most maladaptive would be his way of having to do things in his own certain kind of way. That is rigid and that--it would not take into consideration what impact he is having on other people, and that he would feel that he is correct and the other person is basically incorrect in this matter.

And he's very strong and rigid in sticking by this.

Q Is there a--something that is the best example of that?

A Well, I think, again, I don't have--other than the interview material I have itself, which shows that he, again, is going through, again, this situation with this behavior with his lawsuit, again, many people of the compulsive or paranoid nature do get involved in lengthy litig--litigious kind of interactions with people, so that they can't

(EXHIBIT #38c)

give up. They want to stick in there and prove that they're the ones who are right, and this, I guess, would be the best example of that that we could come up with here.

Q Okay, but you didn't come up with that example. That was from Dr. Rappeport; is that right?

A Well, part of it can be based upon what I obtained from Dr. Connolly in my interview in terms of what he said, the nature of some of what he said in regard to his seeing these other doctors against him and being the ones who dismissed him, and so on.

So there was somewhat of a flavor, although, in my interview, it wasn't to that degree that I could be very definite about it.

Q So even though you couldn't be very definite about it, that's the best example of that kind of behavior?

A Well, I think it's the best example I can think of in terms of his overt behavior. I think we can go in again and again into the psychological testing. If we want to say the best example with the psychological test results, we would talk

(EXHIBIT #39)
-from page 307

1 informal a basis in a patient that was desperately
2 ill. I needed that courtesy -- that patient to have
3 the courtesy to have something done. If he couldn't
4 come in because of his own personal commitments to
5 see her, why didn't he tell me. If he was so
6 concerned about it, why didn't he call the patient.
7 There was just no communication, and I was refused any
8 communication for my patient that I felt deeply
9 concerned about.
10 Q Is the answer to my question yes,
11 Dr. Levinson?
12 A I have rambled. Possibly you should repeat
13 your question, sir.
14 Q The question is that your consult says
15 "Any contraindication to intrauterine saline for
16 abortion?" Isn't that asking Dr. Connolly to approve
17 or disapprove a method of terminating the pregnancy?
18 A No.
19 Q It's not?
20 A It is not. I am merely asking him is there
21 danger to the kidneys, what is the extent of her
22 medical disorders, would my saline bother that or not.
23 You see, if Dr. Connolly had said, yes, I think it's

is anything that I can help you with."

And I gained--

Q Okay.

A --the distinct impression that Dr. Lang felt helpless in this situation and possibly maybe it would be a good idea if I did proceed.

Q Okay. Fine.

Did you get the same impression from Dr. Labowitz?

A I stated my position just a moment ago with Dr. Labowitz.

Q That he felt helpless and do what you--

A I beg your pardon, sir?

Q --what you thought you should?

A I said I spoke to Dr. Labowitz. I told him what I was going to do and I don't recall him expressing himself one way or another.

Q At any rate, Dr. Labowitz came into the hospital and he did give medical clearance for the abortion; is that correct?

A Yes, he did.

Q Did he approve the method of the abortion, that is, intrauterine saline injection?

A Yes, he did.

Q And would it be fair to say that that was within hours? I don't know how many hours, but it certainly was within 24 hours of Dr. Connolly's telling you that he would not see the patient?

A. Yes. That is correct.

Q Fine.

And would it be fair to say that Dr. Labowitz agreed with Dr. Connolly's assessment when he told you on the phone, on Friday, October the 12th, that the patient's condition was stable and didn't he say that there's no organ--systemic involvement?

A. May I just look at the consult for a moment before I answer you, Mr. Green?

Q Yes, sir. I believe that is--

A. I have this right in front of me, sir.

Q But for the Court's reference, Dr. Levinson, I will refer the Court to--

A. I beg your pardon.

MR. PARKINS: 5-F.

MR. GREEN: Plaintiffs' Exhibit No. 5-F.

THE COURT: Thank you.

THE WITNESS: Do you want me to go

(EXHIBIT #41)
-from page 307

1 desperately ill, in my opinion.

2 Q The letter does not say that the patient

3 was more than five months pregnant; does it?

4 A. No, it doesn't.

5 I don't quite understand your question,

6 but it, indeed, it does not.

7 Q Your letter does say that the abortion

8 had nothing to do with your consult to Dr. Connolly,

9 does it not?

10 A. That's correct.

11 Q And that is your testimony today?

12 A. That's correct.

13 I wanted concommitant care. He was

14 not to be involved in the abortion issue, as I

15 have repeatedly stated. That would have been wrong

16 on my part to even suggest that to this man. I wanted

17 his professional opinion on salt water for her kidneys,

18 in basic language. And, number two, concurrent care

19 for her life-threatening medical disorders.

20 The patient, other consultants and her

21 family all felt that the termination of the pregnancy

22 was in order. We did not wish to burden him with

23 any way--in any way with this.

(EXHIBIT #42 a-b)
-from page 331

1 Flinn, Doctor Levinson, and the list doesn't stop there.
2 He has also named Doctor Richard Morgan, Doctor Alan Fink,
3 Doctor Richard Gordon, Doctor Tom Celello, Doctor William
4 Taylor, Doctor Lee Reese, and so on. All of these have
5 been named by him. You should weigh -- I urge you to weigh
6 in your deliberations what this means, that he has named
7 all of these respectable physicians, leaders in this
8 community, as wanting to conspire against him, as out to
9 get him.
10 You have now actually seen many of those people
11 that he has named. Did they look like sleazy,
12 strike-in-the-dark conspirators? I think instead you may
13 have concluded they looked like what they are, leaders in
14 this community, caring doctors.
15 You saw and listened to Doctor Fink and Doctor
16 Newman testify. Did they sound like conspirators?
17 Scholarly, learned had doctors, who provide top flight
18 medical care to you and me and our families. Is it
19 credible that these are conspirators or is this just a
20 delusion?
21 Isn't it perfectly clear that the Medical Center
22 and that Doctor Flinn were trying to help Doctor Connolly
23 in suggesting he get a psychiatric examination. They were

1 trying to assist him in overcoming a problem. They were
2 trying to protect you and me and other future patients from
3 being exposed to a doctor who was having problems.
4 And these efforts in this courtroom are twisted
5 and distorted and tortured into something entirely
6 different, and you are asked to believe the twisted,
7 distorted, different version. That's what becomes of their
8 good faith efforts.
9 Doctor Connolly has seized on the various steps by
10 others to protect him, to protect future patients, and each
11 one of them, he selected and he has isolated and said,
12 "This is part of a conspiracy against me." And he has
13 distorted that and twisted it and presented it to you as
14 part of a crazy, fantastic plot.
15 Doctor Levinson's efforts to see that future
16 patients would not be abandoned and that abandonment was
17 treated as the serious thing that it is -- is characterized
18 as a conspiracy. Doctor Flinn's efforts to protect future
19 patients by requesting Doctor Connolly to have a
20 psychiatric examination -- he didn't say, "I want you
21 committed." He didn't say, "I want you treated." He just
22 said, "Go find out if there is something that maybe is a
23 problem." That is condemned here in this courtroom.

1 Center had an obligation to make sure an impaired physician
2 didn't continue to practice there.
3 It is going to be argued that with all this smoke
4 there must be fire. We submit there is a fire. And it's
5 in Doctor Connolly's mind. That's the only fire, twisting,
6 turning, distorting every little event into some kind of a
7 fantastic plot. Not a single doctor came here from
8 Wilmington to support Doctor Connolly's charges, only his
9 hired expert, Doctor Groves, attempted to snipe at the
10 doctors who did testify, Doctors Rappeport and Olsson,
11 appointed by the Court.
12 Yes, this has been a long case. It has been an
13 unpleasant case. And it has been a sad case. I'm sure
14 it's long and unpleasant for Doctor Connolly and for you,
15 but most of all, it's long and unpleasant and sad for the
16 victim, the real victim in this case, Doctor Labowitz. I
17 urge you to return a verdict vindicating him, finding in
18 his favor. He is the one who has suffered in this case.
19 Thank you.
20 THE COURT: Thank you, Mr. Carpenter. We'll take
21 a fifteen minutes recess at this point, please.
22 (A brief recess was taken at 3:07 o'clock p.m.)
23 THE COURT: Mr. Green, you will have 35 minutes.